"Hugh Ross always causes me to think new thoughts, consider new models, and walk roads I haven't walked before. This book is no exception. If you affirm biblical inerrancy properly understood (and I do), you will find this book a powerful tool in the defense of that position. It's different, brilliant, and profound. *Rescuing Inerrancy* is a reminder of the greatness of the God we worship and the clarity and trustworthiness of the truth he has so carefully revealed to his people. Read it and give it to everyone you know who is uncertain on the inerrant nature of Scripture."

—Steve Brown
Seminary professor, broadcaster, and author of
Laughter and Lament: The Radical Freedom of Joy and Sorrow

"Hugh Ross presents a spirited defense of the inerrancy of Scripture. Like him, I also believe that the Chicago Statement on Biblical Inerrancy still works as a good summary of the Bible's self-attestation. As Christian scholars—scientists and theologians alike—explore how best to integrate recent scientific discoveries with our faith, we must continue to do so with a clear affirmation of the Bible's inspiration, infallibility, and inerrancy."

—Ken Keathley
Senior Professor of Theology
Southeastern Baptist Theological Seminary

"It is hard to overstate the global impact that Hugh Ross's writings have had. And being the fruit of a lifetime of scholarship, *Rescuing Inerrancy* may well be his best book to date. Moreover, it comes at a crucial hour in church history where the nature of biblical revelation and authority are needlessly eroding. That's why this book should be at the top of your reading list. It's not a rehash of ideas already presented. Rather, it contains a lot of new and fresh evidence and arguments that are quite informative. The result is a feast of ideas that covers an incredibly wide range of topics with rigor and care.

As is typical of Ross, he doesn't hide from the hard issues. And by wisely adopting a moderate concordism, he deftly guides the reader through the contentious topics in science and Christianity integration. The result is a set of intellectually satisfying answers that are consistent with scientific findings and give proper respect to the inerrant Word and solid hermeneutics. I could not recommend this book more highly."

—J. P. Moreland
Distinguished Professor of Philosophy
Talbot School of Theology, Biola University
and author of *Scientism and Secularism*

"I stand in awe. I stand corrected. Repeatedly. On several issues. A lifetime of study by Hugh Ross enlightens and frightens me. As exposed by Ross: Can Western Christianity survive with such contortions of biblical truth and doubting of biblical inerrancy? It will, but not without judgment and purging, I fear. I'll need to read this book again and again. Thank you, Hugh, for pointing me on a surer course of scientific interpretation and biblical hermeneutics."

—James Tour
T. T. and W. F. Chao Professor of Chemistry
Professor of Computer Science
Professor of Materials Science and Nanoengineering, Rice University

"The integrity I've come to expect of Reasons to Believe publications is once more on display in Hugh Ross's latest book, *Rescuing Inerrancy*. He cites recent discoveries in biology and archaeology that have emboldened some evangelical authors to rekindle old challenges to biblical inerrancy and its cousins, dual revelation and concordance.

Dr. Ross, with his signature gentleness and respect, calls them out then documents why inerrancy matters today. It's a sobering but edifying read that expertly takes the reader through current Scripture-and-science controversies. He also takes us on a deep dive into how science can support, not undermine, critical theological doctrines and closes with 'a modest defense of biblical inerrancy.'

Did the Holy Spirit allow untrue mythology to taint his story? Find out when you read this profoundly readable book. And please pass it on to your pastors."

—Nick Tavani, MD, PhD (Biophysics & Physiology)
ABFM Board Certified and Member of the American Academy
of Family Physicians

"*Rescuing Inerrancy* by Hugh Ross rightly portends a looming disaster within evangelicalism. Ross exposes the alarming trend of trusted teachers abandoning or reconceiving biblical inerrancy to suit contemporary evolutionary orthodoxy. Denials that the Bible concords with scientific truth are hardly new. But evangelicals traditionally have come to expect such from theological liberals.

Dr. Ross closes with his own 'modest defense of biblical inerrancy.' Yet the whole of this crucial book represents his mature thinking as to why inerrancy is 'consistent with settled scientific evidence that the universe of space-time, matter, and energy came into existence from a transcendent Source.' If you care about the issue, *Rescuing Inerrancy* is essential reading."

—Theodore Cabal
Professor of Philosophy of Religion
Southwestern Baptist Theological Seminary

"This is perhaps the most important book recently written defending the truth of Scripture as pertaining to modern scientific discoveries. In a time when both skeptics and believers are claiming that the Bible does not accurately reflect current scientific knowledge but, instead, gives an ancient narrative based on archaic ideas, Hugh Ross provides an irrefutable defense of biblical scientific accuracy and puts to rest the notion that the Bible and science are in conflict or that they deal with nonoverlapping themes. This is a must-read book that will elevate your view of the inspiration and authority of Scripture and should lead the church back to the correct and historical understanding of how God's Word and created works declare the same truth."

—Michael G. Strauss
David Ross Boyd Professor
University of Oklahoma

"After a lifetime of writing, speaking, and debating in defense of Reasons to Believe's integrative and testable creation model, Ross brings his vast knowledge of the natural sciences to bear on one of the central theological issues of our day. Can the historic Christian doctrine of biblical inerrancy be reconciled with the findings of modern science? Ross's confidently affirmative answer will challenge those scholars who now (mis)use modern science to dismiss inerrancy. His evidence will comfort Christians who feel embarrassed over what they read in Genesis as they listen to many modern scientists and biblical critics. And his faithful adherence to holy writ will help to anchor all of us in our hope in Christ, who gave us his inerrant and inscripturated Word to strengthen our faith and sanctify our souls."

—Travis James Campbell
Director/President of Consider This
Author of *The Wonderful Decree: Reconciling Sovereign Election and Universal Benevolence*

"Hugh Ross comes to you as your *friend*. Among the qualities that you will find here—careful reasoning, clear exposition, and comprehensive coverage—what stands out is his *joy*: his joyful delight in both the Bible and the sciences, and his joyful confidence that they support one another. And your friend Hugh wants to share that joy with you in this book. I am deeply grateful for his work and think you will be as well!"

—C. John "Jack" Collins
Professor of Old Testament
Covenant Theological Seminary

"Like an anvil, the doctrine of biblical revelation (particularly, dual revelation) has been hammered time and again by critics and skeptics alike. Over the years, it has withstood the onslaught. Today, the same belief is once again being put to the test by a few leading thinkers. In *Rescuing Inerrancy*, Hugh Ross faces these questions head-on.

Like a skilled craftsman, he sifts through the different evidences available both from nature as well as Scripture to demonstrate that while the hammers (old and new) may continue to beat upon the anvil, the anvil of biblical revelation remains unharmed. I wholeheartedly recommend this book as a must-read, especially if you are interested in the truthfulness and reliability of the Holy Bible."

—Balajied Nongrum
Lead Consultant & Managing Director
Reasons to Believe APAC

"In *Rescuing Inerrancy*, astrophysicist Dr. Hugh Ross shocked me with the news that a significant number of well-known evangelical theologians teaching at our seminaries and schools have abandoned the truthfulness and historicity of Scripture due to evidence from naturalistic biological evolution. Many believe Genesis 1–11 is nothing more than ancient Near Eastern myth firmly rooted in the worldview of that time.

But Ross, an actual scientist, points out that the more science discovers, the more accurate the teachings of Scripture are shown to be. I believe every pastor, teacher, seminary student, master's and doctoral student in all disciplines should read this book."

—Dr. John Ankerberg
Founder and President of *The John Ankerberg Show*

"Every evangelical Christian under the age of 30 must read this book. Why? Because in recent decades, a wave of widely published 'conservative' theologians has been telling us that we can't trust the Bible anymore because of science, and this pessimism has become commonplace in many websites, Christian colleges, and churches. Strikingly, these theologians tell us that we must accept the arguments from skeptical and critical scholars about fallacies and errors in the Bible, the very same arguments that earlier generations of evangelical scholars had answered well.

A scientist has now responded to this crisis, saying 'Not so fast! There are powerful ways that science affirms the Bible!' Graciously working through their arguments and the evidence, Ross shows there is no scientific reason to make these dangerous concessions. In fact, when one separates the naturalistic philosophy from the data, science is increasingly pointing to the glory of God as revealed in his creation, and the truth of his Word.

This book is a breath of fresh air, a much-needed antidote to the alarming direction that 'conservative' biblical scholarship is heading today."

—John A. Bloom
Professor of Physics
Founder and Director of the Master's Program in Science and Religion
Biola University

HUGH ROSS

RESCUING
INERRANCY

A SCIENTIFIC DEFENSE

Covina, CA

Cover design: 789, Inc.
Interior layout: Christine Talley
Figure design: Kim Hermosillo

Names: Ross, Hugh Norman, author.
Title: Rescuing inerrancy : a scientific defense / Hugh Norman Ross.
Description: Includes bibliographical references and index. | Covina, CA: RTB Press, 2023.
Identifiers: ISBN: 978-1-956112-03-0
Subjects: LCSH Inerrancy. | Apologetics. | Bible--Evidences, authority, etc. | Science and religion. | BISAC RELI-GION / Christian Theology / Apologetics | RELIGION / Religion & Science | RELIGION / Theology | SCIENCE / Physics / Astrophysics | SCIENCE / Life Sciences / Biology
Classification: LCC BL240.3 .R67 2023 | DDC 239.8--dc23

Printed in the United States of America

First edition

1 2 3 4 5 6 7 8 9 10 / 27 26 25 24 23

For more information about Reasons to Believe, contact (855) REASONS / (855) 732-7667 or visit reasons.org.

Contents

List of Figures and Tables

Figures

Tables

Acknowledgments

M y Sunday Paradoxes class participants, including seminary professors and students, scientists and engineers, and many laypeople both in person and through live streaming, provided a sounding board for me in my content development. Their questions, challenges, critiques, and suggestions helped shape many of the book's arguments, explanations, and descriptions. Big thanks to all.

My colleagues at Reasons to Believe (RTB) and a number of our visiting scholars took time to discuss dozens of theological books and articles and scientific and biblical research findings, and to offer helpful recommendations, for which I am grateful. In particular, RTB staff scholars Kenneth Samples and George Haraksin organized a scholar workshop on dual revelation where theologians Ted Cabal, C. John "Jack" Collins, Ken Keathley, and Vern Poythress, philosophers Joe Miller and Kenneth Samples, and scientists John Bloom, Fazale Rana, and Jeff Zweerink all responded to the first draft of this book's manuscript.

This book is much improved thanks to the excellent peer reviews I received on the latest draft from John Bloom, Joe Miller, Vern Poythress, Fazale Rana, and Michael Strauss.

My partner in life and ministry, Kathy, took on whatever extra tasks she could to ensure that I had time to research and write. She also took the lead role in editing the manuscript. Hers was the nearly impossible task of balancing my demand for theological and scientific accuracy and thoroughness with the lay reader's desire for accessibility. I'm convinced she came remarkably close to achieving that goal.

The editorial team at Reasons to Believe further improved the book's contents. Sandra Dimas, Joe Aguirre, Brett Tarbell, Maureen Moser, Jocelyn King, Helena Heredia, and Karrie Cano devoted themselves to editing and fact-checking, preparing the index, and more. Thanks go to Charley Bell, Richard Silva, and Kimberly Grochow at 789 Inc. for the cover design, Christine Talley for the interior layout design, Kim Hermosillo for the figure designs, and Stacy Nagai and Anastasia Young for their expertise in promotion. I wish I were better at expressing how much I appreciate their efforts and skills.

Others who deserve special mention include my executive assistant, Diana Carrée, as well as RTB's entire support staff. You went beyond the call of duty to allow Kathy and me to focus intensely for many months on writing and editing. I am truly blessed by the love and encouragement I receive from my entire Reasons to Believe team.

Chapter 1

Surprising Theological Developments

This book responds to a growing crisis among conservative evangelical theologians and pastors—the abandonment or radical revision of the doctrines of dual revelation and biblical inerrancy. The push to abandon or radically revise the biblical doctrine of revelation has gained momentum in recent years. The long-standing conviction that the facts of nature, including human and natural history, do now and always will align with biblical revelation has been pushed aside as antiquated and no longer significant—or even possible.

This seismic doctrinal shift among theologians and pastors has already impacted a large segment of the Christian community. According to a survey conducted in 2020 by George Barna, director of research at the Cultural Research Center at Arizona Christian University, American Christians are undergoing a "post-Christian Reformation."[1] A majority of adults aligned with evangelical churches are rejecting once-foundational teachings. More than a quarter deny that the Bible is the Word of God, that it is "trustworthy and reliable."[2] More than half reject the notion that "there are absolute moral truths that apply to everyone, all the time."[3] Three quarters reject the belief that people are *not* "basically good," that we all are "sinners" in need of redemption.[4]

While one might expect the erosion of these foundational doctrines to come from outside the faith community, it has come—with stunning effect—from inside, from theologians widely considered "conservative" in their view of the Bible. So why would a scientist take on the challenge of responding to this theological tsunami? Let me offer a few reasons.

The first is that these theologians view scientific advance as necessitating a change in perspective on foundational doctrines. They have become convinced by bold proclamations that natural processes alone can and do explain the origin and entire history of Earth and Earth's life, including humanity. What rational choice is left, they say, but to reinterpret the Bible's creation texts and the apostle Paul's teachings on them in his letters to the churches he founded?

Second, although I'm a scientist, my primary calling in life is that of an evangelist. In my experience, evidence for the scientific and historical accuracy of the Bible serves as an essential aid in capturing the attention and interest of people who have had little, if any, exposure to Christianity and the Bible. It helps people see that the Bible and the Christian faith are worth their investigation. Jesus expressly commissioned his followers to make disciples among all the world's people groups (Matthew 28:19). One of the most significant resources for fulfilling this commission is stripped away if the Bible—the special revelation on which our faith stands—is stripped of scientific and historical accuracy.

My own experience illustrates the point: The Holy Spirit worked through the Bible *alone*, apart from any human witness, to establish my faith and seal my adoption as a child of God. The Bible came into my hands through the generosity of the Gideons, who deposited a box on my school teacher's desk and left the room without saying a word, other than to let my teacher know the Bibles inside were free for the taking. As a poor kid who loved books, I took one, of course. However, it sat on a shelf for several years because I was too busy studying the required curriculum along with my extracurricular focus on astronomy and physics to pick it up.

Ultimately, "the heavens" had been speaking to me so loudly about a transcendent entity of some kind as the source of the cosmos, I decided to investigate whether this "source" could be identified with any specificity or certainty. If you have read or heard my story, you already know where this two-year-long investigation led. As I journeyed through philosophy to mythology, and to the many texts held sacred by the world's religions, the imaginative and often nonrational scenery held some interest and beauty and glimpses of truth, but the Bible stood apart. It proved unexpectedly unique in multiple ways.

Although written by many authors in diverse genres over several centuries, this one Holy Book held together as one unified and consistent story. What struck me as a virtual impossibility, at least in terms of the probability theory I was studying at university, was the accuracy of its claims about natural history, not to mention sociopolitical history. I asked myself how these people in the ancient Near East could have guessed with such precision what scientists only recently began to discern with the aid of advanced instruments and technology.

This is not to say I understood every passage and did not encounter any mysteries or difficult-to-grasp concepts, but the same was (and is) true of my studies in astrophysics and other science disciplines. Our gaps in comprehension are the drivers of virtually all ongoing study in theology, science, technology, history, and every other subject yet identified by humans. However, what I did find appeared more than sufficient to warrant the transfer of my trust to the Being whose written revelation matched what the heavens and Earth declared.

Please do not assume that I consider my approach—and response—to Scripture as the *only* one or even the *best* one. What disturbs me most deeply in the current discussion and debate is the tendency toward "either-or" thinking. The idea that readers must choose either the Bible's scientific-historical veracity *or* its poetic beauty, mythical scope, and spiritual revelation lies at the very core of unnecessary disunity. Such an idea represents to me the acceptance of a diminished view of our transcendent God. I wish I could adequately describe the power and precision required to create even one quantum particle, one living cell, or one tiny tendril of the cosmic web. If I could, perhaps more people would understand why it seems entirely plausible that God revealed Truth (with a capital T) in the words of a unique book that wholly aligns with the unfolding facts of the physical realm in which we reside.

For me to sit on the sidelines of this either-or controversy over "concordance," the belief that the Bible is reliable in *all* it reveals (also referred to as dual revelation and biblical inerrancy) would be tantamount to a betrayal of the God whose glory is my aim, the God who is worthy of worship. By assuring my fellow Christians—including scholars who lead seminaries, train pastors, and influence congregations around the world—that science is an ally and not an enemy where the accuracy and authority of the Bible are concerned, I hope to embolden others to join me in presenting an effective exegetical and theological defense of our faith.

Indeed, others have joined me and added their rich insights to make an even stronger case for biblical inerrancy. Many participated in a workshop with me in June of 2022 and contributed significantly to the book you now read. However, what I have written is not just for theologians and scientists. The questions, confusion, and erosion of confidence regarding inerrancy emerge in churches, Bible study groups, book clubs, coffee shop dialogues, and personal contemplation, as well as in interactions with seekers and skeptics. My hope and prayer is that this book ignites in each reader a new (or renewed) passion to plumb the depths of God's self-disclosure in all its magnificent forms.

Chapter 2

Dual or Dueling Divine Revelation?

Anyone who has served on a jury as part of a courtroom trial or watched a legal drama unfold on the big (or small) screen understands the value of both eyewitness and expert testimony in deciding a case. When the testimonies of eyewitnesses and qualified experts agree, the verdict becomes clear. When they do not, tensions arise and a struggle ensues. Today, the "truthfulness" of the Bible is once again on trial, and in this case the disturbance has arisen among a group who once considered the case firmly settled: biblically conservative Christian theologians.

In this case, certain experts have stepped forward with claims of "new evidence" so convincing that it demands a retrial, or at the very least a revision or redefinition of the former verdict, which affirmed *biblical inerrancy* and *concordism*. These terms appear repeatedly in the pages ahead, and, in short, they refer to the factual accuracy of the biblical text in all matters it addresses—history, geography, astronomy, biology, and more, including God's character and the plan for humanity's redemption.

My purpose in writing is to sort through the current controversy from the perspective of someone who has for decades researched and written as an expert witness, so to speak, in the subject area from which this disruptive evidence has emerged: the physical and life sciences. What complicates this task, however, is that pure objectivity is all but impossible to come by. Many reputations seem to be at stake, including my own. For this reason, among others, I have invited multiple voices to join me in addressing the jury—that is, you, the reader. These voices, from today and the past, offer insight that can help us all move closer to settling this case with confidence.

Let us start by agreeing on some foundational issues. First, we consider the veracity of the 66 books of the Bible to be significant, both to our Christian worldview and to personal relationship with God—Father, Son, and Holy Spirit. Unless the truthfulness of Scripture matters to you, this book will be of little or no interest to you. Second, we affirm that God has intentionally disclosed himself to humanity in person through the incarnate Christ, as well as by two other means: through the created realm, the world of nature, and through the words of God's chosen spokespersons—prophets, historians, poets, biographers, teachers, and more. These two means are what I refer to as "dual revelation."

Christianity's Two Expert Witnesses

As the source of all reason, *logos*, God has graciously provided humanity with these corroborating testimonies—the "two books" referred to in the Belgic Confession. Dual revelation in a Christian context is the doctrine that God has revealed himself and his personal attributes through two wholly reliable and trustworthy expressions: the book of Scripture (the Bible) and the book of nature. The Bible affirms in multiple passages that God is the personification of truth. Deception is counter to his being (see chapter 6). From a biblical perspective, given that both of these revelations come to us from God, each must be trustworthy and reliable in every way.

This observation in no way challenges the Protestant doctrine of *sola Scriptura*. In stating that the Bible is the only authoritative revelation from God, the framers of this doctrine understood that for God's Word to be clearly authoritative, direct (verbal, propositional) rather than indirect communication is required.

Those of us who already believe in the God of the Bible are not the only ones who benefit from seeing that both the book of Scripture and the book of nature are trustworthy and reliable. As we will examine in later chapters, each book presents an internally consistent message, further affirmation of its freedom from error or contradiction. Given that the whole of Scripture proves internally as well as externally consistent, those who do not already believe in the God of the Bible can become convinced, as I did, that this communication originated from a source beyond mere human imagination. It is worthy, even demanding, of careful study and consideration.

Pathway to Relationship

On the basis of dual revelation, God's revelation of himself and his attributes is made available to all, including those with only limited or (as yet) no direct access to the written Word. As the apostle Paul writes in his letter to Christ's

followers in Rome, "For since the creation of the world God's invisible qualities—his eternal power and divine nature—have been clearly seen, being understood from what has been made, so that people are without excuse" (Romans 1:20). As theologian C. John Collins has explained, the original Greek
text translated "since the creation of the world" implies that the history, extent,
and other features of the physical realm serve to reveal God's invisible qualities.[1] Every human exposed to the book of nature is offered a pathway toward
knowing and entering into a relationship with the Creator.

At this point I have opened the door to a theological debate that may dis-
tract readers from continuing to turn pages. So, allow me to offer a brief comment here. According to John 1:9, God gives "light" to every person. (In his
first epistle, John defines this "light" as a combination of God's life, love, and
truth.) Anyone who embraces God's light, with a yearning for more, will receive more, according to God's promise.

The Current Challenge

From the birth of the church (the body of those adopted as children of God
through grace, by faith) until the latter years of the twentieth century, the cor-
nerstone tenets of at least major segments of Christianity (the conservative
branches of Protestant, Catholic, and Orthodox Christianity) included belief
that God reveals himself to humanity in a wholly trustworthy, reliable way
through nature and the written Word and that nothing humanity can discover
about the world, when rightly understood, will contradict what is written in
the pages of the Bible. Today, however, this belief that the two books faithfully
corroborate one another is being vigorously assailed—by leaders within the
church. The next two chapters briefly describe and document the main sources
of controversy.

Chapter 3

A New Challenge Arises

Throughout church history, Christ's followers have revered the Scriptures as the true and trustworthy revelation from God. The rich history of the preservation and protection of its texts has been well documented. While for many centuries most members of the Christian community of faith had only indirect or limited access to its written message, Christianity grew to become one of the world's great religions. Many historians attribute the rise of Western culture and the scientific age to growing familiarity with and reverence for the Bible.

Until the eighteenth century, much of the Western world considered the Bible as a reliable, in some cases the final, arbiter of truth. Whenever some new discovery about the world appeared to contradict what church leaders interpreted it to say, the church leaders prevailed. Galileo and the Copernican revolution come immediately to mind. So does the spiritual impact of such stories. Since the so-called Enlightenment, inquiring minds have been prone to read and interpret the book of nature without reference to the supernatural, treating nature as the primary source of what is true and trustworthy about the physical realm, regardless of what the Bible might have to say.

By the mid-nineteenth century, the Protestant Christian community had more or less split into two segments: a "liberal" camp that denied both the importance and plausibility of dual revelation and biblical inerrancy and a "conservative" camp that firmly defended both. Further splintering occurred in both of these camps throughout the twentieth century, with the rise of innumerable denominations and sects, as well as independent congregations. (See chapter 4 for a more detailed historical background).

The twenty-first century has seen the growth of a further divide within the so-called conservative sector of Christianity. A significant number of theologians who identify as biblically conservative Christians, often referred to as evangelicals, has begun to call for a redefinition of biblical inerrancy as well as a revision of the long-established principles of biblical interpretation. What has fueled this dissension? Many among the most influential Christian leaders, from seminary professors to cultural icons, have become convinced that nothing less than a radical change in the doctrines of biblical inerrancy and dual revelation, as well as in hermeneutical (interpretive) methodology, can successfully accommodate what they view as unassailable scientific and historical findings that contradict the words of Scripture.[1]

This challenge has arisen and gained momentum a mere quarter century after the most highly regarded biblically conservative scholars from around the world came together to define and defend these core doctrines and principles. They were responding to the publication of Harold Lindsell's book *The Battle for the Bible* in 1977. Lindsell's book sounded an alarm,[2] and the response to it took on unprecedented proportions. Christian leaders rallied to form the International Council on Biblical Inerrancy (ICBI), reminiscent of the Jerusalem Council described in Acts 15.

Scholars Convene

The ICBI convened three major summits: October 26–28, 1978; November 10–13, 1982; and December 10–13, 1986, all held in Chicago. More than 300 theologians, pastors, and ministry leaders devoted hundreds of hours to dialogue, discuss, ponder, and pray over how to document clear and consistent guidelines for faithfully and rationally understanding the Word of God, all 66 books of the Bible. One of the ICBI organizers, Jay Grimstead, described the outcome of this monumental endeavor, *The Chicago Statement on Biblical Inerrancy* and *The Chicago Statement on Biblical Hermeneutics*, as "probably the first systematically comprehensive, broadly based, scholarly, creed-like statement on the inspiration and authority of Scripture in the history of the church."[3]

Each summit focused on a specific issue of controversy: the first, on clearly defining biblical inerrancy; the second, on delineating sound principles of biblical interpretation; and the third, on responding to challenges raised by the documents from the first two summits. The inerrancy statement was published on November 7, 1978. Although no longer available in print, it remains, with the entire set of ICBI documents, publicly and permanently accessible in the online archives of Dallas Theological Seminary. It presents nineteen numbered articles, each comprised of affirmation(s) and denial(s).[4]

Five of the nineteen articles in *The Chicago Statement on Biblical Inerrancy* have direct relevance to the current theological clash among "expert witnesses" in the case for dual revelation:

Article IX
We affirm that inspiration, though not conferring omniscience, guaranteed true and trustworthy utterance on all matters of which the Biblical authors were moved to speak and write.

We deny that the finitude or fallenness of these writers, by necessity or otherwise, introduced distortion or falsehood into God's Word.

Article XI
We affirm that Scripture, having been given by divine inspiration, is infallible, so that, far from misleading us, it is true and reliable in all the matters it addresses.

We deny that it is possible for the Bible to be at the same time infallible and errant in its assertions. Infallibility and inerrancy may be distinguished, but not separated.

Article XII
We affirm that Scripture in its entirety is inerrant, being free from all falsehood, fraud, or deceit.

We deny that Biblical infallibility and inerrancy are limited to spiritual, religious, or redemptive themes, exclusive of assertions in the fields of history and science. We further deny that scientific hypotheses about earth history may properly be used to overturn the teaching of Scripture on creation and the flood.

Article XIII
We affirm the propriety of using inerrancy as a theological term with reference to the complete truthfulness of Scripture.

We deny that it is proper to evaluate Scripture according to standards of truth and error that are alien to its usage or purpose. We further deny that inerrancy is negated by Biblical phenomena such as a lack of modern technical precision, irregularities of grammar or spelling, observational descriptions of nature, the reporting of falsehoods, the use of hyperbole and round numbers, the topical arrangement of material, variant selections of material in parallel accounts, or the use of free citations.

Article XVIII

We affirm that the text of Scripture is to be interpreted by grammaticohistorical exegesis, taking account of its literary forms and devices, and that Scripture is to interpret Scripture.

We deny the legitimacy of any treatment of the text or quest for sources lying behind it that leads to relativizing, dehistoricizing, or discounting its teaching, or rejecting its claims to authorship.

The current controversy over dual revelation seems especially evident in the twenty-five articles that comprise *The Chicago Statement on Biblical Hermeneutics*, published on November 13, 1982.[5] Nine articles relevant to dual revelation particularly stand out:

Article VIII

We affirm that the Bible contains teachings and mandates which apply to all cultural and situational contexts and other mandates which the Bible itself shows apply only to particular situations.

We deny that the distinction between the universal and particular mandates of Scripture can be determined by cultural and situational factors. We further deny that universal mandates may ever be treated as culturally or situationally relative.

Article XI

We affirm that translations of the text of Scripture can communicate knowledge of God across all temporal and cultural boundaries.

We deny that the meaning of biblical texts is so tied to the culture out of which they came that understanding of the same meaning in other cultures is impossible.

Article XIII

We affirm that awareness of the literary categories, formal and stylistic, of the various parts of Scripture is essential for proper exegesis, and hence we value genre criticism as one of the many disciplines of biblical study.

We deny that generic categories which negate historicity may rightly be imposed on biblical narratives which present themselves as factual.

Article XIV

We affirm that the biblical record of events, discourses and sayings, though presented in a variety of appropriate literary forms, corresponds to historical fact.

We deny that any event, discourse or saying reported in Scripture was invented by the biblical writers or by the traditions they incorporated.

Article XVII

We affirm the unity, harmony and consistency of Scripture and declare that it is its own best interpreter.

We deny that Scripture may be interpreted in such a way as to suggest that one passage corrects or militates against another. We deny that later writers of Scripture misinterpreted earlier passages of Scripture when quoting from or referring to them.

Article XIX

We affirm that any preunderstandings which the interpreter brings to Scripture should be in harmony with scriptural teaching and subject to correction by it.

We deny that Scripture should be required to fit alien preunderstandings, inconsistent with itself, such as naturalism, evolutionism, scientism, secular humanism, and relativism.

Article XX

We affirm that since God is the author of all truth, all truths, biblical and extrabiblical, are consistent and cohere, and that the Bible speaks truth when it touches on matters pertaining to nature, history, or anything else. We further affirm that in some cases extrabiblical data have value for clarifying what Scripture teaches, and for prompting correction of faulty interpretations.

We deny that extrabiblical views ever disprove the teaching of Scripture or hold priority over it.

Article XXI

We affirm the harmony of special with general revelation and therefore of biblical teaching with the facts of nature.

We deny that any genuine scientific facts are inconsistent with the true meaning of any passage of Scripture.

Article XXII

We affirm that Genesis 1–11 is factual, as is the rest of the book.

We deny that the teachings of Genesis 1–11 are mythical and that scientific hypotheses about earth history or the origin of humanity may be invoked to overthrow what Scripture teaches about creation.

None of these articles represent a denial of the scientific method, nor do they diminish the value and plausibility of scientific experiments and observations. The ICBI framers simply acknowledge that the content of Genesis 1–11 represents something more than myth and that the interpretive methods employed by scientists may be as subject to misuse as interpretive approaches to the biblical text are. The potential for misapplication exists both in science and in biblical hermeneutics. A contradiction between what the biblical text apparently declares and what the science apparently states represents a misunderstanding or misapplication of one or both sets of data.

A new generation of theological scholars has become convinced, however, that these articles—reflecting the historic teachings of the church, doctrines confirmed by the Reformers and embraced by the church for centuries—can no longer be defended and must be altered. Such was the message proclaimed by various presenters at the 73rd annual meeting of the Evangelical Theological Society (ETS) in November 2021.

Belief in biblical inerrancy appears in the list of criteria for ETS membership. Nevertheless, a number of highly regarded speakers at the November 2021 ETS meeting either stated or implied the following message: twenty-first-century scientific knowledge now renders the work of the once-revered ICBI scholars naïve, anachronistic, and essentially out of touch with the emerging "facts" of nature.

During this same ETS meeting, theologian Wayne Grudem, author of the textbook *Systematic Theology: An Introduction to Biblical Doctrine*,[6] and a participant in the deliberations from which the *Chicago Statements* flowed, countered this message with a challenge of his own. He called those who filled an overflowing lecture hall to remember these words: "Every generation of Christians must fight the battle for biblical inerrancy."[7] This book is but one response to Grudem's call.

Atheists' Challenges to Supernatural Revelation

The first atheist to explicitly reject the notion of dual revelation—at least in a surviving written treatise—is Titus Lucretius Carus, the Roman poet and philosopher more popularly known as Lucretius. In his 7,400-line poem, *De Rerum Natura* ("On the Nature of Things"), written circa 55 BC, Lucretius aimed to dispense with all the questions that trouble people's minds, including the fear of death, by claiming that nature alone offers sufficient answers.[8] He argued, in verse, that there is no need for any gods or revelations from a supernatural source. His conclusion is echoed in the memorable words of famed astronomy and cosmology popularizer Carl Sagan: "The Cosmos is all that is or ever was or ever will be."[9]

In 1875, John William Draper, first president of the American Chemical Society and a founder of the New York University School of Medicine, wrote in his best-selling book, *History of the Conflict between Religion and Science*, "Christianity and Science are . . . absolutely incompatible; they cannot exist together; one must yield to the other; mankind must make its choice—it cannot have both."[10] In context, Draper was focusing on Roman Catholic doctrine as anti-science, but he felt that as long as people of faith made concessions to what he viewed as science, their faith was fine.

Later in the nineteenth century, Robert Green Ingersoll became known as the most public American opponent of divine, authoritative revelation. His

1884 public lecture entitled "Orthodoxy" included this bold declaration:

> Charles Darwin . . . has removed in every thinking mind the
> last vestige of orthodox Christianity. He has not only stated,
> but he has demonstrated, that the inspired writer knew noth-
> ing of this world, nothing of the origin of man, nothing of ge-
> ology, nothing of astronomy, nothing of nature; that the Bible
> is a book written by ignorance. . . . There is nothing left but
> faith in what we know could not and did not happen. Reli-
> gion and science are enemies. One is superstition; the other is
> a fact. One rests upon the false, the other upon the true.[11]

More recently, University of Chicago professor Jerry Coyne published a
New York Times bestseller entitled *Faith Versus Fact: Why Science and Religion Are Incompatible*. In the book's opening sentences, Coyne reiterates Ingersoll's statement: "The greatest scripture-killer ever penned [*On the Origin
of Species*] demolished an entire series of biblical claims by demonstrating that
purely naturalistic processes—evolution and natural selection—could explain
patterns in nature."[12] One of the book's endorsers, fellow best-selling author
Richard Dawkins, likewise argues that science can and will explain everything,
including the entire history of Earth's life and even why so many people believe
in God.[13]

Christendom's Challenges to Dual Revelation
Friedrich Schleiermacher, a German theologian of the late eighteenth and early
nineteenth centuries, is widely known as the father of so-called "liberal" theology (referring not to politics but to a contrast with traditional or "conservative"
Christian theology). He questioned any reliance on a body of written objective
truth. He repeatedly proclaimed that the Christian faith is a matter of feeling,
not adherence to doctrines.[14]

Johann Gottfried Eichhorn, perhaps the most famous theologian of the
first half of the nineteenth century, earned recognition as the father of "higher
criticism" theology. In a five-volume commentary on the Old Testament, Eichhorn asserted that geological discoveries of the previous fifty years had clearly
refuted both the descriptions and chronology of the creation and Flood events
recorded in Genesis 1–11.[15] His interpretive approach eventually led him to
conclude that all the claimed supernatural events in both the Old and New
Testaments have natural explanations.

In the following years, Eichhorn was joined by a community of German theologians in further developing this naturalistic (or antisupernatural) school of theology. This school, known as the "documentary hypothesis," claimed that the Old Testament is primarily a compilation of unreliable documents written between 800 and 500 BC. Additionally, it denied Moses's authorship of the Torah (Genesis, Exodus, Leviticus, Numbers, and Deuteronomy), arguing that these books were written by four priests at different times and later assembled by other priests who overlooked apparent contradictions between the documents. The "higher critics" also introduced the idea that the creation and Flood accounts in Genesis are edited versions of various myths borrowed from nations bordering Israel. ?. | don't think so!

Hermann Gunkel, the founder of biblical "form criticism," published *The Legends of Genesis* in 1901. Gunkel argues that the narratives of Genesis must be legends, on the basis that ancient Near Eastern peoples "are incapable of reproducing their experiences objectively, and have no interest in leaving to posterity an authentic account of the events of their times."[16] He goes on to list nine specific physical descriptions recorded in Genesis 1–8 that he deems scientifically impossible.[17] Thus, he concludes that the book of Genesis cannot possibly be a credible account of actual events of history or science.

Throughout the twentieth century, the divide widened over which "book" to trust as true—the book of nature, as understood by its researchers and interpreters, or the book of Scripture, as traditionally understood and interpreted by biblically conservative Christians. Members of the latter group, facing mounting pressure from rapid scientific advance, chose to close ranks and set forth a declaration of Christian "fundamentals." Their approach took on a defiant attitude toward science, especially during and (even more so) after the infamous and humiliating Scopes Trial. From this event and others, a shoot sprang up and grew into a new branch, "scientific creationists," within the Christian community. They charged mainstream scientists with deliberate deception, especially with regard to the dating of major events in the scientific record.

In an effort to distance his Christian denomination from this outspoken branch, Episcopal bishop John Shelby Spong wrote a book entitled *Rescuing the Bible from Fundamentalism* (1991). The first six chapters of this bestseller purport to show that the Bible totally lacks credibility in scientific matters.[18] An article published in 1998 by the Westar Institute quotes a lecture by Spong, in which he says, "The biblical story of the perfect and finished creation from which humans fell into sin is pre-Darwinian mythology and post-Darwinian nonsense."[19]

Meanwhile, a group of Roman Catholic theologians including David Tracy, Francis Schüssler Fiorenza, and Anne Clifford began to develop and promote still another new approach to the dual revelation dilemma: "process theology."[20] This interpretive model, now shared by a number of Protestant theologians as well, avoids outright rejection of dual revelation. Rather, it takes the perspective that revelation in nature, revelation in Scripture, and God himself are all undergoing a substantial evolutionary process, though not necessarily in a consistent or parallel manner. In other words, truth is still emerging, and claims of certainty in the interpretation of either nature or Scripture can only be considered premature. This is "divine revelation" redefined.

Neoorthodox Challenges to Biblical Inerrancy

Many of my theologian friends and acquaintances would agree that Karl Barth may well be the twentieth century's most influential theologian. His voluminous written works serve as textbooks in Christian seminaries of various theological branches and denominations around the world.

In 1914, Barth broke from his early theological training and practice, then referred to as "liberal," and moved in a more conservative direction. In his first major book, *The Epistle to the Romans*,[21] he sought to demonstrate that the God revealed in the Bible overthrows every attempt to ally Jesus Christ with human worldviews, cultures, or achievements.

Barth's last published work, however, an unfinished six-million-word tome titled *Church Dogmatics*, reflects another change in his perspective on Scripture. Volume one (of four) says that the Old Testament biblical authors and, thus, the texts they wrote were capable of error.[22] Barth expressed his view that the Old Testament reflects the errant scientific and historical views of its human authors and their contemporaries.[23] He considered the Old Testament creation narratives "sagas," blends of history, legend, and fable,[24] or, as theologian Colin Brown would describe Barth's use of the term, "actual history though expressed in the form of a symbolic tale."[25]

Cumulative Effect of Ongoing Challenges

Biblically conservative Christian theologians have for centuries resisted compromise on the reliability of the Bible as divine revelation, affirming that the Holy Spirit enabled its human writers to record what God revealed, even that which exceeded the writers' full comprehension. (See chapter 5 for a historical overview of this doctrine.) The twenty-first century, however, has seen an accelerating erosion of this doctrine.

Early signs of this shift appeared in January 1991, when I came to Trinity Evangelical Divinity School in Chicago for the Kenneth S. Kantzer Lectures in Systematic Theology. During this biennial event, Old Testament theologian Bruce Waltke and I gave daily lectures on the first chapter of Genesis and responded to questions from faculty and students. Each day we also met for lunch and conversation with Gleason Archer, Kenneth Kantzer, and Walter Kaiser, all of whom had participated in the ICBI and in the preparation of its published documents.

A distinguished professor at Reformed Theological Seminary, Waltke was expected to offer a strong theological defense of Genesis 1 as an accurate historical chronology of creation events. After all, he had built a reputation for theological conservatism at both Dallas and Westminster Theological Seminaries and as an editor of the *Theological Wordbook of the Old Testament*.[26] Instead, his lectures set forth a different view, a "literary-framework" interpretation of the passage, proposing that the account conveys merely a developmental process rather than specific creative acts by God.

When pressed to explain his reluctance to view Genesis 1 as a historical chronology, Waltke could only point to seemingly plausible claims that science no longer permits such an interpretation. On the last day of lectures, a doctoral student came to the microphone to comment, "I find it ironic that the scientist here has no problem with a literal, historical interpretation of Genesis 1 while the theologian says science makes such an interpretation impossible."

Many Christians who self-identify as evangelical or biblically conservative point to books by theologians Peter Enns and Kenton Sparks as the source of this literary-framework view of Genesis 1. In 2005, Peter Enns, at that time a professor of Old Testament and biblical hermeneutics at Westminster Theological Seminary and editor of the *Westminster Theological Journal,* published *Inspiration and Incarnation: Evangelicals and the Problem of the Old Testament*.[27] In this book, endorsed by Waltke and several other respected theologians, Enns argues that just as Jesus in his incarnation was both fully human and fully divine, so, too, the Bible is fully human and fully divine. Enns seems, at first glance, to echo what generations of Christian theologians have written before him and what the ICBI strongly affirmed: the Bible is inspired by God and written by men in the language and writing style of the human authors.

There is a key difference, though. Based on his view that the Old Testament is "problematic"—containing apparent scientific and historical errors—Enns proposes that the Holy Spirit partnered with the Bible's human authors in a limited way. He asserts that while the Holy Spirit ensured the complete inerrancy of everything pertaining to the Bible's primary theological message, he tolerated, or accommodated, mistaken beliefs of the human authors in matters deemed theologically unimportant.

These unimportant matters, according to Enns, included statements about geography, history, and science, as well as what he sees as theological contradictions among the human authors. Enns writes, "Things like historical inaccuracies, myth, and theological diversity in Scripture are not errors needing to be explained."[28] On these "trivial" matters, he says, the authors incorporated myths and legends from the nations surrounding Israel. He describes the Genesis creation story as an account "firmly rooted in the worldview of the time,"[29] with "a firm grounding in ancient myth."[30] According to Enns's interpretive approach, God's Word can reveal truth about God and, at the same time, include some "mythic incidentals safely marginalized in formulating an orthodox doctrine of Scripture."[31]

Similarly, in his 2008 book, *God's Word in Human Words*, Kenton Sparks, then and still a professor of biblical studies at Eastern University, asserted that God accommodated his written revelation in Scripture to "the finite and fallen perspectives of his human audience."[32] He affirmed his belief in biblical inerrancy while redefining the term to allow for divine accommodation of human errors. In his words, "Accommodation does not introduce errors into Scripture; it is instead a theological explanation for the presence of human errors in Scripture."[33]

Sparks proposes that "God has selected to speak to human beings through *adequate* rather than *inerrant* words" (emphasis in the original).[34] According to his interpretive model, "In many cases God does not correct our mistaken human viewpoints but merely assumes them in order to communicate with us."[35] He adds, "God does not err in the Bible when he accommodates the errant views of Scripture's human audiences."[36]

In agreement with Enns, Sparks adopts an "accommodationist" approach to Scripture interpretation, seeing it as perhaps the best—or only—way to preserve long-held doctrinal commitment to the reliability and authority of biblical revelation. It allows for apparent conflict between the ancient text and advancing scientific research. Sparks sees Christians' adoption of belief in biological evolution, in particular, as inevitable. Why? Because the Christian movement must come "to grips with scientific reality."[37]

Silent Progression of a Seismic Shift
One might expect this call by three prominent, biblically conservative Christian

theologians for the radical redefinition of core Christian doctrines dating back centuries to sound an alarm, to signal a major crisis within the evangelical community. The declaration that foundational beliefs must be relinquished to avoid complete marginalization, alienation, and isolation from reasonable, reality-based discourse seems a significant threat to historic Christianity.

So where are the defenders, the "expert witnesses," to counter this disturbing testimony? The next chapter explores the basis for the relatively quiet acquiescence by many leading conservative theologians to a seismic doctrinal shift.

Chapter 4

Disturbing Concessions

You may have read that in 1914, a teenaged terrorist carried out an initially botched assassination in Sarajevo that subsequently escalated into World War I. One of the many tragedies of "the Great War" is that reasonable diplomatic measures, or even appropriate security measures, could have avoided untold misery and devastation.

Similar stories of missed opportunities to avoid major conflict abound, and although reference to them here may seem overly dramatic, the clash over the reliability of biblical revelation also holds weighty ramifications. Reasonable diplomacy on this issue appears well worth the effort, given the stakes for the plausibility of the Good News the Bible presents. This book aims to play a part in bringing about a resolution.

The Problem of Specialization

One reason for the unprecedented rejection of dual revelation and inerrancy in the twenty-first century is that we live in an age of extreme specialization. Gone are the days when clergy comprised the leading edge of scientific endeavor. Likewise, gone are the days when students pursuing advanced degrees in the sciences were required to study natural theology.

College curricula requiring coursework in both of God's two books no longer exist in most universities and seminaries, even in those associated with churches or other religious bodies. Students studying science at an advanced level, amid the intense competition (and cost) of twenty-first-century research, have little choice but to specialize, typically focusing on a single scientific discipline or, more often, subdiscipline.

During my years of research at the California Institute of Technology, my fellow astronomers would fill multiple lunch tables at a nearby burger place. Each of us quickly learned to sit at the "right" table, whether with the gamma ray and X-ray astronomers, the infrared astronomers, the radio astronomers, the ultraviolet astronomers, the theoretical cosmologists, the galaxy modelers, or the stellar evolutionists. The astronomer who sat at the wrong table would most likely fail to comprehend the lunch conversation.

Similar specialization, perhaps to a lesser extreme, occurs at seminaries as well. Old Testament scholar Walter Kaiser often joked with colleagues that he once took time to read the New Testament and found that he liked it. Kaiser's peers commented that these words were no joke. Their goals for academic and research success compelled many of them to focus intensely on a single book of the Bible or a single biblical topic.

The consequence of such specialization is that scientists and theologians tend to function as if there is only one book. Lacking sufficient training in science, theologians are apt to interpret the Bible with little, if any, regard to its scientific content. Similarly, scientists are apt to interpret nature's record with little, if any, regard to its theological significance or implications.

Singular Focus
Especially in the twenty-first century, scientists and theologians have been prone to consider new data emerging in their disciplines (or subdisciplines) as sufficient basis for overturning prior understandings of one or both of God's two books. For those lacking in-depth training in the discipline from which the new data comes, rejection or alteration of dual revelation may seem reasonable, if not necessary.

For example, when a scientist hears a Pentateuch scholar claim that the Genesis reference to the heavens means a solid dome over a flat Earth, the scientist sees an irreconcilable contradiction with fact. When a theologian hears from a scientist that natural processes alone fully explain the history of life—its origin and ongoing evolution—the theologian sees an irreconcilable contradiction with the biblical text.

In either situation, the accommodationist approach to Bible interpretation might seem to offer a reasonable way to preserve the doctrine of biblical inerrancy. Another approach is to concede that the two books address separate realms of truth that do not overlap. In fact, several twenty-first-century theologians have argued that the Bible is essentially free of any content relevant to science, or at least any content pertaining to the origin and history of the universe, Earth, and Earth's life. For their part, many scientists argue that nature's record is essentially free of any theological content or implications. With no significant overlap, no possibility exists for contradiction or inconsistency between the two books.

According to this model, theologians need not fear that established science or scientific discoveries will ever encroach upon or oblige them to modify their biblical interpretation. They see no need to delve deeply into the study of nature. Similarly, many scientists see no necessity to read and understand the Bible, or any other "holy book." For them, any claim of supernatural revelation about nature's realm remains irrelevant.

While research specialization falls short of fully explaining why confidence in dual revelation and biblical inerrancy has been so deeply and widely shaken in the twenty-first century, its significance deserves attention. Given that the major challenges have come from the life sciences and physical sciences, it is troubling that virtually none of those who pursue advanced degrees in theology and become professors of theology have any in-depth science education in their backgrounds. As a result, the weight of "expert testimony" on how to interpret the Bible shifts strongly in one direction.

Unnecessary Concessions

An important moment for diplomatic discussion passed unnoticed in 2009. Bruce Waltke published an article that year in the *Westminster Theological Journal* that might have helped hold back the seismic shift in perspective on biblical inerrancy. In his review of Peter Enns's book *Inspiration and Incarnation*, he points out that what Enns had identified as the most problematic contradictions and historical errors in the Bible were not what they seemed.[1] In fact, Waltke shows how, for each one of the problems identified, a closer look at context and a reasonable exegesis would transform the "contradiction" or "error" into an example of biblical accuracy. In conclusion, he writes, "I find none of Enns' data supports his understanding of inspiration."[2] However, Waltke offered no comment on Enns's claims of scientific errors, or misstatements, in Genesis 1–11.

A year later, Waltke made his position on science and Genesis clear. At a BioLogos conference in New York, he declared that for Christians to deny the reality of biological evolution would be "spiritual death."[3] Subsequently, Waltke resigned from the faculty of Reformed Theological Seminary and became a leading theological proponent of a view commonly known as theistic evolution. He began passing along this view to his students and fellow faculty at Knox Theological Seminary in Florida and at Regent College in British Columbia.

Theistic evolution, as defined by most scientists and theologians in the twenty-first century, is the belief that God guided—in a way that science cannot discern—natural evolutionary processes (mutations, gene exchange, epigenetics, natural selection, and perhaps others very minor, yet unknown) over the past 3.8 billion years, without intervening, to bring forth what we now observe of life's history. Variations on this theme go by slightly different terms, even among scholars associated with BioLogos, the leading advocacy group for "evolutionary creation." However, the message is essentially the same: The Bible reveals God's attributes and moral standards, teaches us how to serve and relate to God and to one another, and presents the truth of God's redemptive plan through faith in Christ's incarnation, death, and resurrection, but that is the extent of its "inerrancy." All else the Bible conveys is open to figurative interpretation and subject to the limited understandings and erroneous beliefs of its human writers—especially with respect to the sciences.

Direct Challenge to the ICBI Statements
As the culture became increasingly accepting of a naturalistic explanation for the origin and history of Earth's life, so did many Christian scholars and theologians who self-identified as theologically conservative. The need for doctrinal revision, or at least a redefinition of terms, seemed essential, even urgent.

In a 14-part blog series in 2011, Peter Enns took particular aim at the work of the International Council on Biblical Inerrancy (ICBI), describing its impact "on the science/faith discussion"[4] as "largely counterproductive."[5] Expounding on the question "What is truth?"[6] Enns asserted that the ICBI gave the wrong answer in declaring that "*since* Scripture is divine revelation, and *since* God is Truth and can speak only truth, *therefore* that revelation cannot be 'untrue' in, say, the creation story or in how biblical authors describe historical events" (emphasis in the original).[7] Enns also maintained that the ICBI assigned incorrect definitions to the words "affirm," "instruction," "requires," "authority," and "embrace."[8]

Throughout the blog series, Enns criticizes the ICBI for dismissing the general principle that "God condescends to human cultures."[9] He asserts that the ICBI went too far in stating that "Paul's view of Adam (in Romans 5 and 1 Corinthians 15) must necessarily be fully in line with what we read in Genesis 2–3."[10] He adds that "maybe not all of the Bible is inspired, just the parts that get it right."[11]

Enns concludes that the Bible's "creation stories are minimally historical (if at all)."[12] While he acknowledges that they are inspired, he insists that they are inspired "to 'do something' other than give historical or scientific information."[13]

In the ICBI definition of biblical inspiration, the Holy Spirit allowed the Bible writers' personalities and writing styles to remain intact while guarding them from committing factual errors. Enns advocates for a view of biblical inspiration that allows not only the Bible writers' personalities and writing styles to remain intact but also their worldviews and cultural assumptions.[14] He claims that the writers' worldviews and cultural assumptions were the same as the imaginative beliefs of the ancient cultures surrounding them, especially concerning the origins of the universe, Earth, and Earth's life.

Enns introduced the idea, which has since become widely accepted, that Old Testament authors and their contemporaries saw history and science as "irrelevant categories"[15] and that they cared little about either factual history or science. In the final blog of the series, Enns asserts that science-and-faith issues have moved far beyond where they stood in the 1980s, and that, for this reason alone, the ICBI doctrines of biblical inerrancy and dual revelation "must be revisited."[16]

Not long after publishing this extensive critique, Enns unequivocally made clear his outright rejection of the term "inerrancy." His contribution to the book *Five Views on Biblical Inerrancy* is entitled "Inerrancy, However Defined, Does Not Describe What the Bible Does."[17] An article on his personal website opens with these words: "I am not an inerrantist."[18] One is left to wonder how he became so firmly convinced that irreconcilable differences exist between scientific "facts" and the Bible's creation texts. Whatever the case, Enns elaborates on these supposed discrepancies in two books, *The Evolution of Adam*[19] and *Genesis for Normal People.*[20]

When I had the opportunity to meet Enns in person at the first of several private meetings between the leaders of BioLogos and Reasons to Believe, I shared my own faith journey. I related how I started, as a young scientist, with no belief in the Bible, but after two years of studying and testing the Bible, my mind was changed. I came to recognize the supernaturally inspired scientific accuracy of its creation texts, as well as the accuracy of the historical events it described. I shared how God led me, through this research process, to trust the Bible and to commit my life to Jesus Christ. Enns's response made me wonder if he had been listening. He said he was glad I had come to Christ and that I had been able to overlook all the Bible's scientific errors.

A Literary Argument for Revision Emerges

Fresh support for alteration of the historic understanding of biblical truth about creation came into view with the publication of *The Lost World of Genesis One*.[21] Written by John Walton, a popular Wheaton College professor of Old Testament, the book claims that until the recent recovery of ancient literature from the sands of the Middle East, a "right reading" of Genesis 1 was impossible. Why? Because "the worldview of antiquity was lost."[22] Walton argues that only now, in the twenty-first century, has an accurate understanding of the creation story been possible for Christians, and that for nearly 2,000 years of church history, no one could have come close to correctly interpreting Genesis 1.

Walton asserts that the ancient Near Eastern (ANE) peoples surrounding Israel focused almost exclusively on how things function, not on their material nature or origin. Therefore, he claims, when Genesis 1 describes God as "creating," "making," or "forming" the universe, Earth, light, water, land, vegetation, animals, and humans, the text is *not* referring to the appearance of material substances at specific times and locations. Rather, he says, it is unveiling the function of all things in the context of "the cosmos as a temple."[23]

Concerning the Bible, Walton declares that it "was never intended to offer an account of material origins,"[24] that "there is no biblical view of material origins,"[25] and that Genesis 1 "does not offer scientific explanations."[26] After all, he says that for the ancient Israelites and the surrounding ANE peoples, "the material cosmos was of little significance to them when it came to questions of origins."[27] According to Walton, "They did not know that the earth was spherical and moving through space; they did not know that the sun was much further away than the moon, or even further than the birds flying in the air."[28] He adds, "The Israelites, along with everyone else in the ancient world believed . . . no 'natural' laws governed the cosmos."[29] Walton concludes, "Science cannot offer an *un*biblical view of material origins because there *is no* biblical view of material origins" (emphasis added).[30]

Walton sees science as impotent to address theological matters. He writes, "Science cannot offer access to God and can neither establish his existence beyond reasonable doubt nor falsify his existence."[31] He goes on to say, "Science is not capable of exploring a designer or his purposes."[32]

Walton also sees science as untrustworthy and unreliable. He claims, "Science is in a constant state of flux"[33] so that "all scientific frameworks are dynamic and subject to change."[34]

The seeming benefit of this literary approach is that it offers complete freedom from the need to make a science-based defense of—or even a critique of—the biblical creation story (or any other Old Testament account subject to plausibility challenges, for that matter). Once *The Lost World of Genesis One* caught the attention of the Templeton Foundation, a philanthropic organization "dedicated to supporting progress in religious and spiritual knowledge, especially from a scientific perspective," the popularity of Walton's view grew exponentially. A substantial grant enabled Walton to tour the globe, promoting the book and the positions it expounds.

With this significant boost, Walton was able to enlist some widely known and highly regarded conservative theologians to coauthor or contribute to five additional *Lost World* books:

1. *The Lost World of Scripture*, coauthored with D. Brent Sandy (2013)[35]
2. *The Lost World of Adam and Eve*, with contributions from N. T. Wright (2015)[36]
3. *The Lost World of the Israelite Conquest*, coauthored with his son, J. Harvey Walton (2017)[37]
4. *The Lost World of the Flood*, coauthored with Tremper Longman III, along with a contribution from Stephen O. Moshier (2018)[38]
5. *The Lost World of the Torah*, coauthored with J. Harvey Walton (2019)[39]

In *The Lost World of Scripture*, Sandy supports the assertion that ANE peoples, including the Israelites, had little interest in science and little capacity for scientific endeavor. Walton and Sandy claim, "The workings of the material world . . . were of very little interest to them."[40] They assert that for ANE peoples, the Moon "was not understood to be an object"[41] and "to the ancients . . . geology, hydrology, and chemistry were unknown."[42] They say the ancients believed that the "Sun and Moon share space with the birds, . . . a matter of deduction on the part of ancients who had no reason to know any better."[43] Walton and Sandy write, "Everyone believed that there was a body of water suspended above the earth by some sort of solid dome"[44] and "everyone believed that the earth was round (but disk, not sphere)."[45]

In *The Lost World of Adam and Eve*, Walton concedes that while Adam and Eve could have been historical persons, both Genesis and the apostle Paul (in the epistles) treat them merely as archetypes. Walton argues that Genesis 3:20, which says that Eve "would become the mother of all the living" must not be a reference to all humans, given that the word "living" could refer to other animal life as well.[46] Wright agrees with Walton in asserting that God chose Adam and Eve from an already existing population of humans.

In *The Lost World of the Israelite Conquest*, Walton's son Harvey reiterates the claim that for the past two millennia, Christians have misinterpreted and misunderstood Genesis due to mistranslation of key Hebrew words. The Waltons propose that people have similarly misinterpreted the book of Joshua. They allege that the Hebrew verb *kherem*, in the context of Israel's conquest, has been misunderstood for centuries to mean "utterly destroy" when it actually means "remove from use."[47] The authors go on to suggest that the book of Joshua offers no moral insight beyond what was common in Joshua's time. They write, "Providing us with moral knowledge is not its purpose as *Scripture*; consequently, any moral knowledge we can derive from it does not carry the *authority* of Scripture, but rather only the authority of human wisdom" (emphasis in the original).[48]

In *The Lost World of the Flood*, Tremper Longman III joins Walton in affirming that Noah's Flood was, indeed, an actual event. Nevertheless, the two allege that the Bible describes the Flood's theological significance only. According to their view, the Genesis depictions of Noah's ark and Flood serve as examples of "hyperbole."[49] Their reasons for this view include the absence of physical evidence for ancient ships the size of Noah's ark, the implausibility of a large concentration of humanity in one region, and the absence of physical evidence for a Flood that encompassed more than a million square miles. Regardless of what the Old and New Testaments say,[50] the authors conclude that a large population of humans must have survived Noah's Flood.

Finally, as *The Lost World* books strip creation and science from the book of Genesis and morality from Joshua, *The Lost World of the Torah* attempts to strip "law" from the Torah (Genesis, Exodus, Leviticus, Numbers, and Deuteronomy). In this fifth book of the series, the Waltons offer the following comment: "If God did not give rules, . . . there are no rules to follow. If God did not provide legislation, there are no laws to obey."[51] The Torah, they say, is all about "wise living," without the constriction of "following rules."[52]

More Inerrancy Challenges Follow

As the message of these authors and the efforts of BioLogos have gained a growing audience, Christian publishers have produced more books that challenge, redefine, or deny biblical inerrancy and dual revelation. Limited space here allows me to comment on only a select few from the past decade. These examples help to highlight the magnitude of a spiritually significant conflict churning beyond the awareness of most churchgoing, Bible-believing Christians today.

Johnny Miller and John Sodem, each with earned doctorates from Dallas Theological Seminary, served as teaching pastors at conservative evangelical churches. In 2012 they authored *In the Beginning . . . We Misunderstood*.[53] They write that Genesis "is not revealing the science of creation,"[54] that "Genesis 1 does not have to fit science and science does not have to fit Genesis 1,"[55] and that "God does not correct some ancient expressions of how the world functions."[56] According to their interpretation, if Genesis 1 is a historical, chronological account of physical events, then (1) the Sun, Moon, and stars do not exist until after vegetation appears on Earth's continents;[57] (2) creation day two describes a solid dome above a flat earth with liquid water everywhere above the dome, where the Sun, Moon, and stars later become attached to the inner surface of the dome;[58] and (3) the universe and Earth are less than 10,000 years old.[59] Since these conclusions are scientifically false, they say, generations of Christians have misunderstood the Bible's creation texts. These texts, they claim, have nothing to do with natural history and everything to do with spiritual truths.[60]

Like Enns, Sparks, and the Waltons, these authors hold an "accommodation" view, belief that the Holy Spirit tolerated (that is, made no effort to correct) the mistaken scientific and historical beliefs of the Bible's human writers.[61] They agree with Walton that rejection of a "concordant" interpretation—one that attempts to integrate science with Genesis—is needed to preserve the doctrine of dual revelation because, in their words, "science continually changes."[62]

Tremper Longman III, emeritus professor and Distinguished Scholar of Biblical Studies at Westmont College, has joined other theologians who contend for a revised view of biblical inerrancy. In his book *How to Read Genesis*, Longman agrees with Walton and others that Genesis "is not concerned to tell us the process of creation. Rather it is intent on simply celebrating and asserting the fact that God is Creator."[63] In his contribution to the book *Reading Genesis 1-2*, Longman further elaborates that Genesis 1-11 describes real events through figurative language for the purpose of making theological, not scientific, points.[64]

Longman also interprets the many statements on creation and nature in the book of Job as mythological or allegorical allusions. For example, he asserts that "Behemoth and Leviathan are not actual animals but imaginary ones."[65] He concludes, "Job is not at all atypical of the literature of the Hebrew Bible, which is filled with mythological allusions."[66]

The basis for Longman's adoption of such a view appears in his foreword to *Adam and the Genome*, by biologist Dennis Venema and theologian Scot

McKnight.[67] There he writes, "The persuasiveness of the theory presented by Darwin" and genetic evidence that "humanity begins not with a single couple but rather with an original population of some thousands of people" required such a revised interpretation.[68] In his book *Confronting Old Testament Controversies*, Longman advocates for interpreting the Old Testament's teaching on creation and the fall of humanity into sin in the context of naturalistic biological evolution.[69]

In *Adam and the Genome*, Venema and McKnight state that "Genesis 1 concerns the *purpose* of what is created and not the *physical origins* of what is created"[70] (emphasis in the original). They claim that (1) the evidence for naturalistic biological evolution; (2) the descent of humans, Neanderthals, *Homo erectus*, chimpanzees, and gorillas from a common ancestor; and (3) an ancestral human population in the thousands are now so overwhelmingly scientifically established that interpretations of Genesis, Romans, and 1 Corinthians must be altered to correspond. Therefore, they deduce "that the Adam and Eve of the Bible are *a literary Adam and Eve*" (emphasis in the original), not a "historical" Adam and Eve,[71] which is now "an anachronism."[72] They conclude, "Neither the Old Testament nor Romans 5 blames Adam for the sin of others or blames Adam for our own death."[73] They say that Paul in Romans was referring to an archetypal Adam, not a literal, historical Adam.[74]

Denis Lamoureux, who holds doctoral degrees in dentistry, theology, and biology, has written five books on science and the Bible. Although he expresses belief in biblical inerrancy, his definition clearly differs from the ICBI's. He rejects the reality of "alignment between the Bible and the facts of science."[75] His book *The Bible & Ancient Science* includes two chapters and an appendix aimed at dismantling any "concordance" between science and the Bible—based primarily on theologians' assertions that the Bible portrays Earth as a flat surface with a solid dome above it.[76]

Michael S. Heiser, theologian and author of more than twelve books and hundreds of articles on the Bible, agrees. He writes, "The story of Adam and Eve then, as the product of a pre-scientific culture, isn't about science in any way. As with respect to theology, it could be viewed as only a story (not the record of a literal event)."[77] In the same article he adds, "Romans 5:12 does not teach that all humans need Jesus because they inherited Adam's guilt."[78]

William Lane Craig, founder of Reasonable Faith (with over 200 chapters worldwide) and arguably today's best-known Christian apologist, still strongly upholds biblical inerrancy but not as defined by ICBI's *Chicago Statement on Biblical Hermeneutics*, article XXII in particular. Craig endorses the integration of "independently discovered findings of contemporary science and biblical theology" but labels day-age interpretations of Genesis 1 and reading big bang cosmology into Genesis 1:1 as a "flawed hermeneutic."[79] In this sense, Craig views "concordism" (a term for science-Scripture alignment) a mistaken view or unnecessary component of inerrancy.[80] In his book *In Quest of the Historical Adam*, he describes Genesis 1–11 as "mytho-history,"[81] adding that "these chapters need not be read literally"[82] just as poetry or apocalyptic literature need not be read literally. He writes, "The accounts of the origin and Fall of man are clearly metaphorical or figurative in nature."[83] As support for this assertion, he lists a number of "fantastic" elements (impossible to be true if understood literally) in Genesis 1–11, including a talking snake, Eden's magical trees, vegetarianism, extremely long life-spans, Eden's rivers, cherubim with a flashing sword, Noah's Flood, the table of nations, and the Tower of Babel.[84] With regard to the New Testament, Craig states that though Paul's epistles commit to an historical Adam, some of Paul's references could refer to a literary Adam, a truth in story form, rather than historical truth.

In his recent book on Adam and in his *First Things* essay, "The Historical Adam," Craig identified Adam and Eve as members of *Homo heidelbergensis*, living 750,000–1,000,000 years ago.[85] He proposed that God selected a male and a female from "an initial population of, say, five thousand hominins, animals that are in many respects like human beings but that lack the capacity for rational thought"[86] and "furnished them with intellects by renovating their brains and endowing them with rational souls."[87] This ancient Adam and Eve, Craig claimed, are the sole genetic progenitors of all Neanderthals, Denisovans, and modern humans, all of which are bearers of God's image. However, in an email communication to me dated 4/6/23, Craig says, "My aim is not to affirm evolutionary origins of humanity, but simply the consistency of the existence of a founding pair with evolutionary theory. The whole thing is hypothetical: assume evolutionary theory; now ask, is the existence of a founding human pair compatible with that theory? I argue that it is."

Each of the individuals whose published works are cited in this chapter carries significant influence in the training of Christian pastors, professors, apologists, and ministry leaders. Already, the impact of some has been profound, persuading Christian seminaries, colleges and universities to incorporate biological evolution—common descent through strictly naturalistic mechanisms—into their biblical instruction. The spiritual significance of this view has been largely ignored or minimized. Not only does it imply that readers are free to decide which parts of the Bible are true and which are mistaken human ideas, but it also implies that human evolution is ongoing. In this view, we humans represent not just the end of a nearly four-billion-year chain of natural events but rather a single temporary placeholder in a still-unfolding continuum.

Biblical Theology before the Twenty-First-Century Crisis

According to the "expert testimony" offered by some of today's highly regarded scholars and authors, Christians have for 2,000 years been mistaken in their understanding—and defense—of Scripture's trustworthiness as divinely revealed truth, and nothing but the truth. For centuries, these scholars suggest, the brightest lights of Christendom have missed the mark—misconstruing what God has revealed about his part in creating and redeeming human beings for eternal fellowship with him. Any response to such assertions must begin with a review of what church leaders previous to the twentieth century actually said about these matters. The next two chapters provide an overview of historic church teachings on dual revelation and biblical inerrancy, teachings diligently preserved in the Christian creeds and confessions.

Chapter 5

Dual Revelation and Inerrancy in Church History

Some late twentieth- and twenty-first-century Christian scholars claim that belief in dual revelation and biblical inerrancy represent merely recent doctrinal developments. Their point is that interest in such subjects rarely shows up in writings from the first fifteen to eighteen centuries of church history. In *The Authority and Interpretation of the Bible*, theologians Jack Rogers and Donald McKim argue that the early church fathers, the medieval scholars, and the Reformation leaders cannot be cited as a source of the twentieth-century belief in biblical inerrancy.[1]

Ironically, the absence of historical references to such terms as "dual revelation," "biblical inerrancy," and "concordance" may have a more reasonable and nearly opposite explanation. Their absence in early writings more likely results from the largely unquestioned acceptance of the beliefs these terms represent—previously known by different words than those we use today. After all, the challenges to these beliefs arose relatively recently, toward the beginning of the nineteenth century, and almost exclusively in Europe.

Early Church Fathers' Perspectives
One measure of how seriously the earliest church leaders took the subjects of creation, dual revelation, and biblical inspiration and inerrancy is the quantity of their writings on these subjects. The leaders who published works prior to the crafting and dissemination of the Nicene Creed (AD 325) produced nearly a thousand still surviving pages on the meaning of Genesis 1 alone. Although they expressed a wide range of interpretations of the creation events described, they were unanimous in asserting that Genesis 1 was a factual account of the historical creation of the universe, Earth, and life on Earth. They also agreed

that Genesis explicitly declares a beginning to nature's realm rather than its eternal preexistence and that it speaks of creation *ex nihilo*, the belief that God created the universe out of nothing. In other words, they acknowledged that the universe we can detect did not come from anything we can conceivably detect (Hebrews 11:3).

Several early church fathers, including Justin Martyr (ca. AD 100–ca. 165), Clement of Alexandria (ca. AD 150–ca. 215), and Origen (ca. AD 184–ca. 253), expressed that truth is not limited to the Bible and that all truth, wherever encountered, is "God's truth," a gift from God. Clement and Origen introduced the idea that philosophy and science should be approached as "handmaids"[2] to Christian theology.

Tertullian (ca. AD 155–ca. 220) is often cited as an early church father who rejected nature as a reliable revelation of truth. However, his apparent rejection targeted heretical beliefs pagans drew from their misunderstanding of nature. In *On the Resurrection of the Flesh*, he wrote, "Some things are known even by nature: the immortality of the soul, for instance, is held by many; the knowledge of our God is possessed by all."[3] A consensus among early church fathers was that nature should neither be worshipped nor repudiated.

Irenaeus (ca. AD 130–ca. 202) wrote, "The Scriptures are indeed perfect, since they were spoken by the Word of God and His Spirit."[4] Clement of Rome (ca. AD 35–99) stated, "Look carefully into the Scriptures, which are the true utterances of the Holy Spirit. Observe that nothing of an unjust or counterfeit character is written in them."[5] Tertullian declared, "The statements of Holy Scripture will never be discordant with truth."[6]

The early church fathers were likewise resolute in affirming that the Bible never contradicts itself. Justin Martyr wrote, "I am entirely convinced that no Scripture contradicts another."[7] Origen commended the person who shows that what "appears to be a conflict in the Scriptures is no conflict, and exhibits their concord and peace."[8]

Post-Nicene Fathers' Views

Christian scholars who wrote on theology from the time of the Council of Nicaea (AD 325) until AD 600 wrote even more on Genesis 1 than did their predecessors. Basil (AD 330–379), Ambrose (ca. AD 339–397), and Augustine (AD 354–430) each wrote lengthy treatises on the creation account. In his *Homilies on the Hexaemeron* (six days of creation), Basil displayed a strong commitment to dual revelation in that he applied everything he knew from the natural realm, much of it from biology and Greek cosmology, in his defense of Genesis

1.[9] In his 280-page homily on Genesis 1–4, Ambrose commented extensively on the integration of the first chapter with observed facts about plants, trees, insects, birds, meteorology, and human physiology and anatomy.[10]

Augustine, in the *Literal Meaning of Genesis,* offered many still relevant insights on dual revelation and the care that must be taken in integrating God's truth revealed in nature with God's truth revealed in Scripture:[11]

> If they [non-Christians] find a Christian mistaken in a field which they themselves know well and hear him maintaining his foolish opinions about our books, how are they going to believe those books in matters concerning the resurrection of the dead, the hope of eternal life, and the kingdom of heaven, when they think their pages are full of falsehoods and on facts which they themselves have learnt from experience and the light of reason?

Augustine applied a careful integration of Genesis 1 with natural philosophy (science) to discern that Earth is spherical, not flat,[12] and that the Sun illuminates the Moon's surface.[13] He trusted God's book of nature to reveal truth. Augustine wrote, "In your great wisdom you, who are God, speak to us of these things in your Book, the firmament made by you."[14]

Writing on biblical inerrancy, Augustine affirmed and expanded upon an earlier statement by Athanasius (ca. AD 293–373), who declared that the entirety of all the books of the Bible is "divinely inspired Scripture."[15] In a lengthy letter to Jerome (ca. AD 345–ca. 420), Augustine wrote, "I have learned to yield this respect and honour only to the canonical books of Scripture. Of these alone do I most firmly believe that their authors were completely free from error."[16] In other correspondence he warns,

> It seems to me that most disastrous consequences must follow upon our believing that anything false is found in the sacred books: that is to say that the men by whom the Scripture has been given to us and committed to writing, did put down in these books anything false. . . . For if you once admit into such a high sanctuary of authority one false statement, as made in the way of duty, there will not be left a single sentence of those books which, if appearing to anyone difficult in practice or hard to believe, may not by the same fatal rule be explained

away, as a statement in which, intentionally, and under a sense
of duty, the author declared what was not true.[17]

Concerning the doctrine of dual revelation, Anthony the Great of Egypt
(ca. AD 251–356) wrote, "My book is the nature of created things, which is
present for me to read when I will the words of God."[18] During the sixth century, John Philoponus (ca. AD 490–ca. 570) published four books on science
and theology.[19] He strongly promoted the compatibility of Christian faith and
teaching with natural philosophy (science), affirming concordance between
the Bible's creation texts and physics.

Medieval Church Leaders' Views

Anselm of Canterbury (1033–1109) dedicated his life and writings to the integration of Scripture, reason, and philosophy. His mission was to show that
God's existence and the truth of Scripture can be established apart from Scripture itself. He is acknowledged as the originator of the ontological argument
for God. Concerning biblical revelation, Anselm affirms, "I see the truth of all
that is contained in the Old Testament and New Testament. . . . The God-man
himself originates the New Testament and approves the Old. . . . No one can
dissent from anything contained in these books."[20]

Hugh of St. Victor (ca. 1096–1141), a Saxon theologian who led the Abbey
of Saint Victor in Paris, also firmly endorsed the doctrine of dual revelation.
Drawing upon a metaphor that appears in Psalm 19:1–4, he declared, "The
whole sensual world is, as it were, a book written by the finger of God."[21]

Arguably the best-known and most prolific medieval proponent of dual
revelation and biblical inerrancy would be Thomas Aquinas (1225–1274). His
life's work, including his 765,000-word *Summa Theologica* and many other
writings, focused heavily on evidential apologetics (the systematic, evidence-
based defense of one's beliefs.) He strongly encouraged the scientific study of
the natural realm, confident that it would increasingly demonstrate complete
harmony between the Bible and the record of nature.

Aquinas saw the Bible as authoritative and truthful in everything it communicated. He wrote, "It is plain that nothing false can ever underlie the literal
sense of Holy Writ."[22] He added, "It is unlawful to hold that any false assertion
is contained either in the Gospel or in any canonical Scripture, or that the writers thereof have told untruths."[23] In his commentary on John, he stated, "Those
who wrote the canonical scriptures, such as the evangelists and apostles and
the like, so constantly and firmly affirm this truth that it cannot be doubted."[24]

Roger Bacon was another famous medieval scholar who strongly endorsed dual revelation and biblical inerrancy. In his *The Relation of the Sciences to Theology*, Bacon explains "the bearing which all sciences have upon theology." He describes theology as "the mistress of all sciences."[25]

Later medieval scholars and clergy reaffirmed belief that the Bible is entirely trustworthy and error-free. Hervaeus Natalis (ca. 1260–1323) expressed certainty "that God cannot speak falsehood."[26] Alphonsus Tostatus (1400–1455) believed that "all Scripture . . . is a divine revelation by the agency of the Spirit, who not only inspires but also preserves the writer from error."[27]

The Christian doctrine that the Creator God is revealed in the pages of Scripture *and* in the realm of nature would provide rich soil for the flourishing of science during the Reformation era (sixteenth and seventeenth centuries). One of the great motivators behind in-depth investigation of nature was the Christian belief that ongoing scientific study would increasingly reveal the beauty, wisdom, and wonder of God as Creator of all.

Reformation Church Leaders' Views

Although the Reformation led to division of the Western church into two camps, Roman Catholic and Protestant, leaders on both sides of the divide remained steadfast in their commitment to the doctrine of biblical reliability as a source of total truth. Spurred by Roger Bacon's writings and scientific experiments, the development of science accelerated during this era. Emphasis shifted from scholastic pronouncements to direct observations and experimentation. As Protestants turned their theological pursuits from quoting medieval scholars to direct study of the Bible, they likewise turned their scientific pursuits from quoting Aristotle and the church fathers to hands-on and technology-aided investigation of the physical realm.

Martin Luther (1483–1546), the seminal figure of the Protestant Reformation, approached theology more as a polemicist than as an apologist. The 95 Theses he posted on the Wittenberg church door were intended to provoke debate over who or what held final authority in the life of the church. Luther argued for the ultimate authority of God's written Word, the Bible, above any contrary church teachings, traditions, and practices. Concerning biblical truthfulness, he wrote, "The Scriptures cannot err,"[28] and "The Scriptures have never erred."[29] He further commented, "Scripture, which though it also has been written through men, is not of or by men but by God."[30] He affirmed, "I believe that in the Scriptures the God of truth speaks"[31] and "We refer all of Scripture to the Holy Ghost."[32] While some scholars have criticized him for failing to stand against the mainstream scientists of his era who opposed the work of Copernicus, the restorer of ancient Greek and Egyptian heliocentrism, Luther clearly acknowledged astronomy as "the most ancient of all the sciences" and "the introducer of vast knowledge . . . familiarly known to the Hebrews."[33]

Like Luther, theologian John Calvin (1509–1564) held firmly to belief in dual revelation. In his best-known theological treatise, *The Institutes of the Christian Religion*, Calvin wrote, "[God] revealed himself and daily discloses himself in the whole workmanship of the universe. As a consequence, men cannot open their eyes without being compelled to see him."[34] He argued, "If we regard the Spirit of God as the sole fountain of truth, we shall neither reject the truth itself, nor despise it wherever it shall appear, unless we wish to dishonor the Spirit of God."[35] Calvin went so far as to say, "If the Lord has willed that we be helped in physics, dialectic, mathematics, and other like disciplines, by the work and ministry of the ungodly, let us use this assistance. For if we neglect God's gift freely offered in these arts, we ought to suffer just punishment for our sloths."[36]

Calvin argued more emphatically than anyone of his era for the total reliability of the Bible. In his words, "We owe to the Scripture the same reverence as we owe to God; since it has its only source in Him alone, and has nothing of human origin mixed with it."[37] Explaining why he was convinced that 2 Maccabees should be excluded from the Old Testament canon, Calvin noted that its author "implores pardon" if he has written anything amiss. "Surely," Calvin says, "he who admits that his writings are in need of pardon does not claim to be the oracle of the Holy Spirit."[38] Here, Calvin leaves no doubt that he considered inerrancy as a requisite of biblical authority. He also implied that it would be slothful for a Christian not to study both theology and science and integrate God's truth revealed in both.

A century later, Swiss theologian François Turrettini (1623–1687)—the seventeenth century's staunchest defender of Calvinist orthodoxy—raised a still resounding challenge to those who would deny Scripture's inerrancy. In his best-known work, *Institutes of Elenctic Theology*, he provocatively asked, "What will become of this sacred book [the Bible], if everyone is allowed to wield a censorious pen and play critic over it, just as over any profane book?"[39]

Abraham Kuyper (1837–1920), a theologian who studied physics, founded the Vrije Universiteit Amsterdam (Free University of Amsterdam), and served as the prime minister of the Netherlands, wrote the following concerning dual revelation:[40]

Our best Calvinistic Confessions speak of two means whereby we know God, viz., the Scriptures and Nature. And still more remarkable it is that Calvin, instead of simply treating Nature as an accessorial item as so many Theologians were inclined to do, was accustomed to compare the Scriptures to a pair of spectacles, enabling us to decipher again the divine Thoughts, written by God's Hand in the book of Nature.

Reformation Era Scientists' Perspectives

Sir Thomas Browne (1605–1682), physician, polymath scholar, and author of *Religio Medici*, writes that his knowledge of divinity comes from "two books, . . . the written one of God"[41] and the observed one of nature. He refers to nature, appropriately, as God's servant, "that universal and public manuscript, that lies expanded unto the eyes of all—those that never saw him in the one [written], have discovered Him in the other."[42]

Reformation-era astronomer Johannes Kepler (1571–1630) also commented on dual revelation. In a letter to his teacher, Michael Mästlin, he writes:[43]

May God make it come to pass that my delightful speculation [in *Mysterium Cosmographicum*] have everywhere among reasonable men fully the effect which I strove to obtain in the publication, namely that the belief in the creation of the world be fortified through this external support, that thought of the creator be recognized in its nature.

Robert Boyle (1627–1691), widely regarded as the founder of modern chemistry and a pioneer in the modern experimental scientific method, also wrote on Christian theology—seven books, in fact. In *The Excellence of Theology, Compared with Natural Philosophy*, he affirmed that because "the two great books—of nature and of Scripture—have the same author, the study of the latter does not at all hinder an inquisitive man's delight in the study of the former."[44]

The Protestant-Catholic Divide?

While the Reformation did, indeed, split the Western church in two, both Protestants and Roman Catholics have continued to uphold Scripture as the authoritative, inerrant Word of God. Because Protestants and Catholics accepted biblical inerrancy, neither group felt compelled during that era and for centuries beyond to develop formal, lengthy treatises on that issue.

Since the time of the Reformation, the Catechism of the Catholic Church has consistently included the following view, stated today in these words:[45]

> Since therefore all that the inspired authors or sacred writers affirm should be regarded as affirmed by the Holy Spirit, we must acknowledge that the books of Scripture firmly, faithfully, and without error teach that truth which God, for the sake of our salvation, wished to see confided to the Sacred Scriptures.

The acknowledged difference between Protestants and Catholics resides in their response to other sources of authority. Catholics deem the tradition of their clergy to be authoritative, whereas Protestants deny an authoritative oral tradition outside of Scripture, as the Westminster Confession declares:[46]

> The Supreme Judge, by which all controversies of religion are to be determined, and all decrees of councils, opinions of ancient writers, doctrines of men, and private spirits, are to be examined, and in whose sentence we are to rest, can be no other but the Holy Spirit speaking in the Scripture.

A New Development or a Long-Held Perspective?

The claim by some of today's prominent theologians that the doctrines of dual revelation and biblical inerrancy are recent developments[47] contradicts a comprehensive survey of church history. Neither can it be said that only certain fringe elements of the Christian church held these views in past centuries or that these beliefs have been subject to changing definitions throughout the church age. As Norman Geisler wrote in the *Journal of the Evangelical Theological Society*, "Inerrancy was indeed believed by Augustine, Aquinas, Calvin, Luther and virtually all the great theologians in the history of the Church till modern times."[48]

Are the framers of the ICBI statement out of step with the history of the church, at least its conservative branch, or are the ICBI challengers out of step? Is not the God who brought the cosmos of space, time, matter, and energy into existence capable of communicating truth through his chosen spokespersons? Would the Holy Spirit, who lives and operates within the life of every faithful follower of Christ, allow centuries of his disciples to believe and teach untruths?

In the next chapter I argue that those who call for radical redefinitions or outright rejection of dual revelation, biblical inerrancy, or "concordance" are out of step not only with the great theologians in church history but also with the historic Christian creeds and the biblical text itself.

Chapter 6

Dual Revelation and Inerrancy
in the Bible and the Creeds

Does the Bible really claim to be "factually" true and trustworthy, as the ICBI affirms—and as the historic creeds declare? Or, do the defenders of this doctrine perhaps rely on out-of-context, misinterpreted, and mistranslated passages to uphold an anachronistic (mis)understanding of the Bible? These are two of the core questions on which the current controversy over dual revelation crucially hinges. Another, to be addressed in later chapters, has to do with the "facts" on which the conflict hinges.

Let's start by considering the character and capacity of God, as revealed in the pages of Scripture, from the Old Testament to the New. Both sides in the conflict agree at least on the meaning of the opening words of the sacred text: "In the beginning, God created . . ." First and foremost, God does exist and takes action. The issue at stake is the accuracy of the biblical account of *what* action and to *what effect*.

Old Testament Passages on God's Integrity

For God to make himself known in a deceptive or misleading way would carry alarming implications about his transcendent moral character as well as his power to communicate effectively. The prophet Isaiah was moved to utter these words: "I, the Lord, speak the truth; I declare what is right" (Isaiah 45:19).

Psalm 19 specifically connects God's divine attributes to the words of the people he chose to express them to in writing. The law, statutes, precepts, commands, and ordinances of the Lord reveal that he is (according to unquestioned translation from Hebrew) perfect, trustworthy, correct, righteous, radiant, pure, sure, precious, sweet, and rewarding (Psalm 19:7–11). Other passages of the Old Testament can be cited as well:

- God is not a man, that he should lie. (Numbers 23:19)
- The words of the Lord are flawless. (Psalm 12:6)
- All [God's] words are true. (Psalm 119:160)
- Every word of God is flawless. (Proverbs 30:5)
- The word of the Lord is flawless. (2 Samuel 22:31)

Psalm 19 also declares that this book of Scripture is complemented by a second kind of divine revelation (metaphorically comparable to a book), the realm of nature. Verses 1–4 describe nature's features in this way:

> The heavens declare the glory of God; the skies proclaim the work of his hands. Day after day they pour forth speech; night after night they display knowledge. There is no speech or language where their voice is not heard. Their voice goes out into all the earth, their words to the ends of the world.

God's glory, including evidence of his creative acts, pours forth from the physical, observable, researchable realm, the realm we humans occupy and interact with. Psalm 19 serves as the basis for the apostle Paul's words in Romans 10:18, "Did they not hear?" Paul responds, "Their voice has gone out into all the earth, their words to the ends of the world." Such a statement implies that the book of nature is not silent on theological matters. Nature's ability—and reliability—to communicate is affirmed in other psalms as well:

> The heavens proclaim his righteousness, for he is a God of justice.
> —Psalm 50:6

> The heavens praise your wonders, Lord, your faithfulness too.
> —Psalm 89:5

> The heavens proclaim his righteousness, and all peoples see his glory.
> —Psalm 97:6

> The Lord's word is flawless.
> —Psalm 18:10

The words of Job recorded in Job 7–19 illustrate an awareness of God's redemptive plan in the era *before* the written Scriptures were available. We notice that in Job, patriarchs rather than priests perform sacrifices to God. Other clues, such as the mention of city-states rather than any higher levels of organized government, suggest that the content of Job predates the development of Hebrew as a written language—and, thus, of the written Scriptures.[1]

These chapters record in memorable poetic form Job's claim, based on what he observed in nature and within himself, to *know* certain truths: (1) God exists; (2) God is powerful, knowledgeable, wise, and loving; (3) as a human, however righteous, he, Job, fell short of God's moral perfection; (4) for this reason, he stood in desperate need of an Advocate-Intercessor (Job 16:19–21); and (5) God in his power, wisdom, and mercy has already provided for Job's redemption. Despite his friend's objections to such talk, Job makes this emphatic and ecstatic statement:

> I know that my redeemer lives, and that in the end he will stand on the earth. And after my skin has been destroyed, yet in my flesh I will see God; I myself will see him with my own eyes—I, and not another. How my heart yearns within me! (Job 19:25–27)

If one accepts the Old Testament as spiritually authoritative, then, by itself, the Old Testament sufficiently establishes belief in dual revelation, as defined in chapter 1, and in biblical inerrancy, as defined by the ICBI (see chapter 1). The New Testament makes a case that's equally strong and clear.

Jesus as the Embodiment of Truth

Jesus of Nazareth came to Earth as "the visible expression of the invisible God" (Colossians 1:15, J. B. Phillips New Testament). One of the more familiar passages of the New Testament is John 14:6, quoting Jesus's words: "I am the way and the truth and the life." Jesus, the personification of truth, refers to the Holy Spirit as "the Spirit of truth."[2]

According to Matthew, Mark, and Luke, even Jesus's enemies publicly acknowledged him as "truthful" and as "a teacher of truth," partial to no one (Matthew 22:16, Mark 12:14, and Luke 20:21), and John records Jesus's response to Pilate in these words: "For this I was born, and for this I have come into the world, to testify to the truth. Everyone who is of the truth hears my voice" (John 18:37).

The book of Titus opens with a reference to God as one "who does not lie" (1:2), and the author of Hebrews echoes Old Testament prophets in saying, "It is impossible for God to lie" (6:18). In 2 Timothy 2:15 and James 1:18, the Bible is called "the word of truth." These passages imply that when God speaks, whether directly as God incarnate or through words or visions as God the Spirit—as to the apostle John on the Isle of Patmos—his message is truth and nothing but truth.

More New Testament Confirmation

The most frequently cited New Testament text upholding the doctrine of dual revelation is Romans 1:18–32. This passage affirms that God has given us an accessible, trustworthy revelation of himself—his existence *and* divine attributes—in nature. The part of the text most relevant to dual revelation appears in verses 18–20:

> The wrath of God is being revealed from heaven against all the godlessness and wickedness of people, who suppress the truth by their wickedness, since what may be known about God is plain to them, because God has made it plain to them. For since the creation of the world God's invisible qualities—his eternal power and divine nature—have been clearly seen, being understood from what has been made, so that people are without excuse.

According to this passage, "what has been made" (the natural realm) speaks so plainly and clearly about God that humanity has no excuse for missing his message. The only explanation for human failure to comprehend and act upon God's revelation is deliberate suppression of the truth. Romans 1:23 clarifies that this suppression occurs when people assign credit for the existence, qualities, and purposes of nature not to the Creator but rather to nature itself. Such transference of credit, as irrational as it is, will be seen by many or most as "wise" (verse 22).

The very character of God, as revealed in the pages of Scripture, Old Testament and New, would seem to imply that everything communicated therein can be trusted as truthful. When Jesus says, "Scripture cannot be broken" (John 10:35) and that "the smallest letter, not the least stroke of a pen, will by any means disappear from the Law [the entire Old Testament as implied by Psalm 19 and 119] until everything is accomplished" (Matthew 5:18), he affirms biblical inerrancy. When he confronts the Sadducees for their error because they "do not know the Scriptures" (Matthew 22:29; Mark 12:24), he affirms biblical inerrancy. When Paul reminds his young colleague, Timothy, "All Scripture is God-breathed and is useful for teaching, rebuking, correcting, and training in righteousness" (2 Timothy 3:16), he affirms biblical inerrancy and rejects accommodation. When Jesus rebukes Satan, saying, "It is written, 'Man does not live on bread alone, but on every word that comes from the mouth of God'" (Matthew 4:4), he is quoting Deuteronomy 8:3 and affirming that every word from God is life-giving and true.

The apostle Peter makes statements recorded in the New Testament that confirm the truthfulness of Old Testament writings. He says that "no prophecy of Scripture came about by the prophet's own interpretation of things. For prophecy never had its origin in the human will, but prophets, though human, spoke from God as they were carried along by the Holy Spirit" (2 Peter 1:20–21). This passage alone seems sufficient to rule out various modern-day theologians' claims of "accommodation."

Peter Enns[3] and Kenton Sparks[4] dismiss defenses of dual revelation and biblical inerrancy that rely on the citing of biblical proof texts. What they and their theologian allies overlook is that the biblical case for dual revelation and biblical inerrancy is not merely founded on a few isolated, out-of-context passages. The Bible repeatedly asserts both doctrines in a variety of contexts, and none of its passages contravenes them.

Church Confessions on Dual Revelation

The rarity of access to the Bible for the first several centuries of Christian history prompted early church leaders to prepare succinct statements presenting the fundamentals of the gospel message. These easy-to-recite creeds, used in liturgical worship, proved helpful not only in growing the church but also in quelling emergent heresies. Given their timing and purpose, they included no specific comment on dual revelation and biblical inerrancy. As the canon of Scripture became more firmly established and Christianity spread, these statements grew into longer and more detailed declarations, or "confessions," of the faith.

The most explicit reference to dual revelation, the "two books" doctrine, appears in one of the early documents outlining the essentials of the Reformed faith, the *Belgic Confession* (1561). Article 2 of this document, penned by Protestant pastor and theologian Guido de Brès (a student of John Calvin), says this:[5]

> We know God by two means: First, by the creation, preserva-
> tion, and government of the universe, since that universe is
> before our eyes like a beautiful book in which all creatures,
> great and small, are as letters to make us ponder the invisible
> things of God: God's eternal power and divinity, as the apostle
> Paul says in Romans 1:20. All these things are enough to con-
> vict humans and to leave them without excuse. Second, God
> makes himself known to us more clearly by his holy and divine
> Word, as much as we need in this life, for God's glory and for
> our salvation.

Here, the Reformer proclaims the revelatory power of the record of nature side by side with that of Scripture, acknowledging that nature's revelation is less detailed and specific, of course. Originally printed in French, this confession was revised at the Synod of Antwerp in 1566 and then further revised, translated (into Dutch, German, and Latin), and given final acceptance at the Synod of Dort in 1619. Ultimately, it became one of the standard creeds of the Reformed Churches in the Netherlands, the Reformed Church of America, and many other Reformed denominations around the world.[6]

A few decades after ratification of the *Belgic Confession*, the British Parliament called for a meeting of learned and highly regarded theologians and church leaders at Westminster Abbey to produce a systematic exposition of Church of England theology. This group, the Westminster Assembly, worked for nearly five years to create a governing document for both the Scottish and English churches, the *Westminster Confession of Faith*, as well as the *Westminster Larger Catechism* and *Westminster Shorter Catechism* to go along with it. While some revisions have been made since to account for differences in church governance, especially here in America where church and state are separate authorities, for more than 300 years, Anglican, Presbyterian, Congregational, and Baptist denominations around the world have embraced it as their own, subordinate only to the Bible.[7]

Appropriately, the *Westminster Confession* (1647) begins with ten articles "Of the Holy Scripture," listing the biblical canon, "All which are given by inspiration of God, to be the rule of faith and life" (Article II). The statements that appear most relevant to the current controversy over biblical inerrancy include these:[8]

Article IV. The authority of the holy Scripture . . . dependeth not upon the testimony of any man or church, but wholly upon God (who is truth itself), the Author thereof . . .

Article V. . . . The heavenliness of the matter, the efficacy of the doctrine, the majesty of the style, the consent of all the parts, the scope of the whole (which is to give all glory to God), the full discovery it makes of the only way of man's salvation, the many other incomparable excellencies, and the entire perfection thereof, are arguments whereby it doth abundantly evidence itself to be the Word of God . . .

Article VIII. The Old Testament in Hebrew . . . and the New Testament in Greek . . . , being immediately inspired by God, and by his singular care and providence kept pure in all ages, are therefore authentical . . .

Article X. The Supreme Judge, by which all controversies of religion are to be determined, and all decrees of councils, opinions of ancient writers, doctrines of men, and private spirits, are to be examined; and in whose sentence we are to rest, can be no other but the Holy Spirit speaking in the Scripture.

Though I have not included them there, the official document includes multiple Bible references in support of each article.

Two "Books," Same Author, Similar Purpose

From an examination of the Scripture itself and of the creeds and confessions Christians have followed for centuries, it seems reasonable to infer that readers really can trust what the Bible reveals about the natural realm, as well as what the natural realm reveals, through illustration, about God. Each shows its readers or observers the transcendent glory, power, and care of its Author, one in verbal form, the other in nonverbal yet discernible representation. Thus, we can realistically expect to discern a harmonious relationship—and overlapping content—between the Word and the world. As a student of both, I see similarities in how they are to be studied and understood, as the next chapter describes.

Chapter 7

Concordism and Science

The word *concordism* isn't included in my massive *Oxford English Dictionary*. It does show up, however, in Wiktionary, where it is defined as "the attempt to make scientific discoveries (especially on the origin of the world) coincide with the teachings of the Bible."[1] This term, *concordism*, has come into use relatively recently, and primarily among Christian authors. They take the familiar word *concord*, defined as "a state of harmony," and add "ism," the suffix for "a set of beliefs or doctrines," in this case, the doctrine of harmony between Scripture and modern science. The *Cambridge English Dictionary* adds an intriguing comment in the definition of "ism," saying that it is most commonly used by those who disapprove of a particular set of beliefs or doctrines.[2] Perhaps you have noticed (in preceding chapters) some reluctance on my part to use the term *concordism*. Among many twenty-first-century theologians, it carries a negative connotation.

Another reason for my hesitancy is that the term *concordism* can be more confusing than clarifying in that it refers to a wide range of perspectives. So, the term often requires additional clarifying adjectives—scientific, historical, moral, theological, hard, soft, moderate," etc. Concordism, in practice if not in vocabulary, dates back at least to the Middle Ages, when Jewish scholars sought to harmonize the Torah with the science and metaphysics of their era.[3] However, I first encountered the term in Bernard Ramm's book, *The Christian View of Science and Scripture*.[4] Ramm applied it in a positive sense as he described something I had observed before becoming a Christian. In my initial reading of the Bible, it occurred to me, as it did to him,[5] that a day-age understanding of Genesis 1 brought harmony, at least pertaining to timescales, between the biblical creation story and the geological and biological records.

Concordance Rejected—or Not?

A logically consistent view of biblical inerrancy implies that the three primary spheres of concordance—historical, scientific, and theological—are essentially intertwined. If the Bible is historically concordant, it will also be scientifically and theologically concordant. If the Bible is scientifically concordant, it will also be historically and theologically concordant. If the Bible is theologically concordant, it will also be historically and scientifically concordant.

Although some leaders within the Christian church even prior to the time of Charles Darwin embraced concordance between the Bible and science, in different ways and to different degrees, all held to some level of accord. Christendom's conservative evangelical branch upheld threefold concordance until the twenty-first century's Human Genome Project. Within a decade after completion of the project, the leading lights within this branch began to redefine, disregard, or deny concordance altogether.

Denis Lamoureux claims that we must move beyond concordism, "a constraining hermeneutic," to a "more peaceful and God-honoring relationship" between modern science and our evangelical Christian faith.[6] John Walton and Brent Sandy see concordism, or their preferred term, convergence, as cherry-picking, "seeking statements in the Bible that are compatible with modern science."[7] Johnny Miller and John Soden define concordism as reading the Bible "as if it is in concord (agreement) with a scientific worldview (emphasis added)."[8] William Lane Craig has declared that a proper interpretation of Genesis 1 "requires shunning concordism."[9] Craig further comments that concordism is "the attempt to read modern scientific discoveries into biblical texts," scientific truth that isn't really there.[10]

Peter Enns, Michael Heiser, Kenton Sparks, and Denis Lamoureux all reject concordance by asserting that the Holy Spirit tolerated the mistaken scientific notions of the biblical authors, permitting such mistakes to remain in Scripture. John Walton, Brent Sandy, Scot McKnight, Johnny Miller, and John Soden express the view that the Bible is virtually devoid of content on science. Walton, for example, states that science is "not capable of exploring a designer or his purposes"[11] or even of "affirming or identifying the role of God."[12] The grounds on which this rejection rests is essentially the same for all: the false assumption that a historical reading of the original Hebrew text of Genesis 1–2 requires interpreting the creation days as seven 24-hour days.[13] Because such a reading is clearly at odds with well-established measurements of the ages of the universe and Earth, this false assumption compels intellectually honest readers to abandon a concordant interpretation of at least these early chapters of Scripture.

Walton and Enns express further reasons for the abandonment of concordism. Walton considers science "impotent" to address theological issues, based on his belief that "all scientific frameworks are dynamic and subject to change"[14] and "science is in a constant state of flux."[15] He adds, "The combination of 'scientific truth' and 'divine intention' is fragile, volatile and methodologically questionable."[16] Enns, meanwhile, regards the "fact" of biological evolution as the crucial "game changer."[17] He writes, "the Human Genome Project, completed in 2003, has shown beyond any reasonable scientific doubt that humans and primates share common ancestry."[18] On this basis, he says, we can be sure that "human beings are not the product of a special creation act by God as the Bible says but are the end product of a process of trial-and-error adaptation and natural selection."[19]

Evidence that a rejection of concordism leads to further doctrinal erosion may be seen in Walton and Sandy's book, *The Lost World of Scripture*. There they argue that Old Testament prophetic books should not be interpreted as "future telling."[20]

They contend that both Isaiah and Daniel were written by multigenerational communities of the prophets' disciples and that what may appear to be fulfillments of the prophets' predictions are actually amendments and addenda made by these later followers—after the "predicted" events occurred. Concerning New Testament writers, Walton and Sandy see the fulfillment of prophecy referenced in the apostles' writings as "not the same thing as the message proclaimed by the prophets."[21] Most likely, they say, the Old Testament prophets were unaware that they were predicting future events.

The great irony of recent dismissals of concordism—prompted primarily by concerns over apparent contradictions between science and Scripture—lies in their advocacy of a new and more strongly doctrinaire version of concordism. This revised version requires reinterpreting Scripture to fit, or at least to disallow any conflict with, the latest naturalistic models adopted and defended by evolutionary scientists.

The Bible as Springboard for Modern Science

According to Genesis 1:28–30, responsibility for "dominion" over the earth, its natural resources and all forms of life, rests with humanity, placed there by the Creator. God tells the first humans to manage everything on Earth for the flourishing of all life, a mandate that essentially requires them to engage in what we now call "science." Clearly, their assignment calls for ongoing investigation, analysis, and practice, under God's direction.

The major creation passages in the Bible, especially those in Job, Psalms, Proverbs, and Ecclesiastes, portray God as a rational Being who exquisitely, deliberately, and continually orders the universe for the sake of his plan for humanity. These same biblical texts exhort us to exercise and grow in the virtues of discernment, analysis, reflection, and understanding. Jeremiah 33:25 confirms that the entire universe is governed by laws that remain fixed. In these and other passages, the Bible implies that the pursuit of science will yield knowledge—logical, consistent, trustworthy, valuable truth.

The declaration in Genesis 1:26–27 that humans uniquely reflect God's image implies, among many things, that we are endowed with the capacity to discover and comprehend to a significant extent the underlying principles, purposes, and characteristics of our intelligible natural realm. Thus, a biblical worldview makes scientific inquiry both possible and desirable.

In ancient cultures that lacked a biblical worldview, science was essentially "stillborn," to borrow Stanley Jaki's word. Jaki, a philosopher of science, documents how sparks of scientific endeavor arose in some cultures apart from biblical influence, but these sparks were snuffed out. They could not survive the stifling or distorting effects of such things as cyclical theories of time, polytheism, astrology, and various metaphysical views that either denied or deified nature's reality.[22]

The Bible has always stood alone in proclaiming the universe to be neither absurd nor magical; an effect, rather than a cause; a realm governed by linear time that points back to a beginning; a comprehensible and logically consistent reality, capable of revealing what's true. Successful science is possible *only* within such a worldview, a biblical worldview.

Test Everything

During my late teens, I studied the works of Descartes, Hume, and Kant and then turned to the "holy books" and other writings undergirding the world's major religions. I noted that the Bible, unlike the other books I examined, invited objective testing. As a curious and still skeptical science student, I was surprised and impressed to see how frequently and in what variety of contexts the Bible exhorts truth seekers to put their beliefs (and actions based on those beliefs) to the test.

The Bible encourages thoughtful contemplation: "Fools believe every word they hear, but wise people think carefully about everything" (Proverbs 14:15, Easy-to-Read Version). The Bible recommends acquisition of greater knowledge and insight on any given subject: "Wise men and women are always learning, always listening for fresh insights" (Proverbs 18:15, The Message). It instructs us to consider different sides of an issue before drawing conclusions: "There are two sides to every story. The first one to speak sounds true until you hear the other side and they set the record straight" (Proverbs 18:17, The Passion Translation).

The Bible instructs us to test everything we observe and discover and to test the message of those who instruct us. The apostle Paul is strikingly succinct: "Test everything. Hold on to the good" (1 Thessalonians 5:21). Here, Paul not only urges us to test everything, but when through our testing something proves to be true, we are to act upon—that is, embrace—what has been determined to be correct. This exhortation aligns with both the biblical and Greek concepts of faith, which encompasses not just intellectual assent but also an investment of trust.[23]

First John 2 hints at ways to test for truth. For example, if a message reflects "the lust of the flesh, the lust of the eyes, and the pride of life," we can be sure it "comes not from the Father" (verse 16). What's more, those preachers and teachers who distort the gospel of Christ "did not really belong to us. For if they had belonged to us, they would have remained with us . . ." (verse 19). First John 4 further warns Christians to test the message of a previously unknown teacher or preacher: "Every spirit that acknowledges that Jesus Christ has come in the flesh is from God, but every spirit that does not acknowledge Jesus is not from God" (verses 2–3).

The approach to testing set forth in 1 John holds relevance for the study of science. Hearers must evaluate what scientists say not simply by the weight of their fame, but more importantly on the soundness of their evidence and reasoning. In Acts 17:11–12, we read Luke's compliment of the Bereans: "Now the Bereans were of more noble character than the Thessalonians, for they received the message with great eagerness and examined the Scriptures every day to see if what Paul said was true."

The peer-review process that guides scientific advance has its roots in Scripture. From beginning to end, the Bible reminds readers that determination of "fact" requires corroboration. We see this principle affirmed in Numbers 17; Deuteronomy 11, 22, 28; Job 12, 38–39; Proverbs 3, 18; the historical record of 1 Kings 3; and Isaiah 55. According to Malachi 3:10, God himself challenges people to "test" the veracity of his promises to reward their obedience. In the New Testament, Paul instructs early church leaders, "Two or three prophets should speak, and the others should weigh carefully what is said. . . . The spirits of prophets are subject to the control of prophets. For God is not a

God of disorder but of peace" (1 Corinthians 14:29, 32).

Consensus and Consistency

The primary basis on which various written documents were determined to be "God-breathed," sacred texts may be summed up in two words: consensus and consistency. As evidenced by the Septuagint (the Greek translation of the Tanakh), Jewish rabbis had by the third and second century BC established what today we recognize as the Old Testament canon. By their agreement, the 39 books were deemed Scripture. The early church, under the leadership of Athanasius, Bishop of Alexandria, established a consensus list of 27 books (AD 367) that was then confirmed within 30 years by two bodies, the Synod of Hippo Regius (AD 393) and the Council of Carthage (AD 397). The internal consistency of these books served as a core criterion for consensus.

A similar story comes from the history of science. For centuries, scholars debated over what "facts" comprise nature's book. Over the past four hundred years, the scientific revolution succeeded spectacularly, not only in developing the data to form multiple disciplines of research and knowledge but also in applying consistency as a basis for confirming facts. When seeming contradictions arise between or among the scientific disciplines, scientists acknowledge that more research is necessary. Scientists often encounter anomalies—observations, measurements, and/or experiments that initially appear to conflict with the firmly established scientific record or appear to make one scientific discipline contradict another. However, in case after case, ongoing research has resolved the apparent conflict and led to greater insight.

No wonder scientists excitedly welcome anomalies. Anomalies represent opportunities to discover greater harmony and consistency ("concordance") among the various disciplines and subdisciplines of science. As astronomers have gained the capability to detect and measure the laws of physics throughout the universe, and throughout virtually the entire history of the universe, confidence in the immutability and reliability of these laws[24] has justifiably risen to a once-unimaginable height. Science proceeds without concern over emergence of an intractable contradiction between any two scientific disciplines.

While some theologians may still debate the consistency of the biblical books, evangelical scholars generally do not. When Peter Enns[25] and Kenton Sparks[26] raised concern over what they considered a contradiction between two books of the Bible, other evangelical theologians provided a compelling resolution.[27] Claims of contradiction usually come from reading one or more biblical texts in the worst possible interpretive light. When the biblical writers are granted even a reasonable benefit of the doubt, however, the Bible remains free of contradiction. This is not to say anyone, scholar or otherwise, possesses complete and perfect understanding of every word, but I'm confident in asserting sufficient understanding.

For decades, even centuries, anti-theists have taken pains to convince people that the Bible abounds in inconsistencies and contradictions of fact. Skeptics and "free thinkers" still meet regularly to mock Christianity, in particular. One organization headquartered in Redmond, Washington, published a book touting *136 Contradictions in the Bible*.[28] Reading the book, with its obvious and easily resolved interpretive twists, served only to confirm my confidence in the Bible's freedom from inconsistency and contradiction. Theologian Brad McCoy has a written response to all 136 claimed contradictions.[29] The website defendinginerrancy.com provides an extensive collection of responses to other false claims about the biblical text.[30]

Broad consensus on the internal consistency of Scripture as well as on the noncontradictory relationship between one scientific discipline and another points to a reasonable expectation of consistency, or concordance, between the Bible's words and nature's record.

Origin of the Scientific Method

The public schools I attended in British Columbia introduced the scientific method as early as grade one and continued in each grade-level curriculum to emphasize its applicability. By the time I picked up a Bible for the first time, I had been thoroughly saturated in that method and its diverse representations and applications. It had become familiar to me even outside of school from my extracurricular reading and hands-on study of physics and astronomy from age seven onward.

While various step-by-step outlines of the scientific method appear in the many books on this subject, the most familiar from my own education is as follows:

1. Identify the phenomenon (or set of phenomena) to be studied and explained.
2. Identify the frame of reference, or point of view, from which the phenomenon is to be examined.
3. Determine the initial condition(s) from which the phenomenon begins.
4. Carefully and completely note what occurs—the what, when, where, and how the phenomenon proceeds.

5. Describe the final conditions.
6. Form a tentative explanation (hypothesis/interpretation) of the phenomenon.
7. Test this initial explanation with further observations, experiments, and data.
8. Revise or refine the explanation accordingly.
9. Consider whether (or to what degree) the explanation matches with established understanding of related phenomena.
10. Repeat these steps for further insights, validation, and/or revision of the explanation.

As was my habit with other books, I started my examination of the Bible by opening to its first page. As I read the narrative, slowly and thoughtfully, a familiar pattern unexpectedly emerged. I was struck by the parallels between the Genesis 1 account of origins and the stepwise method of observation and analysis I knew so well.

After the bold and accurate introductory declaration, which referenced the long-debated but later confirmed "beginning" of physical history, the passage set forth an account of Earth's transformation into a suitable home for life and then presented a history of life, from its earliest, least complex form to its more recent, complex form, humanity. A particular phrase in the first verse, "the heavens and the earth," stumped me initially. However, I was aware that the English Bible in my hands had been translated from ancient Hebrew, a language with a much smaller vocabulary. So, I reasoned that it could be an idiom or merism the ancients used for what we now refer to as the universe. Later, I discovered that specific words for "universe" and "cosmos" appear nowhere in the Old Testament. The phrase "the heavens and the earth," however, appears thirteen times and always, as the context indicates, with reference to the totality of physical reality.

When I came to Genesis 1:2, I noted a shift in the frame of reference. No longer looking on from out in the heavens, the narrator spoke from the perspective of Earth's surface, as indicated by reference to "the surface of the deep" and to the Spirit of God as "hovering over the waters." Next came a listing of the primordial Earth's initial conditions: (1) the entire surface covered by water; (2) the entire surface wrapped in darkness; (3) the entire surface without form and void, which the context suggested as meaning unfit and devoid of life.

The account of Earth's transformation during the six creation "days" (verses 3–27) appeared to be a stepwise chronology of major events leading up to the planet's suitability for human habitation. Genesis 1:28–2:4 depicted the final state of Earth and its life, now including human life, once God had completed his creative work. Needless to say, I was sufficiently intrigued by this first reading to continue my examination of this unusual book.

Before long, I could identify multiple unique features of the Bible as compared with the writings on which other belief systems are based. One such feature was the quantity and quality of references to creation and to the natural realm. This abundance of testable references allowed for corroboration, another connection with the scientific method. It afforded many and diverse opportunities for testing tentative interpretations (hypotheses) of the Genesis account. Job 38:8–9, for example, affirmed my hunch that Earth's initial darkness (Genesis 1:1–2) resulted from the thickness and opacity of Earth's primordial atmosphere.

Other passages of Scripture brought clarity to other Genesis statements. When I read through the parallel creation texts in Job 37–39, Psalm 104, and Proverbs 8:22–36, I saw Genesis 1:6–8 as a highly abbreviated account of Earth's water cycle formation. Job 37–38 described in much detail Earth's complex water cycle, explaining how three kinds of liquid precipitation (rain, mist, and dew) and three kinds of frozen precipitation (snow, frost, and hail) provided for global human civilization.

A few years later, I decided to read a detailed account of Galileo's debate with the church over heliocentrism. I learned that Galileo defended his view by arguing that the clergy had incorrectly interpreted biblical texts referring to Earth's "immovability" (1 Chronicles 16:30; Psalm 93:1; 96:10; 104:5). He said they had simply misidentified the frame of reference in each case. At that time, the Roman Catholic leaders would not tolerate theological correction from the laity. Despite being correct in his hermeneutics, Galileo was ousted.

I later read a number of books authored or edited by Scottish theologian Thomas Torrance, a man who had dedicated much of his life to the integration of Christian theology and science. When he invited me to participate in a dialogue between theologians and physicists (fifteen of each) to be held in Berkeley, California, I jumped at the opportunity. There I encountered a significant challenge: neither group could speak the other's language. Neither knew where to begin an interactive discussion. If we accomplished anything that day, it was to assure the gathered scholars that Christian theology and the sciences are allies, not enemies, that the two disciplines are founded on similar investigative and interpretive principles, and that the two have much to contribute to each other.[31]

Privately, Torrance spoke to me about "the beauty principle." He emphasized what an extraordinarily powerful tool the scientific method has been for discovering beauty in God's creation. We agreed that the scientific method could just as appropriately be called the biblical testing method and that it was no accident that the scientific revolution exploded from Reformation-era Europe. In books written and edited by Torrance, he explains and documents how the Bible and the theological advances that arose during the Reformation played a crucial role in the development of what is now known as the scientific method.[32]

Scientific Method and Concordance

The fact that both Christian theology and the scientific enterprise passionately seek to discover, explore, and understand what is *true*, what is *real*, argues in favor of concordance between the two. Their similar mission and means of investigation bind them as allies, working together to reveal truths about spiritual and physical reality. Nevertheless, exactly *how* the Bible and science work together as allies has led to vigorous debate within the Christian community. The next chapter describes the wide diversity of Bible-and-science models and comments on their strengths and weaknesses.

Chapter 8

Bible-and-Science Models

More than half a century ago, physicist Ian Barbour observed and described four distinct approaches within Christendom to the relationship between the Bible and science.[1] At the time, he referred to them in these terms: *conflict, independent, dialogue,* and *integration.* Due to changing theological perspectives and scientific advances amid a changing Western culture, Barbour later revised his original categorization, reducing the four to three: *enemies, strangers,* and *partners.*[2] These categories still come close to describing what we see among Christians today, especially within the more theologically conservative branch of the church, where the Bible still holds its long-held position of authority.

Enemies Mutually Rejected

As the naturalistic explanation of life's history gained wider acceptance, the biblical creation account appeared to be under threat. The introduction of biological evolution in public school science curricula stirred up an especially strong response from Christians. Thinking that Earth's age (in the low billions of years) represented the linchpin upholding this naturalistic evolutionary theory, they focused their counterattack on the timescale. Any scientific anomaly (and several do exist) could be exploited to prop up acceptance of the new "creation science" and raise doubts about the plausibility of research findings—especially regarding the age of Earth and the universe.

Although clearly at odds with mainstream science, these creationists asserted that science and the Bible could restore their alliance *if only* scientists would put on biblical glasses crafted specifically to fit a young-earth interpretation of the data. Theologian John Whitcomb and physicist Donald DeYoung wrote that, regardless of training or discipline, scientists "grope in darkness apart from God's special revelation in Scripture."[3] Now, this conflict between young-earth creationism and mainstream science—not just in one or two disciplines, but virtually *all* disciplines—has escalated into a winner-take-all battle. Popular book titles highlight the battle motif. Founder and long-time president of the Institute for Creation Research, Henry M. Morris, wrote (among many other books) *The Long War Against God*.[4] Answers in Genesis founder and president, Ken Ham, wrote *The Lie*,[5] identifying mainstream science and scientists as an enemy to be defeated.

Though accommodationists do not easily fit into Barbour's classification, they do display a conflict element. Accomodationists see multiple conflicts between scientific statements made by authors of the Bible's 66 books, if interpreted historically or literally, and what they view as the established findings of modern science.

Many nontheist and agnostic scientists, assuming young-earth creationist views are those of all "Bible-believing Christians," have responded with belligerence and ridicule toward Christians. Many people (and their reputations) have been injured in the crossfire. Opportunities for dialogue and faith-sharing have been lost. In the midst of the battle, some scientists have come to view Christianity as an enemy of advancing research or, worse yet, as an anti-science belief system.

The conflict approach brings out the worst, not the best, in all who adopt it. Christians, whatever position they may take, are tempted to take aim at *all* views that differ from their own, often launching their most vociferous attacks against fellow Christians.[6] This clash has done significant damage to the advance of the gospel and to the unity that Jesus has called Christian believers to.

Strangers on (Mostly) Separate Quests

The term "nonoverlapping magisteria" (NOMA) was coined by Stephen Jay Gould and first appeared in a *Natural History* magazine article. Here's how he describes this approach: "The net of science covers the empirical universe: what is it made of (fact) and why [or how] does it work this way (theory). The net of religion extends over questions of moral meaning and value. These two magisteria [realms of investigation] do not overlap."[7] Gould does acknowledge that what separates the two realms is not "an extensive no man's land."[8] Rather, he notes, "The two magisteria bump right up against each other, interdigitating in wondrously complex ways along their joint border. Many of our deepest questions call upon aspects of both for different parts of a full answer."[9]

While Gould sees a border between the Bible and science, Christian scholars John Walton and Brent Sandy, among others, see a chasm. They claim that the Bible authors and their contemporaries had no interest in science and that science is impotent to address theological issues.[10] Other Christian scholars express a similar view when they advocate for "accommodation." As discussed in chapter 2, they point to what they regard as multiple conflicts or contradictions between the findings of science and the creation passages recorded in the Bible's 66 books. They assert that we need to allow the Bible and science to speak separately, accommodating the apparent differences as artifacts of diverse cultures, languages, and historical eras. They say that while there is minimal, if any, overlap between science and the biblical authors' mistaken scientific and historical notions, the rest of the Bible has been inspired by the Holy Spirit, and that part is truthful.

A slightly different approach agrees with Gould that science and the Bible fully "complement" one another, but with the caveat that the two books remain essentially independent. According to advocates of this approach, science and Scripture address different topics. One may add insight to the other in that each reveals different aspects of God, and thus, they cannot be considered contradictory. While this group recognizes that science and the Bible possess a long "common border," as Gould suggests, they see only a few points of connection between them rather than any significant overlap.

Nearly all theistic evolutionists and evolutionary creationists[11] hold to one of the complementary models.[12] Most framework hypothesis advocates do as well. As discussed in chapter 2, framework hypothesis proponents interpret the seven-day scheme of Genesis 1 as a literary framework in which God's creative works are narrated in a topical, not a chronological, order. They see the Genesis 1 creation days as picture frames containing snapshots of God's creative activity on Earth that mirror his creative activity in heaven.[13]

Nearly all complementary models agree that both the Bible and science point to a cosmic beginning. Many also highlight the fine-tuned quality of the universe that makes physical life possible. A few complementary models allow for a slight degree of overlap between science and the Bible, but in ways that are permanently hidden from human investigation. John Walton, for example, speculates that "God might be working alongside or through physical and biological processes in a way that science cannot detect."[14]

Partners in Discovery and Dialogue
The partnership approach to the Bible and science acknowledges significant

overlap between them. This approach is based on belief that the two books *do* address overlapping subject matter: physical, biological, relational, and spiritual reality. They are seen as forming an alliance, a historically contingent revelation of how the physical and biological realms we inhabit—and we, ourselves—came to be and now function. What's more, if we consider that a single, transcendent Source accounts for both revelations, as science implies and the Bible states, we would anticipate opportunities for science to inform Christian theology and for Christian theology to inform science. What Scripture uniquely brings to the discourse, however, is an all-important revelation of the *why* behind the physical realm as it is, including *why* we have the capacity to discern and describe physical reality and to make sense of its existence and our own.

Both the Old and New Testaments explain why "something" exists rather than "nothing" and why this tangible "something," the physical realm, is intelligible—orderly, principled, and temporal. Science points to a transcendent origin, a beginning of space, time, matter, and energy from beyond themselves, unbounded by them. The Bible explains that a transcendent Being, a relational Being characterized by love, acted to create the cosmos according to purposes and plans prepared before time as we know it.[15]

Those purposes and plans are encompassed in the word *redemption*. As Paul writes in 2 Timothy 1:9, "This grace was given us in Christ Jesus before the beginning of time." In Titus 1:2, Paul states that we humans have "the hope of eternal life, which God, who does not lie, promised before the beginning of time." Peter declares in 1 Peter 1:18–20 that Christians "were redeemed from the empty way of life" . . . "with the precious blood of Christ" who "was chosen before the creation of the world." These and several other Bible passages,[16] from Genesis to Revelation, assure us that God began his works of redemption before he created anything—before he created the universe, where this plan would unfold and ultimately lead us to a realm beyond the limits of this one.

This perspective aligns with the medieval Christian proclamation that every detail of the universe was, and is, superintended by God to allow for the existence and redemption of humans, many humans. Such a claim can be—and has been—put to the test. Revelation 7:9 declares that the host of redeemed humans will be "an uncountable number," especially notable given that when Revelation was written, the Greek numbering system already went up to a billion.

A wealth of scientific evidence indicates that every significant component of the universe, Earth, and Earth's life, and every significant event in their histories, plays a role in making possible the existence and redemption of billions of humans from their self-destructive ways—and within a relatively brief time (astronomically speaking).[17] This theological proposition points us toward the most productive way to investigate the realm of nature—and to care for it, too. It implies that science will progress most rapidly and efficiently from a biblical perspective, and it compels us to keep the Bible's redemptive perspective in mind.

As mentioned in the preceding chapter, God gave humans responsibility to oversee our earthly habitat for the well-being of all life. This responsibility was not removed when the first humans demonstrated a disastrous propensity to sin. Like all humans, they yielded to their own impulses rather than to God's wisdom. Genesis 3 says, "Cursed is the ground because of you" and cites other consequences as well. However, in working to restore the damage sin caused and continues to cause, we humans have an opportunity to learn essential lessons that drive us back to trust in God.

If both the literal book of Scripture and the tangible book of nature reveal our desperate need for—and God's provision of—a divine Redeemer, we can reasonably expect the two books to be concordant. We can anticipate that the two books will exhibit significant and mutually elucidating overlap. We can anticipate that, as scientists learn more about the universe, Earth, and Earth's life, the redemptive connection between the two books will become more clearly evident. As theologians gain more insights into the message of Scripture, we can anticipate that its redemptive theme will remain clear and consistent. We can anticipate that the concordance between the words of Scripture and the book of nature will only grow as understanding of both books deepens.

Most importantly, the partnership approach to the content of the Bible and science keeps the door open for dialogue between students of Scripture and students of nature. Rather than stirring up animosity or driving us apart, this approach leads to a blessed alliance that can only enhance our Christian witness to the world. Like any valuable relationship, it must be mutually protective, as well. Concordance, when taken to the most extreme forms of concordism, can become needlessly divisive, as the following brief chapter explains.

Chapter 9

Concordance vs. Concordism

Confusion over what, exactly, the term *concordism* refers to has significantly complicated the dual revelation/biblical inerrancy debate among
Christians. While many *isms* refer to a specific (or closely similar) set of beliefs (such as relativism), practices (such as stoicism), or characteristics (such
as colloquialism), concordism covers an unusually wide range of beliefs and
practices with the added baggage of a likely negative connotation. The term
has been applied to a range of Bible-and-science positions from one extreme
to another and by an array of descriptors, some more emotional than logical.
The descriptors I've chosen for this chapter are those I've encountered most
frequently in the theological literature.

The one so-called concordist position omitted from the discussion here
would be more accurately called "fusion." Harmony requires at least two notes,
but this position acknowledges only one: the Bible or science. Some Christians
claim that the Bible is the sole source of truth about the history and features of
the universe, Earth, and all life, up to and including human life. On the other
hand, I meet people of diverse backgrounds, religious or not, who claim that
science is the sole source of truth about the history and features of the universe,
Earth, and life. In either case, the possibility for reasonable dialogue seems limited, and yet a gentle nudge toward logical consistency can open a door.

Hard (or Bold) Concordism
Concordists most often described as "hard" or "bold" by fellow theologians are
Christians who tend to draw as much science from the Bible as the text can conceivably hold—and then some. Hard concordists would include individuals who
hear or read science headlines and then scour the Bible looking for verses that

seem to connect in some way with the findings. Because of my dual identity as a Christian and a scientist, people often send me their excited claims of having discovered scientific statements or insights no one else has yet found in the Bible. Some point to passages in Genesis, Job, Psalms, Proverbs, Ecclesiastes, Isaiah, Ezekiel, or another book of Scripture that purportedly speaks about space travel, galaxies, atoms, quantum mechanics, string theory, special and general relativity, Neanderthals, dinosaurs, television, nuclear weapons, helicopters, or tanks, for example.

One helpful response to this extreme type of concordism, a response I try to use when presented with such "findings," is to raise questions that highlight some of the fundamental principles of Bible interpretation:

1. Given that the Bible is a book for all generations, is there some scholar from a past generation who recognized, at least in general terms, this same (or a closely similar) insight within the text? If not, perhaps this new "finding" is something the Holy Spirit did not intend to reveal.
2. Are there any other Bible passages, especially in other books of Scripture, that convey this same (or a closely parallel) message? Any important truth the Holy Spirit intends to reveal will appear in more than one passage and typically in more than one book of the Bible.
3. Does the Bible passage actually "teach" a certain scientific discovery, or does it merely show consistency with that discovery?
4. Has anyone from the past drawn a similarly specific and detailed scientific message from the text, or does the text instead reveal truth in more general terms? A scientific truth may, indeed, be there in the text but perhaps less specifically or clearly so.
5. Does the text communicate a message of importance to previous generations apart from its recently observed concordance with scientific truth?
6. Is the claimed scientific message constructed from the linkage of two unrelated verses or contexts? For example, Job 31:4–7 refers to a man walking, and Job 31:26 extols the splendor of the Moon. To suggest, as several concordists have, that this chapter predicted a man would walk on the Moon seems an unreasonable stretch. It is especially unreasonable given that Job is the man walking in Job 31:4–7 and also the one extolling the Moon's splendor in Job 31:26.

The most popularly known example of hard concordist assertions may be the claim that the book of Job describes dinosaurs.[1] No Bible teacher or scholar prior to the nineteenth century considered the "behemoth" in Job 40 and the "leviathan" in Job 41 as gigantic, prehistoric creatures. In fact, the text implies that Job and his friends were familiar with these two creatures. Until the nineteenth century, commentaries on Job typically referred to the behemoth as a hippopotamus or elephant and the leviathan as a crocodile or whale.[2]

Until William Buckland's discovery of Megalosaurus bones in 1819,[3] no fossils had been discovered and identified as belonging to lizard-like creatures larger than any land animal on Earth today. Fossils of such creatures date to tens of millions of years ago, long before humans existed. Large dinosaurs were driven to extinction by a giant asteroid collision that ignited huge volcanic eruptions around the world 66.04 million years ago—again, long before humans existed.[4]

The descriptions in Job 40–41 of the behemoth and the leviathan present a poor fit with any known dinosaur species. On the other hand, once the literal descriptions are separated from the metaphorical descriptions, Job 40–41 provides excellent portrayals of the behemoth as a hippopotamus and the leviathan as a crocodile. Critics of this view cite Job 40:17 as evidence against it. This verse says, "his [the behemoth's] tail sways like a cedar." Hippopotamus (and elephant) tails are relatively small, whereas dinosaur tails were large enough to resemble a cedar's trunk. However, the range of meanings of the biblical Hebrew word for "tail" in Job 40:17, *zanab*, includes "tail," "end," and "stump."[5] The hippopotamus possesses a massive muscular rump. Job 40:16–17 links the behemoth's tail (*zanab*) with its loins, belly, and thighs. For millennia, people observed that hippopotami use their large, heavily muscled hind quarters as a weapon against intruders who dare to come into their territory.

The most glaring problem with interpreting the behemoth and leviathan as dinosaurs is that it misidentifies the larger context of Job 38:39–42:9. This portion of the book focuses on *nephesh* (soulish animals), some of which are easy for humans to tame, such as goats, and some of which are extraordinarily difficult to tame, such as the hippopotamus and the crocodile. However, whether the *nephesh* animal is a goat, a lion, a raven, a deer, a donkey, an ox, an ostrich, a horse, a hawk, an eagle, a behemoth, or a leviathan, only a higher Being can tame such a creature. God's point, here, is that only a higher Being can humble a proud human's heart (Job 40:9–14). While dinosaurs are not *nephesh*, both the hippopotamus and the crocodile are.[6]

Another familiar hard concordist claim is that the Bible predicted the future use of military vehicles such as tanks. The two texts cited as references to tanks are Nahum 2:3–4 and Revelation 9:17–19.

The idea that the Bible predicted the future use of tanks in warfare is based on descriptions of chariots and horses rushing back and forth through city streets and squares with heads spewing out fire, smoke, and sulfur. Although one cannot absolutely rule out the possibility that these are seventh-century BC and first-century AD descriptions of tank warfare, alternate explanations certainly do exist. Roman charioteers, for example, were known to shoot flaming arrows into strategically positioned bales of hay as well as into oncoming chariots and warriors. Here, concordists would be wise to couch their claims with caveats.

Another glaring example of hard concordism comes from twenty-first-century, self-professed *anti*-concordists. They claim that the description of Earth's sky in Job 37:18, "hard as a mirror of cast bronze," reflects Job's belief that the "expanse" referred to in Genesis 1:6–8 was a solid bronze dome.[7] They overlook obvious contextual clues that indicate the use of figurative language. For example, Job 37:21 reads, "Now no one can look at the sun, bright as it is in the skies after the wind has swept them clean." In ancient times, glass mirrors did not exist. The best reflective surface humans could produce was a mirror of polished cast bronze. Job 37:18 and 37:21 compare the brightness of the sky on a windswept day to the painfully bright reflection of light from a cast bronze mirror.

Soft (or Safe) Concordism

"Soft" concordism, by contrast with "hard" or "bold" concordism, refers to the opposite approach to acknowledging scientific content in the Bible. An example of soft concordism is the willingness to say that Genesis reveals a beginning, whether of the universe, the world, or life as we know it, but no more. For soft concordists, to affirm that Genesis contains any further content related to science, natural history, or chronology goes beyond the limits of safety. After all, they believe science is subject to change, and they point out that Christians have embarrassed themselves in the past when using (or rather, misusing) Scripture to defend a scientific "truth" that eventually proved untrue.

Many self-described soft concordists also call into question the veracity of most, if not all, Old Testament miracle stories, seeing them merely as "exaggerations" to make a point.[8] In such cases, the descriptor "concordist" would appear a distortion of the term, or an exaggeration at best. In fact, this response reveals greater concordance with naturalism than with theism.

Scholars associated with the BioLogos ministry take a variety of positions for which the label soft, or safe, concordism seems appropriate. For example, they refer to themselves as "evolutionary creationists." In this way they indicate acceptance of the biblical God as Creator, the Source of the realm we humans occupy, though most reject the possibility that scientific investigation of that realm can or does reveal God's creative involvement or miraculous intervention in the unfolding of cosmic history. They see the process as strictly natural and continuous, guided invisibly and undiscoverably by the hand of God. This level of caution means that scientific findings can neither confirm nor deny the reliability of Scripture. Thus, the term noncommittal concordism seems appropriate. It is "safe" in that the possibility of having to make any corrections or adjustments to current understanding of the Bible is eliminated.

The apostles Peter and Paul exhort all Christians to be courageous in sharing good reasons their faith. Something more than soft (safe) concordism is needed for those who, like the apostle Thomas, need evidence on which to build faith. Thinkers and questioners are among the people God has called his followers to reach, to make disciples of.

Moderate (or Modest) Concordism
While science-Scripture linkages warrant care and must remain within the accepted ICBI hermeneutical bounds, when they do appear reasonable, they deserve attention. If these linkages are discarded out of hand, the Bible ends up being much like any other ancient storybook, without content that differentiates it from merely human thoughts and imaginings. Concordance between the message of ancient and diverse writers and well-established or even still-emerging discoveries about history, medicine, archaeology, geology, and other knowledge disciplines helps readers recognize the Bible's uniqueness as a supernaturally inspired revelation. Only the One who created the universe could reveal truth to all generations and cultures—transcendent truth from the transcendent God.

Moderate concordism means paying attention to whatever the Bible has to say about nature's realm *and* everything it has to say about the spiritual realm. Obviously, each of God's two books, Scripture and nature, has a limited and different scope. However, as noted previously, given that both are revelations from God, we would expect that each also includes some guidelines for their interpretation, including contextual clues to the usage of metaphor and other figurative language. The examples from Job stand out. In the chapters referring to behemoth and leviathan, the words "like" and "as" appear more than a dozen times. Literal reading does not imply the absence of illustrative devices.

To take a moderate, or modest, concordist position, as the Reasons to Believe scholars do, also means being willing to acknowledge that ongoing scientific, historical, and theological research could show our understanding of certain biblical texts inaccurate, or at least partly so. Likewise, ongoing exegetical and theological research on biblical texts can reveal where we have misunderstood the record of nature and also help guide scientific research.[9]

Moderate concordists recognize that no one can claim to have a complete, unbiased, and perfectly interpreted understanding of everything the Bible—and the book of nature—teaches. A moderate concordist approach provides efficient, productive pathways for gaining additional knowledge and understanding from God's two books.

Collision over Cosmology

Anti-concordists and soft concordists have been most critical of moderate concordists' claim that the Bible teaches some of the fundamental features of big bang cosmology. Ironically, many Christian theologians strongly rejected the claim that the Bible aligns well with big bang models, while twentieth-century nontheistic and atheistic astronomers have strongly reacted to the same models' clear theological, specifically biblical, implications. Some of the most famous astronomers of the past century—Sir Arthur Eddington, Sir Fred Hoyle, Thomas Gold, Hermann Bondi, Robert Dicke, John Gribbin, and Geoffrey Burbidge—mustered all the scientific clout they could in a vain attempt to overthrow big bang cosmology.[10]

Sir Arthur Eddington protested, "Philosophically, the notion of a beginning of the present order of Nature is repugnant to me . . . I should like to find a genuine loophole."[11] John Gribbin wrote, "The biggest problem with the Big Bang theory of the origin of the Universe is philosophical—perhaps even theological—what was there before the bang?"[12] Many more quotes could be cited, but these suffice to demonstrate that while some twenty-first-century evangelical Christian theologians see no links between the Bible and big bang cosmology, non-Christian astronomers consistently have and still do. As a skeptical young astronomy student, I did as well.

In my first serious reading of the Bible, I noted that the Bible repeatedly declares three distinct features of the universe: (1) the universe had a single beginning of everything humans could possibly detect, namely matter, energy, space, and time (Genesis 1:1; 2:3–4; Psalm 148:5; Isaiah 40:26; 42:5; 45:18; John 1:3; Colossians 1:16–17; 2 Timothy 1:9; Titus 1:2; Hebrews 11:3); (2) the laws governing the universe are constant, unchanging throughout cosmic history (Genesis 1–3; Jeremiah 33:19–26; Romans 8:22); and (3) one of these unchanging laws is a pervasive law of decay, termed by physicists as the second law of thermodynamics (Ecclesiastes 1–3; 9–12; John 16:33; Romans 8:20–22; Revelation 21:4–5).

These three biblically referenced features of the universe were consistent with the big bang model but contradicted by that model's twentieth-century competitors: the steady state, the quasi-steady state, the hesitation, the plasma, and the oscillating universe models.[13] In this regard, the Bible showed predictive power. If, in fact, ongoing astronomical observations proved the big bang model correct and its competition false, such validation would stand as strong evidence that the Bible had been supernaturally inspired by the One who created and designed the universe. Seeing features of big bang cosmology in the Bible was one of several evidences that led to my signing my name in the back of a Gideon Bible, committing my life to Jesus Christ.

The Benefits of Moderate Concordism

Moderate concordism allows for respectful dialogue over what may seem either under- or overinterpretation of various passages with respect to science. A personal example comes to mind. Upon hearing me speak about the wonder of the Bible's accuracy in identifying three distinct, recently confirmed features of the universe, a theology professor in my audience approached me afterward to say that I had missed one: cosmic expansion. Although I was aware of the possibility, I felt unsure that the biblical mentions of "the stretching out of the heavens" were literal references to the expansion of the universe.

The professor, John Rea, began by explaining that the three Hebrew verb forms are different from verb tenses in English. He listed eleven texts that say (in English translations) that God stretches out—and stretched out—the heavens. In seven of these passages (Job 9:8; Psalm 104:2; Isaiah 40:22; 42:5; 44:24; 51:13; and Zechariah 12:1), the verb *natah* is used in the form that implies continual or ongoing stretching of the heavens. In the four other passages (Isaiah 45:12; 48:13; and Jeremiah 10:12; 51:15) the form of *natah* indicates that the stretching out of the heavens was completed in the past. Isaiah 40:22 uses two different Hebrew verbs, *natah* and *mathah*, in two different forms to imply that God *continually stretches* out the heavens and that God *has stretched* out the heavens. I explained to Rea that the simultaneously ongoing and finished aspect of cosmic expansion he had deduced from these Bible verses matches astronomers' observations of the universe and their theoretical construct of the big bang model.[14] Therefore, cosmic expansion *could be* an example of moderate concordism.

Independent of Rea, I was impressed that Job's list of wonders God has performed includes the stretching out of the heavens. Job grants God exclusive credit in Job 9:8, which says, "He [God] alone stretches out the heavens."

Astronomers have determined that the physical constants governing cosmic expansion manifest by far the most spectacular, measurable fine-tuning of the cosmos (10^{96} times greater than anything designed and manufactured by humans) to make physical life possible in the universe.[15]

On the other hand, this view that the Bible refers to cosmic expansion in multiple passages may represent an example of reaching too far for concordance. Vern Poythress, also a respected theology professor, takes a different view of these same passages. In response to our discussion during a recent workshop on dual revelation,[16] Poythress sent me this explanation of these biblical passages. Here is an excerpt from what he wrote:

> The Hebrew tense system is very different from English. Context of use is necessary to narrow down the function of any one occurrence. There are a multitude of contexts, and a variety of meaning implications that go with the contexts . . . .
>
> So, what is the point in the poetic image [in Job 9:8–9] of stretching out the heavens? Isaiah 40:22 has one of the fuller renderings, ". . . who stretches out the heavens like a curtain, and spreads them like a tent to dwell in . . ."
>
> Both lines draw an analogy with a piece of cloth, "a curtain" or "a tent (cover)." The image evoked in Isaiah 40:22 "is likened to one unfurling and stretching out a tightly wrapped tent." Psalm 104:2 is not as elaborate, but similar. The occurrence of a number of such passages in the Bible does not show that some special information is being conveyed. Rather, it is a reinforcement of the point made in any one of them.
>
> The comparison with a tent brings God's work into connection with Israelite work. The poetic association that is primary is probably the ease and mastery and confidence with which God has structured creation . . . .
>
> It need not supply any technical information as to how God is dealing with spatial measurements of the size of the cosmos. We can evoke Calvin's principle (with which I basically agree), discussed in his commentary on Genesis, that Moses writes about what ordinary people could observe.

Both John Rea's explanation and Vern Poythress's response have been highly abbreviated for this book. Interested readers will find in the endnotes an unabridged version plus a review of how theologians many centuries ago interpreted biblical texts relevant to the universe.[17] One significant value of a modest or moderate approach to concordism is the opportunity it provides for diverse interpretations and respectful debate over differences, with the goal of discovering, integrating, and better understanding truth from God's two books—all within the boundary of dual revelation and biblical inerrancy, not outside it.

The Spiritual Impact of Concordance

My surprising discovery that the Bible made statements about the natural realm that were undoubtedly beyond the scientific knowledge of its human authors and their contemporaries—revelation that appeared in no other written or oral source I had found—persuaded me that the Bible could only have been inspired by God. Years of experience in sharing my Christian faith with people who lack exposure to the Bible tells me that these connections between the ancient text and established science stir a willingness to consider that Scripture may, indeed, come from the Being who created and shaped the universe. A soft concordist position removes the opportunity for testing and demonstrating the Bible's unique standing as God's Word. A denial of what seems obvious—such as the textual clues indicating that Genesis conveys a chronology of events in Earth's history—is most often seen as a concession that the Bible cannot be wholly trusted as a book of truth.

My experience may be a bit unusual in that I have lived and worked for decades in the vicinity of the California Institute of Technology, the Jet Propulsion Laboratory, and the headquarters of the Skeptics Society. In all these years, I have yet to meet a non-Christian who respected, rather than ridiculed, the claim that Genesis 1 presents *no* chronology of creation, just a general statement about beginnings. Both Christians and non-Christians can be spiritually encouraged when scientific research produces discoveries and theories that coincide with what Scripture long ago stated. They can also be discouraged or spiritually shaken when science appears to contradict what the Bible says.

What are Christians to do, then, with the duality of God's revelation? As previously stated, no one can claim to have a complete, unbiased, and perfectly interpreted understanding of all that the Bible reveals, and the same goes for the book of nature. We humans exist within nature and its limits. Nevertheless, the Bible calls us to be diligent and discerning students of theology and nature, thoroughly and humbly researching both revelations. It also provides guidelines for this task (see chapter 6) of developing a reasonable, compelling case in support of the hope we have in Christ (1 Peter 3:15). When we overreach, we are to humbly back up. If we underreach, we are to courageously move forward. To stop moving is not an acceptable option (Philippians 3:13–15). As we press forward to embrace more and more truth, we become better equipped to share our faith (Philemon 6).

In pressing forward, we need to be aware that other religions and cults are also attempting to win converts and bolster the confidence of adherents by making their own concordist claims. They attempt to show how their religious books and beliefs have always aligned with what are now well-established facts of science and history. The next chapter examines various concordance efforts in other religions and cults and contrasts it with the Scripture-science concordance in Christianity.

Chapter 10

Concordism in Other Faiths

Growing up in a neighborhood of more immigrants than fellow Canadians, I encountered followers and proponents of many other religions years before getting to know Christians or learning about the Bible. After becoming convinced that the universe had a beginning (and consequently a Beginner), I looked into the beliefs of some of my school friends—Hinduism, Buddhism, Islam, Baháʼí, Zoroastrianism, Confucianism, and Mormonism—exploring to some extent their foundational books and commentaries.

I noticed that virtually all these religions' apologists sought to attract converts by showing how their foundational books/texts aligned with data from modern science. What follows are brief summaries of their scientific concordism attempts.

Concordism in Hinduism

Before some of my classmates nudged me to examine the Vedas, I had already been exposed to some Hindu beliefs through my studies of astronomy, especially cosmology. Many astronomers at that time were attracted to Hinduism because it explicitly taught a cosmology consistent with one of the prevailing cosmological theories, the oscillating or cyclic universe. In Vedic cosmology, a *kalpa* is one day in the life of Brahma (a Hindu deity). This day is said to equal 4.32 billion years.[1] According to the Vedas, Brahma creates a new universe at the beginning of each day, a universe that is destroyed at the end of the day (that is, after 4.32 billion years), whereupon Brahma creates another universe. The *Rig Veda* (ca. 300 BC) reports that the present *kalpa* began about 1.973 billion years ago.[2]

In 1976, physicist John Gribbin suggested a version of big bang cosmology that closely resembled Vedic cosmology. He wrote that the best way around what, for him, were the troubling theological implications of a singular cosmic beginning was "provided by a model in which the universe expands from a singularity, collapses back again, and repeats the cycle indefinitely."[3] This reincarnating, or oscillating, universe model (and others like it) drew interest for several years, and it still holds the attention of a few scholars. Nevertheless, astronomical observations and the outworking of the laws of physics have essentially ruled out such models.[4]

Hindu apologists have more recently pointed out that the Rig Veda clued scholars to the fact that Earth is round and orbits the Sun.[5] However, the concept of a spherical Earth that revolves around the Sun was widely known throughout the ancient world at the time the Rig Veda was written (see chapter 12). What is more, as with all the Vedas, its language is vague and highly esoteric.

One of two texts cited by present-day Hindu apologists as proof that the Rig Veda revealed a spherical Earth says this: "Decorated with gold and jewels, they were spreading over the circuit of the earth; but mighty as they were, they triumphed not over Indra; he dispersed them with the (rising) sun" (mandala 1, sukta 33, mantra 8).[6] The other text states, "Thy spirit that went far away, away to the four-cornered earth, We cause to come to thee again that thou mayst live and sojourn here" (mandala 10, sukta 58, mantra 3).[7] In the latter text, Hindu apologists claim that "the four-cornered earth" could be understood as the four-bended-cornered earth. While Earth's spherical shape could conceivably be deciphered from these texts, that interpretation seems neither probable nor specified.

Cited as a proof text for Earth's orbit around the Sun, another passage from the Rig Veda reads, "When the earth which has neither hands nor feet flourished through the acts of (devotion paid) to the adorable (deities), then you did smite down Susna, circumambulating it on the right, for the sake of Visayu" (mandala 10, sukta 22, mantra 14).[8] In the original Sanskrit, Susna can refer to the sun, fire, or a spirit being. Again, it may be possible to read this Hindu text as implying Earth's revolution around the Sun, but this interpretation seems far from specified or probable—especially given that many Hindu scriptures declare the Sun a deity and a home for other deities.

Still, some Hindu apologists claim Vedic cosmology predicted dozens of modern astronomical discoveries. A few go so far as to accuse Sir Isaac Newton of "scientific robbery" from the Vedas.[9] However, the majority of practicing Hindus are well aware that their Vedas are far from closely or clearly aligned with the findings of astronomy, physics, geology, and chemistry. Therefore, they opt for a softer concordism. For example, they point to the health benefits of Hindu teachings such as yoga, meditation, and dietary practices.[10] These "benefits" do find some support in the social science and life science literature. However, these health benefit teachings are not unique or exclusive to Hindu practices.

Concordism in Islam

When I first examined a copy of the Qur'an (translated into English), I was struck and, to be honest, dismayed by its repetitive, esoteric language. The vague language alone raised doubt that this book could be a message inspired by the person or power responsible for the existence and features of the universe. Far more importantly, where the Qur'an did include a specific statement about science, it stood at odds with firmly established science. For example, the Qur'an speaks about seven concentric spherical layers of heaven, one above another, centered around Earth (Sura 67:3; 71:15). From the lowest of these seven layers, the stars are said to be suspended like lamps (Sura 6:97; 37:6; 41:12; 67:5). These lamps are described as missiles, made to drive away the devils (Sura 67:5; 37:6–10).

In an attempt to get around the Qur'an's erroneous statement that the stars are in the nearest of seven heavenly layers, some Muslims speculate that the seven layers refer to seven atmospheric layers around the Earth or to extradimensional layers beyond the universe. However, Sura 71:15–16 contradicts both of those interpretations in declaring that the Moon and Sun are in the midst of the seven heavens (see also Sura 25:61).

Despite these and other notable conflicts between the Qur'an and science, followers of Islam promote the concordance of their holy book with modern science more ardently than do apologists for any other religion. While among Christians, extreme or bold concordists are a fringe element, among Muslims, they represent the mainstream.

The most well-known advocate for the concordance of the Qur'an with modern science is French physician Maurice Bucaille, author of *The Bible, The Qur'an, and Science*.[11] Bucaille launches with an attack on young-earth creationism, demonstrating how advances in scientific knowledge have demolished that biblical origins story, which he claims is *the* biblical origins story. He goes on from there to interpret biblical statements in the worst possible way to show that the Bible is full of contradictions. Bucaille claims that the Bible and the Christian faith are completely lacking in scientific or rational credibility.

Lack of biblical literacy leaves many readers vulnerable to his arguments.

Bucaille illustrates what concordist overreach looks like. He attempts to show how the Qur'an predicted dozens of modern scientific discoveries, such as the existence of multiple Earth-like planets in the universe. He claims, "The Qur'anic text clearly indicates the existence of more than one single Earth, our own Earth (*ard*); there are others like it in the Universe."[12] He bases this conclusion on the appearance of multiple appearances of the word "worlds" in the Qur'an, and on "their symbolic numerical quantity: 7."[13]

Christian physician William Campbell has taken up the challenge of refuting Bucaille's wild assertions. His book *The Qur'an and the Bible in the Light of History and Science* exposes Bucaille's distortions of Scripture as well as of the Qur'an.[14] In the same book, Campbell, who has devoted his life to bringing Muslims to faith in Jesus Christ, demonstrates how the Qur'an has, in fact, proclaimed more than a few statements about science that are clearly erroneous.

Despite Campbell's thoughtful and thorough refutation, a number of Islamic apologists have pushed Bucaille's brand of concordism to even greater extremes. Many claim, for example, that the Qur'an predicted the discovery of pulsars.[15] The claim is based on Sura 86:1–3, which reads, "By the sky and at-Tariq. But what will let you know what at-Tariq is? The Piercing Star."[16] The Piercing Star ostensibly refers to a pulsar, as if there were only one. In fact, a great many have been discovered.[17] Unfortunately for these Islamic apologists, none of the known pulsars is so exceptional compared with the others that it would warrant the title the Piercing Star. Additionally, "piercing star" is a poor description of a pulsar. Virtually any astronomical emitter of radiation could be identified in such terms.

Today's Islamic apologists also assert that Sura 55:33 predicts the future development and deployment of interplanetary space travel. The passage reads, "O society of jinn and humans! If you can pass through the bounds of the heavens and the earth, go ahead and pass. But you will not pass except with authorization."[18] In the Qur'an, "jinn" is a reference to angels, almost always to the evil angels. While passing through "the bounds of the heavens and the earth" is a supposed reference to travel via physical interplanetary spacecraft, it seems more likely a reference to another kind of passage, such as death.

The same Islamic apologists claim that Sura 17:1 predicted the development and use of airplanes. That passage reads, "Glory to Him who journeyed His servant by night, from the Sacred Mosque, to the Farthest Mosque, whose precincts We have blessed, in order to show him of Our wonders."[19] The claim here is that a journey in one night from the Sacred Mosque to the Farthest

---

Did Neil Armstrong Convert to Islam When He Walked on the Moon?

A story told by Muslims across Africa since the late 1980s and early 1990s claims that Neil Armstrong heard the sound of the muezzin's call to prayer while he was on the Moon. At that moment, the story goes, he converted to Islam. Christian leaders I met during a trip to Africa told me that two million printed copies of this story had been distributed throughout Africa, influencing many to embrace Islam. They asked me to contact NASA to see if the claim of Armstrong's conversion were true.

Upon my return to America, I called NASA's public relations office with my question. The person I spoke with asked one of her bosses, who knew Armstrong personally, to call me back, and he did. He told me Armstrong preferred to keep his religious beliefs private, but then he added, "I can categorically assure you Neil Armstrong is not a Muslim and never has been a Muslim." He gave me permission to put this statement in print and to have it distributed throughout Africa.

Armstrong himself requested that the US State Department send a rejection of the claim notice to embassies and consulates throughout the Middle East, North Africa, and Asia stating that "reports of his conversion to Islam are inaccurate."[20]

Mosque would require a modern airplane, yet there is nothing in Sura 17:1 that says how such a journey would be accomplished or even what kind of journey is implied.

Perhaps the most widely known example of Islamic hard concordism is the claim that the Qur'an predicted that men would walk on the Moon and bring back rocks from the Moon. The Qur'an certainly does mention the Moon some 28 times, and Qur'anic references to men number in the hundreds. However, not one passage in the Qur'an mentions both the Moon and a human (or humans) in the same or a nearby verse, nor does any passage even hint that humans would walk on the Moon. This claim is more imaginative than concordist.

Another familiar claim says that the Qur'an predicted the precise date on which the first humans would land on the Moon. This claim is based strictly on (statistically insignificant) numerology. As it turns out, there are 1,389 verses between Sura 54:1, which mentions the Moon, and the end of the Qur'an.[21] The year 1389 on the Islamic calendar (called the Hijri calendar) corresponds to 1969 on the Gregorian calendar, the year Neil Armstrong and Buzz Aldrin landed on the lunar surface. No verses in the Qur'an, even in the most ancient versions of the Qur'an, indicate that the number of verses corresponds to a number of years. Furthermore, a different date would pop up by counting the number of verses following any of the other 27 references to the Moon. This example illustrates what could be referred to as hindsight concordism.

This kind of hard, imaginative, or hindsight concordism has been, and still is, used extensively by Islamic apologists, as well as by proponents of Hinduism. Nevertheless, countless people have been influenced by it, especially in cultures where tradition or authoritative voices trump critical assessment.

Concordism in Buddhism

Buddhism, unlike Hinduism and Islam, is a syncretic religion. Historically, its many and diverse sects have borrowed doctrines and practices from other religions, including Christianity. As one might anticipate, scientific concordism is a relatively recent addition to Buddhist efforts to gain converts. Concordism is used primarily to downplay the mythical elements of Buddhist cosmology and rituals and to highlight, instead, the rational aspects of Buddhism.[22]

Astrophysicist Trịnh Xuân Thuận claims that the Buddhist doctrine of subtle impermanence, the belief that everything is constantly changing, is affirmed by the thermodynamic principle that matter everywhere in the universe is in constant motion.[23] However, as philosopher Evan Thompson comments in his book *Why I Am Not a Buddhist*, Buddhism's "central teachings aren't empirical. . . . They're based on value judgments that aren't subject to independent empirical test."[24]

The best-known spokesperson for scientific concordism in Buddhism is the fourteenth Dalai Lama, Tenzin Gyatso. The happy recipient of the 2012 Templeton Prize emphasizes what he describes as the parallel purpose of Buddhism and science. He writes, "My confidence in venturing into science lies in my basic belief that as in science so in Buddhism, understanding the nature of reality is pursued by means of critical investigation."[25]

Buddhism, however, is fundamentally based on belief in nonduality. This belief makes it appealing to Western scientists and others who agree with astronomer Carl Sagan that the universe is all that is, or ever was, or ever will be. It asserts that the universe, Earth, Earth's life, and humans are simply differing forms of a shared substance. In traditional Buddhism, the universe is not created. It has existed and will continue to exist forever. There is no transcendent realm behind or beyond the physical realm because all is one. Mind and matter are undivided features along a single plane of consciousness. No separation or distinction exists between the observer and the observed. In Buddhism, "the nature of reality," not "the reality about nature," is waiting to be discovered. Despite the Dalai Lama's assertion, Buddhism supports no effort to understand nature by means of scientific investigation.

Concordism in Christian Cults

Christian cults can be defined as religions based at least in part on the Bible but teaching doctrines clearly at odds with the historic Christian creeds. The largest Christian cults to use concordism in proselytizing efforts are Jehovah's Witnesses, Christadelphians, and Mormons (members of the Church of Jesus Christ of Latter-Day Saints). Of these three, Jehovah's Witnesses present the most detailed and comprehensive scientific concordism, for the obvious reason that they base their belief system on one holy book, the Bible, from which they draw a non-trinitarian doctrine of God. Of course, their "translation" of the Bible has been "adapted" to support this specific doctrinal belief.

The Jehovah's Witnesses have long promoted historical concordism in their writings, and their door-to-door spokespersons point to the Bible's prediction of future historical events—especially prophecies about imminent mass destruction, or Armageddon—as a way to draw people into their study groups. After some past embarrassment from inaccuracies in predicting the date of "the final battle," they tend to make slightly less use of doomsday prophecies. Nevertheless, some Jehovah's Witnesses still say that Armageddon will occur in 2034, exactly 120 years after the start of World War I.

In years past, when asked about the early chapters of Genesis, their evangelists presented a young-earth view of origins. However, as scientific evidence for Earth's old age has become overwhelmingly clear and convincing, the official publishing vehicle of the Jehovah's Witnesses, the Watch Tower Bible and Tract Society, has explicitly rejected young-earth creationism. It now promotes a day-age interpretation of Genesis 1, in which the creation days are long epochs,[26] and a chronology nearly identical to what I published nearly five decades ago.[27] In any case, they have begun to affirm that God, the Bible, and science are congruous and mutually supportive. Their fervent commitment to proselytizing gives them strong motivation to use concordance with credible science to show that their New World Translation Bible (which differs from standard

Christian versions by about 400 words)[28] is the inspired, inerrant Word of God.

Christadelphians refrain from altering the Protestant Bible to fit their doctrinal views. However, they align with Jehovah's Witnesses in considering Jesus as subordinate to, not equal with, God the Father. Christadelphians acknowledge the Bible as the inspired, inerrant Word of God. They make use of both scientific and historical concordism to persuade people to trust the Bible while advocating for interpretations that diverge from historic Christian teaching. They take full advantage of the widespread lack of biblical literacy.

The Church of Jesus Christ of Latter-Day Saints (LDS) more closely resembles Islam than it does any branch of Christianity. Like Muslims, Latter-Day Saints (or Mormons) uphold the Old and New Testaments as important (though not preeminent) revelations from God and believe that a latter-day prophet has delivered to humanity an additional book, or books, of divine revelation. Latter-Day Saints look to the *Book of Mormon, Doctrines and Covenants*, and *Pearl of Great Price* as "updates" to the Bible.

Historical and scientific concordism are nevertheless foundational to the spread of Mormonism. The *Book of Mormon* claims that members of the lost tribes of Israel emigrated to America during the sixth century BC and founded a sophisticated civilization that included the building of cities, the minting and use of coins for commerce, and the manufacture and use of steel tools and weapons. To back up this "history," Mormons make the scientific concordist assertion that archaeological relics affirm the history presented in their holy book. To date, however, no archaeologist outside of the LDS church has validated such findings. Meanwhile, genetic evidence fails to support the supposed emigration of Jews from Israel to America previous to the Christian era and, instead, clearly refutes it.[29]

Like the Qur'an, the LDS sacred books present a cosmology clearly distinct from that of the Old and New Testaments. These books deny the doctrine of creation *ex nihilo* and instead teach that matter is eternal. In Mormonism, creation is *ex materia*, God organizing previously existent matter.[30]

According to *Doctrine and Covenants*, our galaxy, if not all galaxies, contains countless planets either already or soon to be inhabited by human-like life. Here, Mormon teaching aligns to some degree with the belief of astronomers engaged in SETI, the search for extraterrestrial intelligent life. According to Abraham 3, the greatest of the habitable planets is Kolob, which is "nearest to the throne of God."[31] Abraham 2–4 describes Kolob as a planet surrounded by many large, nearby stars and with a rotation period of 1,000 Earth years. The same passage says God has established Kolob as the master planet "to govern all those which belong to the same [advanced-life-habitable] order." Meanwhile, astronomy establishes that Kolob, if it existed, would be incapable of sustaining even the simplest microbe, let alone any life-forms resembling humans.[32]

Each of the largest Christian cults claims to uphold the doctrine of dual revelation and makes an attempt to show historical and scientific concordance with their beliefs. These attempts appear to have been somewhat effective. They serve to create an appearance of plausibility or testability. Does this observation have anything to say to Christians today?

In Light of the Great Commission

If Christians abandon *all* forms of scientific concordism, a helpful basis for comparing and contrasting biblical truth claims with those of other faiths will be lost. The risk is that in some cultural arenas, Christianity will be overshadowed by religions that do promote (falsely but boldly) the predictive power of their scriptures. We also risk having our faith dismissed by non-Christians for offering no scientific truth by which to test or falsify it.

In conceding that the Bible has no predictive power, Christians lose a powerful tool for persuading people who lack a Christian background that the Bible is the inspired, inerrant Word of God.

Rather than abandon endeavors to demonstrate the scientific and historical reliability of the Bible, Christian theologians and apologists would do well to show clear and credible examples of its alignment, consistency, and concordance with truth, wherever it may be found—in the facts of history, the facts of human nature, and the facts of the natural realm, to the extent that we can discern them. To do so effectively means being willing to follow the facts wherever they may lead, confident that God's Word and world come from the same source, the One who self-identifies as "the truth."

The accuracy of the Bible in describing historical events and scientific discoveries before they occur makes it a powerful resource for gaining the attention and trust of those who lack a Christian background. Let's neither lose nor abuse the opportunities God has given us to play our part in fulfilling the Great Commission,[33] making disciples especially among people who, like the apostle Thomas, need tangible evidence.

Chapter 11

The Great Genre Debate

A starting point for interpreting any biblical text is to identify its literary genre, its specific type of communication. Each genre is characterized by certain distinctive features and expectations. Genre recognition helps guide our understanding of a particular portion of Scripture, as it provides significant assistance in discerning (1) what the author of the text, inspired by the Holy Spirit, intended to communicate, and (2) how the original, present, and future readers of the text would have understood or understand this communication.

The genre of biblical creation accounts remains at the center of an enduring controversy among theologians concerning the doctrines of dual revelation and biblical inerrancy. With the early nineteenth-century discovery of the first Mesopotamian cuneiform tablets, those inclined toward a more theologically liberal approach to Scripture saw grounds for asserting that ancient Near Eastern (ANE) culture and literature surrounding God's people shaped the composition—and content—of Old Testament creation passages. Other scholars used this same finding to argue for the reverse, influence flowing from God's people to nearby cultures. However, a far more pervasive shift has been occurring in recent years, less about language and ANE cultural influences than may seem obvious.

Genre Upheaval

From the birth of the church until near the end of the twentieth century, theologically conservative Christian theologians held that the biblical creation texts should be understood as historical narratives, essentially literal except where textual clues indicate otherwise. By the end of the twentieth century, however, a number of biblically conservative theologians had begun to lean toward agreement with the claim that ANE culture and literature shaped both the genre and intended meaning of the Bible's creation texts. Since the start of the twenty-first century, that number of theologians has greatly increased. One of the aims before us is to identify the driving force behind this shift—and then to challenge it. Is this new genre designation, an ANE-culture-influenced genre, truly a literary certainty, or is it propelled by something else?

Some of the Christian theologians and authors leading the charge for change strongly suggest that fresh ANE cultural and literary insight warrants the new identification.

> The languages of the ancient Sumerians, Babylonians, Egyptians, and Canaanites were deciphered for the first time only in the past 200 years. The intimate relationship between the OT and the literature and ideas of these civilizations became accessible only after such developments in ancient language studies. This opened an extraordinary window for understanding what the biblical writers meant. These connections significantly impacted our understanding of the early chapters of Genesis.[1]
>
> —Michael Heiser

> The primaeval narratives [Genesis 1–11] belong to the genre of myth principally on the basis of their sharing common mythic themes and their effort to anchor present realities in the deep past.[2]
>
> —William Lane Craig

> The biblical worldview described in Genesis is an ancient Near Eastern one.[3]

> The cultures, religions, and worldviews of the ancient world in which the Israelites lived, thought, wrote, and worshiped have significantly reoriented our expectation of what Genesis is prepared to deliver.[4]
>
> —Peter Enns

> If it [Genesis] was written in an early form of the Hebrew language to people who had lived hundreds of years in Egyptian

culture, then we should expect it to reflect a concept of the universe and a worldview different from ours. . . . If Abraham came from Mesopotamia, we might also expect some religious influence from Mesopotamia.[5] . . . The Mesopotamian creation materials remind us that Genesis 1 uses basic ancient conceptions of the material world to describe creation.[6]

—Johnny Miller and John Soden

Ancient [biblical] texts often seem to be something they are not, primarily because we read them as if they were products of modern society rather than of an ancient and sometimes alien world.[7]

—Kenton Sparks

We need to interpret Genesis 1–3 in the context of some ancient Near Eastern texts like *Enuma Elish*, the *Gilgamesh Epic*, and *Atrahasis*.[8]

—Scot McKnight

Bruce Waltke has suggested that God inspired Moses to compose the Genesis creation account in "the garb of the Mesopotamian cosmogony."[9] John Walton claims that the key to understanding the Old Testament "is to be found in the literature from the rest of the ancient world."[10] Tremper Longman III devotes a lengthy chapter of *Reading Genesis 1–2* to affirming that ANE texts strongly influenced what Genesis teaches.[11] Several other evangelical theologians have written books arguing that Genesis 1–11 and the rest of the Old Testament should be interpreted in the genre of the ancient mythological literature of the Akkadians, Sumerians, Egyptians, and Canaanites.[12]

Before offering a response to the claim that we *must* for the sake of scholarly integrity interpret the biblical creation accounts in this new way, I would like to note where broad theological agreement concerning these passages does exist. First, both liberal and conservative theologians agree that Genesis 1–2, Job 37–42, Psalm 104, and Proverbs 8—the major creation texts—display awe-inspiring majesty and grandeur. Scholars openly admire the exquisite beauty and elegance of the prose and poetry in these passages. Even people who do not believe in God are known to quote from these literary masterpieces.

Second, scholars widely acknowledge that these texts carry theological significance. They agree with Peter Enns that a "christotelic coherence"—"that

Christ is the goal"—is evident in all the major Old Testament creation texts.[13] In other words, these passages all point to Christ as Creator of everything that has been made.[14]

One further point of agreement is that the biblical creation texts differ from various ANE myths in their lack of political motivation. ANE creation literature consistently links cosmology with ancient politics. The Bible's creation texts neither state nor imply a political message.

History, Myth, or Mytho-History?

The genre debate focuses on this question: Do the Old Testament creation texts refer to actual, physical, potentially discernible events of the past, or do they not? From among those who for centuries would have answered with a resounding affirmation ("They do!") now comes a mixed response, as noted by the comments quoted in the previous section. While some still say yes, many now say the texts should be interpreted as creation myths, not as history, and certainly not as literal accounts.

To some extent, the dual meaning of "myth" presents a problem. As a genre, the term refers to a traditional story, often a culture's origin story involving supernatural events or beings. However, *myth* can also refer to a widely held but false belief. Generally speaking, a myth is *not* expected to be "true." So, it seems easy to assume that by referring to Genesis 1–11 as myth, Peter Enns and others who share his perspective expect the passage to have little or no connection with actual history.[15] This "myth vs. narrative" dilemma is further complicated by William Lane Craig's assertion that the passage be regarded as "mytho-history."

As discussed in chapter 2 (see "More Inerrancy Challenges Follow"), Craig holds that Genesis 1–11 includes a few historical elements, including a true, historical human, Adam, from whom all humans are descended, but he denies that it should all be read literally or chronologically because it also contains nonhistorical elements. In other words, as Craig sees it, this portion of Scripture is filled with elements that cannot possibly be true if interpreted literally and historically. Therefore, to a large degree it must be myth.[16]

A Polemical "True Myth"

Both the pre- and post-Nicene church fathers recognized the Genesis creation accounts as foundational to biblical theology. Accordingly, on the first chapter of Genesis alone, they wrote well over two thousand pages. They were also unanimous in their belief that the Bible was polemical, in the sense that it stood against the cultural milieu. For example, they saw Paul's admonition against conformity with the world's thinking (Romans 12:2) as an echo of Joshua's Old Testament calling of God's people to "be separate."[17]

The Bible's message consistently goes against the cultural grain. Certainly, there are similarities between the ANE accounts of creation and the Genesis account. Both address the basic origins questions. However, that is where the similarities end. The differences between the ANE and biblical creation accounts are far greater than their similarities. As theologian Gerhard Hasel observed in an *Evangelical Quarterly* article, Genesis 1 is "not only a complete break with the ancient Near Eastern mythological cosmologies but represents a parting of the spiritual ways brought about by a conscious and deliberate antimythical polemic."[18]

The ANE creation accounts speak of many gods. In the Bible's creation texts, there is only one God. In the ANE creation accounts, matter predates the existence of gods, and gods arise from eternal (or previously existent) matter. In the Bible, God is eternal and is the Creator of all matter, energy, space, and time. The God of the Bible transcends his creation whereas ANE gods are merely deified natural forces. In the ANE creation texts, the gods reflect the fallenness of humans. They engage in immorality and continual conflict with one another. The God of the Bible is morally perfect, and the triune godhead exhibits perfect harmony, peace, and love. In the ANE creation texts, humans emerge as an afterthought or from the remains of a vanquished god. The biblical creation account shows God's purposeful progression toward a climactic act—creation of humans in his own image. In the ANE myths, the gods create humans to serve them. In the Bible, God creates humans to serve others, alongside him. The God of the Bible grants to humans the power and authority to rule over all Earth's resources and all Earth's life. In ANE texts, humans are depicted as subservient to capricious and terrifying nature gods.

In every important respect, the Bible's message differs radically from those of ANE literature. The Old Testament books were written by men best described as countercultural. Moses, Isaiah, and Jeremiah set the tone for all the Old Testament authors in emphatically and consistently countering the surrounding ANE cultures and beliefs.

The form and content of the biblical text should be the indicators of its genre, taking precedence over ANE cultures and beliefs. In this case, even if the biblical text's purpose—to present an account of origins—slightly resembles that of ANE myths, there is no reason to conclude that it must be a merely traditional, nonfactual story. Can it not be considered, as in the words of C. S.

Lewis, "a true myth: a myth working on us the same way as the others, but with this tremendous difference that it really happened?"[19]

The 39 human writers of the Bible's 66 books understood that the Holy Spirit was the guiding voice behind everything they wrote. In many biblical passages, the human authors explicitly declared that what they were writing was inspired by God himself. The phrase "thus says the Lord" appears 427 times in the Old Testament.[20]

Jesus often quoted from and referred to Old Testament passages as true and trustworthy. The apostle Paul assures the early Christians, "All Scripture is God-breathed and is useful for teaching, rebuking, correcting, and training in righteousness" (2 Timothy 3:16), and the apostle Peter affirmed that "prophecy never had its origin in the human will, but prophets, though human, spoke from God as they were carried along by the Holy Spirit" (2 Peter 1:21).

Miraculously, every one of the 66 books of the Bible conveys the same theme: God's redemptive plan and purpose for humanity. Each reveals, in one way or another, that our transcendent Creator is moved by love to create beings who can experience genuine love in a never-ending relationship not only with him but also with countless others—a relationship made possible at infinite cost to him. This message is not for just one generation of humanity. It is for all generations. While the human author of Genesis certainly did have his own generation in mind as he wrote, the divine Author's intent was to communicate to a far broader audience. The biblical text addresses all of humanity's cultures and generations.

The Bible's redemptive theme is sustained by the record of nature. That God began his work of redemption before he created anything[21] implies that all of nature is designed to make possible not only the existence but also the redemption of a vast host of humans.[22]

Even though the language and genres of biblical texts are shaped by the biblical writers' varying times and cultures, the fundamental meaning of the Bible is transcultural. The Holy Spirit knows the meaning of what has been written and promises to guide us toward ever-deeper understanding. He uses genre and prayerfully discerned interpretive principles to help us today, just as he helped ancient peoples of the world and will help future generations.

The Case for Historical Narrative
Most books of the Bible manifest the traits of one particular genre—history, law, wisdom, poetry, prophecy, gospel, epistle, or apocalypse. While some books combine genres, the transition from one genre to another is distinct and

recognizable. In the book of Job, the shift from historical prose to poetry is unmistakable. So is the inclusion of poetry (Mary's song) in Matthew's Gospel. No such change exists at the end of Genesis 11.

I have yet to meet a Christian theologian who would identify the genre of Genesis 12–50 as anything other than historical narrative. The only *literary* basis for labeling Genesis 1–11 as anything other than history is that these chapters point back to a time when oral tradition, rather than written records, accounted for historical events. However, all fifty chapters of Genesis describe history that occurred before Hebrew became a written language.

Genesis includes genealogies (family trees), the longest in chapters 5 and 11. Genesis 1–11 is replete with time markers, names of specific individuals, and geographical locations and directions. Repeatedly, the phrase "these are the generations of" appears as an unmistakable indicator of the progression of historical events. Such references serve as clear indicators of specific historical content, and yet these first eleven chapters of Genesis are most often challenged for their historicity—especially Genesis 1.

Ironically, no other chapter of the Bible contains more historical and chronological indicators than Genesis 1. The chapter is organized into a pattern of numbered days that follow one after the other. Each of the first six creation days is closed out with the phrase "evening was, morning was, day X." The repeated use of this phrase indicates that each of the first six creation days had a start time and an end time within Earth's history.

The repeated use of the phrase "and it was so" implies something physical occurred at a particular juncture in Earth's history. God's comment at the end of each creation day (with the exception of day 2), that "it was good," again communicates that something of great significance had been accomplished at that point in Earth's history. On creation day 4, the first-time appearance of the Sun, Moon, and stars as distinct objects visible from Earth's surface—markers for Earth's creatures to measure the passage of days, seasons, and years—does more than just suggest historical intent. It seems the Genesis 1 author goes overboard to make it clear he is writing a historical, chronologically ordered narrative.

In Genesis 1–2, the use of the Hebrew verbs *bara*, *asa*, *haya*, and *yatsar*, typically translated as "create," "make," "let there be," and "formed" or "fashioned," are not the verbs one would expect to find in passages that have nothing or little to do with history or acts of creation. They are exactly the verbs one would need, however, to describe the origin and history of Earth and Earth's life.

The physical events described in Genesis 1–11, especially those in Genesis 1, are referenced again, with added detail, in Job 37–39, Psalm 104, and

Proverbs 8. No hint appears in any of these other texts that the physical events mentioned did not actually occur. Jesus, Paul, and the author of Hebrews also refer to the physical events described in Genesis 1–2 as real events occurring in history. To deny the historicity of these chapters leads to questioning the reliability of much of the rest of Scripture.

So, one must ask: What would prompt so many wonderful Christian leaders, scholars, and defenders of the faith and the gospel to now take such a strong stance against the long-held doctrine of Genesis as a trustworthy revelation of historical and scientific truth? The answer is provided by one of the movement's most influential and articulate leaders, Peter Enns, whose books and articles have been quoted in this and previous chapters.

Enns and many other theologians have become understandably convinced by the work of a truly brilliant and respected brother in Christ, Francis Collins, who founded the organization BioLogos in 2007.[23] According to Collins and the leaders of BioLogos, the evidence for common descent of all life from the last universal common ancestor (LUCA, a microbe that somehow came into existence ~3.8 billion years ago) through natural selection, mutations, gene exchange, and epigenetics is so overwhelming that all Scripture must be interpreted to fit—or at least to not conflict—with this scenario.[24] This scenario has been firmly embraced by many theologians today.

Genesis 1–11 is neither poetry nor fantastic myth. This portion of the Bible is plainly narrative in the same sense that Joshua, Judges, Ruth, 1 and 2 Samuel, 1 and 2 Kings, and 1 and 2 Chronicles are. Most evangelical theologians who question or deny the historicity of Genesis 1–11 continue to affirm the truthfulness of these other historical narratives.[25]

This affirmation is not surprising. These other books present no conflict with biological evolution. They certainly do, however, contain certain "fantastic" elements—a floating axe head, chariots of fire, and a sundial shadow moving backwards, for example. To claim that we must deny the historicity of Genesis 1–11 because of the text's wildly "fantastic" elements means we must also deny the historicity of these other historical books, at least in part, in order to be consistent. Like Genesis, these books clearly imply God's miraculous intervention. Thus, they set the stage for the unfolding drama of God's direct intervention for the sake of our redemption.

When to Trust Science
To make a case for dual revelation, the concordance of the Bible and the book of nature, requires a high degree of trust in each book. What if the *misreading*

of these books, whether through faulty application of sound hermeneutical principles or through misinterpretation of the scientific data, is what sets them at odds? Theologians, for their part, have been willing to make adjustments to their interpretations, but what about scientists? How willing are we to question the interpretation of our data?

In some disciplines, predominantly the physical sciences, challenging past understandings is both encouraged and rewarded. The response to big bang cosmology serves as a key example. Big bang models initially challenged physicists, but once the basic theory gained wide acceptance through ongoing testing, it remained the focus of relentless questioning. This questioning has led to ongoing refinement of the models to more closely match emerging data. In other disciplines, predominantly the life sciences, a totally different response often occurred.

When evolutionary models initially challenged long-held religious and philosophical beliefs, they sparked a firestorm of controversy in the wider culture. Life scientists came under attack, accused of evil motives, labeled as enemies to belief in God and as advocates for atheism. Countless books written over the past century have traced this storm's destructive pathway. It pushed life scientists into a defensive posture, where further testing would not be rewarded and ongoing questioning would be dismissed or punished. This polarization has severely hampered the pursuit of truth, but I am convinced that resolution is possible *if* we move forward in humility.

We can be grateful that theologians have taken a more respectful stance toward science and scientists. Such an attitude adjustment is admirable and appropriate. Yet, some theologians have gone to a perhaps unnecessary and inappropriate extreme. They claim with certainty that the Bible has been wrong about science all along and that only now are we Christians prepared to admit it. They add that we must charitably lower our expectations of the ancient Bible writers, who were ignorant of science, and allow Scripture to concord with false beliefs of the past without denying our trust in those portions on which our faith more essentially rests. They would say it is our responsibility to decide what parts of Scripture are plausible and what parts are not.

With this increasingly popular perspective on dual revelation in view, is it possible that the scientific case for common descent from LUCA through natural processes has been overestimated? Or that the scientific knowledge and understanding of ANE scholars and ancient Bible writers has been grossly underestimated? The next two chapters address the latter question in some depth.

Chapter 12

Debunking the Dome Myth

Throughout the nineteenth and twentieth centuries, nontheist scholars and liberal theologians promoted the idea that ancient Near Eastern (ANE) peoples—including the early Hebrews and the Old Testament writers—all believed that a solid dome was fixed over a flat Earth,[1] as illustrated in figure 12.1. Theologically conservative Christian scholars consistently rejected such an assertion, seeing no convincing basis for it in the relevant biblical texts. In the twenty-first century, however, some of these theologians have changed their view. Some of their comments appear in the section below the figure.

Some slight variations of this illustration appear in various texts, but most share features in common with this one, showing Earth as a flat disk with supporting pillars above and below. According to this depiction, a solid dome (or vault) stands above Earth, upheld by pillars, while the Sun, Moon, planets, and stars are attached to the dome's inner surface. Above the dome is a huge reservoir of water extending all the way down to the ocean that surrounds and lies beneath the disk-shaped Earth. Small windows on the dome apparently open and close to allow rain to fall intermittently on Earth.

Comments on ANE Cosmology in the Bible
Here is a brief sampling of statements from recent theologians about the supposed beliefs of the ancients:

> Everyone believed that there was a body of water suspended above the earth by some sort of solid dome.[2] Everyone believed that the earth was round (but disk, not sphere).[3]
>   —John Walton and Brent Sandy

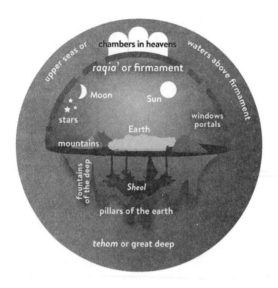

Figure 12.1: Presumed Ancient Near Eastern Cosmology
Image credit: Tom-L, Creative Commons Attribution 4.0 International, based on File: Early Hebrew Conception of the Universe.png and several other depictions, including Understanding the Bible, *Stephen L. Harris, 2003.*

Genesis does not try to correct a perception of reality that assumes a watery mass above the vault of the sky.[4]

He [Moses] leaves intact a completely different view of the universe that is scientifically incorrect.[5]

—Johnny Miller and John Soden

Genesis—as other stories of the ancient world—thus portrays the world as a flat disk with a dome above. Below the earth were the waters threatening to gush up, and above the dome are the waters threatening to drop down.[6]

—Peter Enns

The firmament dome surrounded the earth with its edge meeting at the horizon—"the boundary between light and darkness" (Job 26:10; Prov 8:27–28). It was supported by "pillars"
or "foundations," (2 Sam 22:8) thought to be the tops of mountains, whose peaks appeared to touch the sky. The heavens had
doors and windows through which rain or the waters above
could flow upon the earth from their storehouses.[7]

—Michael Heiser

Earth has a dome over it.[8]

—Dennis Venema and Scot McKnight

What the Ancients Did or Did Not Believe

German and Swiss Old Testament and ANE scholars Othmar Keel and Silvia
Schroer noted in 2015 that no complete image or drawing of an ancient Israelite conception of the world has ever been found.[9] In an exhaustive search
through ancient Mesopotamian literature, British archaeologist and Assyriolo-
gist Wilfred Lambert could find no evidence that the ancient Mesopotamians
believed that a solid dome rested upon the earth.[10] Apparently, it *was not* part
of their physical cosmology.

Lambert's student, Wayne Horowitz, did discover a somewhat altered version of the solid dome concept in an ancient Mesopotamian astrological drawing.[11] In this drawing, a system of "cables" held many planes suspended above
one another. These planes demarked realms in which the many gods related to
one another and to their human servants. The religious priests who invented
this construct showed no concern for how it conformed to physical reality.
Their intent was to tell a religious story for their own purposes.

Just as it would be a mistake for researchers working centuries from now to
interpret J. R. R. Tolkien's *Lord of the Rings* as a depiction of the past centuries'
Western beliefs about geography and cosmology, it would likewise be an error
to interpret Mesopotamian and Egyptian astrology and myths written for political purposes as their understanding of the solar system and the starry realm.
With limited archaeological data, one can expect some difficulties in distin-
guishing myth and fantasy literature from historical and scientific writings.

Both the ancient Mesopotamians and Egyptians invested heavily in astronomy. They employed astronomers to monitor the positions and movements
of celestial bodies with the goal of understanding and predicting the timing
and locations of future astronomical events. (Astrologers were among them,

of course, just as they are today, offering "spiritual" guidance.) These ancient astronomers developed a remarkable depth of knowledge without the aid of modern technology.

For example, they determined that stars do not move relative to one another in the sky, while the planets, comets, Moon, and Sun make dramatic movements relative to the fixed stars. In a world without electric lights to inhibit observation of celestial bodies, all ANE people, not just astronomers, had ample opportunity to observe the fixed stellar patterns (constellations) traversing, east to west, across the night sky. It would have been obvious to them that these bodies were not fixed in place on the inner surface of a stationary dome. Even if the dome were rotated, it would not have accounted for their observations of the Sun, Moon, planets, comets, and stars in their various positions.

Ancient astronomers also noticed that when traveling even a few hundred kilometers to the north or south, some constellations could no longer be seen and others would come into view. They would also have seen that the Sun, Moon, and stars rise and set at different times for observers in different locations.

Ancient astronomers in Mesopotamia, Egypt, and Greece attempted to measure the parallaxes of stars (apparent shifts of positions of nearby stars relative to the background of distant stars). Their inability to do so established for them that all stars must be located at extreme distances from Earth. Their observations and measurements also demonstrated to them that Earth is not a flat disk but, rather, is spherical in shape (see chapter 13).

Meanwhile, ancient engineers in Mesopotamia, Egypt, and Greece gained knowledge from their experience in monumental building projects. They certainly would have understood—even without knowledge of what we know as gravity—that there are limits to the size of a physical dome. They knew, based on their building endeavors, that a dome-like structure large enough to encompass even one portion of the region where humans lived would surely collapse under its own weight.

The ancient civilizations of the Mesopotamians and Egyptians depended heavily on artificial irrigation to produce the crops they needed to feed their populations of humans and domesticated animals.[12] Such dependence no doubt helped them recognize the mythical nature of a solid dome as pictured in figure 12.1. Ancient hydraulic engineers in both Mesopotamia and Egypt learned that the height to which water could be hydraulically drawn up from the Euphrates and Nile Rivers had its limits. On this basis, among others, ANE peoples would have been aware that the notion of liquid water extending from a subterranean ocean up and over a solid dome anchored to the earth represented a physical impossibility.

The twenty-first-century misunderstanding of ancient cosmology exemplifies how an erroneous assumption of ignorance can result in the faulty interpretation of an archaeological find. This misunderstanding has been made worse by its impact on translation of a biblical text.

One Error Leads to Another

Theologians who embrace assertions that such supposedly flawed ANE cosmology was the source of Hebrew cosmology have focused attention on a reinterpretation of the Hebrew noun *raqia'*. Although for centuries this word has been translated as "expanse," "sky," or "firmament," some scholars noted that it might possibly mean "dome" or "vault." Their persistence finally brought about alterations in some of the more popular translations of the Old Testament into English.

The revision made its way into the New International Version (NIV) in 2011. The 1978 and 1984 NIV printings render Genesis 1:6–8 as follows:

> And God said, "Let there be an expanse between the waters
> to separate water from water." So God made the expanse and
> separated the water under the expanse from the water above it.
> And it was so. God called the expanse "sky."

The 2011 NIV substitutes the word "vault" for "expanse" in the translation of *raqia'* throughout this passage. Similarly, the New Revised Standard Version (NRSV), published in 1989, substitutes "dome" for the 1971 Revised Standard Version's "firmament." The Good News Translation (1976), New American Bible (1970), and Contemporary English Version (1995) have recently joined the NRSV in translating *raqia'* in Genesis 1 as "dome." The International Standard Version (2011) translates it as "canopy," while the God's Word Translation (1995) uses "horizon." Prior to 1970, no English language translation used any word other than "expanse" or "firmament" for *raqia'* in this portion of the text.

The translation of *raqia'* as "firmament" was derived from the Latin Vulgate (AD 384) translation, *"firmamentum."* This Latin word refers to anything that supports or provides support.[13] It also can mean the sky above the earth.[14] *Raqia'* occurs seventeen times in the Old Testament—in Genesis 1:6–8, 14–15, 17, 20; Psalm 19:2; 150:1; Ezekiel 1:22–26; 10:1; and Daniel 12:3. The 2011 NIV uses "vault" for *raqia'* only in Genesis and Ezekiel, and the NRSV translates it as "dome" only in Genesis and Ezekiel.

The *Theological Wordbook of the Old Testament* defines *raqia'* as "expanse" or the "broad expanse of heaven."[15] It notes a biblical exception in the case of Ezekiel 1 and 10, where *raqia'* refers to a "canopy" over the cherubim in Ezekiel's vision.[16] Some theologians claim that Ezekiel 1:22 can be interpreted as referring to a solid dome. However, in none of the other seventeen appearances of *raqia'* in the Old Testament is it ever associated with any kind of metal or solid substance. The 1984 NIV says,

> Spread out above the heads of the living creatures was what looked like an expanse (*raqia'*), sparkling like ice and awesome.

The 2011 NIV substitutes "vault" for "expanse" and "crystal" for "ice." However, the use of the word "like" in this passage clearly signals that the *raqia'* is not ice or crystal but rather has the appearance of ice or crystal.

In a further attempt to sustain a solid dome interpretation for *raqia'*, some theologians appeal to *raqa*, the verb root of *raqia'*.[17] *Raqa*, in five of its twelve occurrences in the Old Testament, is associated with metal that is stretched, by hammering, to cover a much larger surface. *Raqa* refers to the process, the action, whereby any substance—metal, earth, cloud, dust, air, space—can be stretched out and expanded. The basic definition of *raqa*, "to expand," suggests that "expanse" is a fitting translation for the noun *raqia'*. But as Old Testament professor Paul Kissling explains, "The meaning of a related verb in Hebrew cannot by itself tell us what a noun which is derived from it means."[18]

Among the church fathers, Basil holds the record for the most extensive commentary on Genesis 1:6–8. Here is what he says about the meaning of the text:

> I have said what the word firmament in Scripture means. It is not in reality a firm and solid substance which has weight and resistance; this name would otherwise have better suited the earth. . . . Imagine a place fit to divide the moisture, sending it, if pure and filtered, into higher regions, and making it fall. . . . Is it not plain to everyone that it has risen in vapour?[19]

Among Christian scholars of the Middle Ages, Thomas Aquinas wrote most extensively on this same passage. He writes,

Another possible explanation is to understand by the firmament that was made on the second day, not that in which the stars are set, but that part of the atmosphere where the clouds are condensed, and which has received the name of firmament from the firmness and density of the air.[20]

Further Comparative Analysis

Raqia' also appears four times in Genesis 1:14–20. Verses 14–17 declare that the Sun, Moon, and stars reside in the *raqia'*. Genesis 1:20 says that birds fly above the earth in the *raqia'*.

It would have been obvious to the ancient Hebrews, even to their young children, that birds fly at various heights above Earth's surface without any concern for bumping into other objects, such as the Sun, Moon, planets, and stars, attached to the inside of a domed cage or vault.

In his second letter to the Corinthians, Paul wrote of being taken up to the third heaven.[21] The reason for his reference to the "third" heaven is that Scripture speaks of three distinct heavens: (1) Earth's troposphere, where clouds float and birds fly; (2) outer space, where the Sun, Moon, and stars reside; and (3) the realm beyond the material world, the heaven where God and the angels dwell with the "great cloud of witnesses" (the host of redeemed humans who have died in Christ).

From Genesis 1:14–17, we gather that the realm where birds fly is the first heaven and that the realm where the Sun, Moon, and stars reside is the second heaven, each fully visible and accessible to God and his "messengers." Nothing in this passage or in Paul's words or in any other passage of Scripture suggests that those who dwell in the third heaven must either peer or pass through a metal dome to see us or reach us.

The frame of reference or point of view for the Genesis 1 creation days is that of an observer on Earth's surface (Genesis 1:2). From this perspective, the *raqia'* in Genesis 1 is the sky above. It would include Earth's troposphere as well as interplanetary and interstellar space. It is the whole sky that can be seen above Earth's surface.

Perhaps the greatest challenge to a clear understanding of Genesis 1:6–8 is its brevity. Of all God's creative acts described in Genesis 1, the events of day 2 receive the least description. These verses simply say that God established water in the expanse above and water below the expanse. One explanation for the compactness of this text may well come from the audience's familiarity with the closely related descriptive passages in the book of Job.[22]

Figure 12.2: A "Window of Heaven"
Image credit: Hugh Ross

Nearly a chapter and a half in Job (36:27–37:21 and 38:22–38) are devoted to portraying, in considerable detail, the physical events of the second creation epoch. Given that Job's epic story predates the writing of Genesis by at least a few hundred years, the author of Genesis could afford to be brief in addressing the events of that day. Job 36, 37, and 38 provide a vivid picture of Earth's water cycle. These texts make it abundantly clear that clouds are full of moisture, that the clouds are the source of rain, snow, hail, thunder, and lightning, and that dew and frost have their origin in the sky above Earth's surface.

Vern Poythress, in a *Westminster Theological Journal* article, shows that seven other Old Testament books in addition to Job (Judges, 2 Samuel, 1 Kings, Psalms, Proverbs, Ecclesiastes, and Isaiah) explicitly state that precipitation comes from the clouds.[23] In light of these texts, the idea that the ancient Hebrews believed that precipitation fell as God opened up portals or windows in a solid dome over the earth seems logically indefensible. As Poythress shows in his article, the context of the rare biblical references to "windows of heaven" makes clear that the writer was using phenomenological language. From many locations on Earth, rain clouds can, indeed, look like windows of heaven (see figure 12.2).

Did the Ancients Believe Earth Is Flat?

Any student of astronomy and of its history can confirm that no factual basis exists for the claim that the ancient Hebrews or ANE peoples believed Earth is flat. As discussed earlier, given their depth of interest and investment in understanding the heavens and earth, ancient peoples would have known that Earth's shape is at least approximately spherical. So, what was the origin of the idea that ANE peoples, ancient Hebrews, and Bible believers up through the Middle Ages believed in a flat earth?

Two historians, Jeffrey Burton Russell and Christine Garwood, have independently documented the fact that this rumor was conceived in the late eighteenth and early nineteenth centuries.[24] Russell credits antireligious scholars, intent on discrediting Christianity, for starting the rumor. Garwood credits biblical hyperliteralist sects for advancing it. Both Russell and Garwood exhaustively scoured books, articles, and letters written by scholars from early antiquity until the Renaissance, searching for comments on Earth's size and shape. They found that only a few obscure individuals thought Earth to be flat. A broad consensus, historically and geographically, saw Earth as an orb.

In a written summary of his lecture at the 1997 conference of the American Scientific Affiliation, Russell made this observation:

> The falsehood about the spherical earth became a colorful and unforgettable part of a larger falsehood: the falsehood of the eternal war between science (good) and religion (bad).[25]

To counter the claim that ANE cultures, including the Hebrews, lacked motivation to pursue what today we call "science," the next chapter presents a brief overview of their astounding research efforts and achievements. No one can honestly describe these cultures as disinterested, ignorant, or nonscientific.

Chapter 13

Ancient Near Eastern Science

For well over a decade, some Christian theologians have made bold claims not only about ancient peoples' lack of concern to understand and describe the cosmos but also about their inability to study the natural realm. In other words, these theologians believe that ancient peoples were unable to do science. Peter Enns makes the claim that "scientific investigation was not at the disposal of ancient Near Eastern peoples."[1] He also writes, "The biblical writers assumed that the earth is flat, was made by God in relatively recent history (about 4,000 years before Jesus) just as it looks now, and that it is a fixed point in the cosmos over which the sun actually rises and sets."[2] John Walton and Brent Sandy agree that nature was of no interest to ancient Near Eastern (ANE) peoples, except for purposes of survival.[3] They attribute a lengthy list of supposed false beliefs to the ancients' ignorance of or disinterest in "the material cosmos."[4]

Based on my respect for the intelligence and integrity of these and other twenty-first-century theologians who have made similar assertions, I can only surmise that their awareness of the history of science has been biased by a selection of tertiary sources. Perhaps they hold that religion prevented ANE people from in-depth study of nature. The most significant bias may be the presumption that ANE people had no more interest in the heavenly bodies displayed in the night sky than many or most people living in the twenty-first century do.

Today, much of the world's population has lost touch with the night sky. Urbanization, with its bright lights and nighttime entertainment options, powerfully prevents and distracts people from noticing the night sky. Both light and air pollution in many parts of the world block people from seeing more than a few planets and a dozen or so stars. In some cities, the only visible heavenly

Figure 13.1: Stonehenge in England's Salisbury Plain
Image credit: Hugh Ross

body after dark is the Moon, and only once it has risen well above the horizon.

The ANE peoples had a radically different experience. No matter where they lived, they saw, night after night, hour by hour, the Milky Way and roughly fifteen thousand shining stars. I have witnessed what happens when twenty-first-century people visit a planetarium. They are awestruck by the simulated view of a night sky, which today shows us only about five thousand visible stars (due to current atmospheric conditions). The ANE peoples had an even more awe-inspiring view than we do on the clearest of nights. They could hardly help but become familiar with the Milky Way, the stars, and the orbital movements of the planets and the Moon, even if they called these objects and actions by different names.

Ancient Near Eastern Observatories
Nearly all ancient cultures—Mesopotamian, Egyptian, Greek, Briton, Chinese, Japanese, Korean, and more—dating back to the time of Moses or earlier

invested heavily in the pursuit of astronomical knowledge. They spent a greater fraction of their gross national product in employing and equipping astronomers than any nation does today. Some 1,800–4,900 years before Christ, people living in Great Britain, Ireland, Normandy, and Germany constructed thousands of stone circle observatories (see figure 13.1), ranging in size from several meters to 330 meters in diameter. The primary purpose of these sites was to allow accurate naked-eye observations of the Sun, Moon, planets, and stars.[5] Egyptians, dating back to at least the fifth millennium BC, constructed similar observatories for the same purpose.[6] Archaeologists have recently identified what are likely astronomical observatories made of stone dating from 3600–2500 BC in the Maltese archipelago.[7]

Egypt, Mesopotamia, Europe, and China employed astronomers to predict the timing of future solar and lunar eclipses and planetary conjunctions (two or more planets coming within a few Moon diameters of each other in the celestial sky) and the locations from which these events would be visible.[8] They did so because the visual proximity of planets to one another and the duration of eclipses differ depending on the observer's location on Earth.

Nearly all ancient governments paid astronomers to detect the timing and relative positions of the Sun, Moon, five (naked-eye-visible) planets, comets, novae, and supernovae. These astronomers were employed for both astronomical and astrological purposes, just as Tycho Brahe and Johannes Kepler were in the sixteenth and seventeenth centuries AD.

Solar and lunar eclipses and planetary conjunctions were of special interest to the ancients. To make accurate predictions of these events required the meticulous monitoring, night after night, year after year, of the positions and movements of the Sun, Moon, visible planets, and occasional comets relative to the fixed background stars.

Ancient astronomers also carefully recorded the timing and brightness levels of variable stars and made note of "guest" stars, novae or supernovae normally too faint to be seen by the naked eye but when undergoing an explosion, bright enough to be visible for a few weeks or months.

ANE Comprehension of Spherical Heavenly Bodies

Ancient astronomers realized through their observations of solar and lunar eclipses that both Earth and the Moon must be spherical bodies. They noted that the shadow of Earth on the Moon during partial lunar eclipses always has a curved edge, a portion of a circle (see figure 13.2). They knew enough about geometry to recognize that only a spherical body would present a consistent

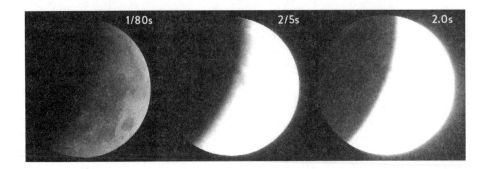

Figure 13.2: October 2014 Partial Lunar Eclipse
The three exposure times represent the approximate range of partial visibility to naked-eye observers. *Credit: Tomruen, Creative Commons Attribution-Share Alike 4.0 International*

curved boundary to its eclipse shadows. Thus, Earth must be a spherical body.

People throughout the ancient world, as today, could observe partial solar eclipses using tiny gaps between tree leaves. These gaps act as "pinhole lenses." During a partial solar eclipse, the light coming through these gaps allows images of the partially eclipsed Sun to show up on the ground or wherever else the light falls. A YouTube video clip shows this effect for the May 20, 2012, annular solar eclipse: youtube.com/watch?v=IgZw72Vtjfo. Such observations made by ancient peoples would have revealed that the Moon's shadow on the Sun during a solar eclipse always has an edge that is a portion of a circle. Thus, ancient astronomers would have concluded that the Moon, too, must be a spherical body.

Ancient mariners and military leaders were also well aware of Earth's curvature due to the crow's-nest effect. They noted that only the tops of mountains could be seen from a distance and that the more distant the mountain, the less of the top was visible. This crow's-nest effect is illustrated in Genesis 8. From the top of the ark, Noah could see distant hills (verse 5), whereas the dove he released, flying low over the floodwaters (verse 9), was unable to see any land.

Many other evidences affirmed that Earth was spherical. As mentioned in the previous chapter, astronomers observed that the Sun, Moon, planets, and stars rise and set at different times of day in different geographical locations, with the difference in time proportional to the distance between locations. They also observed that as someone traveled north or south, some constellations

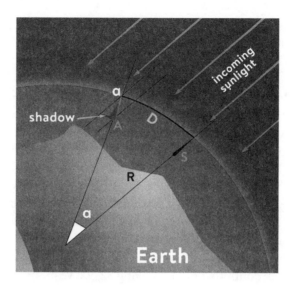

Figure 13.3: Obelisk Shadow Method for Determining Earth's Diameter
Eratosthenes compared the length of an obelisk shadow at Alexandria with that at Syene (modern Aswan), both at the same meridian, at noon on the summer solstice. He then used the distance between Alexandria and Syene and simple plane geometry to determine Earth's diameter. *Image credit: Italian Wikipedia, GNU Free Documentation License*

would disappear from view as other constellations appeared. Again, such observations only make sense if Earth is a spherical body. In fact, the correlation between distance traveled north or south and the appearance or disappearance of stellar constellations provided the ancients with the capacity to even make a rough estimate of Earth's diameter.

ANE astronomers possessed two additional methods to measure Earth's diameter: (1) variation in obelisk shadow length, depending on location, and (2) variation in shadow angles in deep wells, depending on location. Figure 13.3 shows the obelisk shadow method that the Greek-Egyptian astronomer Eratosthenes used to measure Earth's diameter in the third century BC. His measurement of Earth's polar diameter was 7,850 miles.[9] The current measurement is 7,899.8 miles. Eratosthenes's measurement came within 0.99% of the true value.

Eratosthenes's measurement is the earliest surviving precise determination of Earth's shape and diameter. Aristotle, writing a century earlier, referred to the curved shape of shadows of lunar eclipses and the visibility of stellar constellations at different geographical locations as proof that the world must be a spherical body.[10] Given ancient peoples' ubiquitous curiosity and preoccupation with astronomy, Aristotle could not have been the first to correctly discern Earth's shape. No doubt, this knowledge predated the earliest surviving published sources.

Given how labor intensive and costly written publications were in ancient times and how challenging it was to preserve such publications, we should not be surprised that earlier written descriptions of Earth's shape and size have not yet been found. By analogy, there is no written record of ancient peoples manufacturing flour and baking bread until about 5,500 years ago. Yet, the discovery of grinding stones, hearths, and charcoal residues of roasted grains establishes beyond reasonable doubt that humans living 32,600 years ago indeed were engaged in such activities.[11] Likewise, the thousands of astronomical observatories constructed by ancient peoples and the ease by which ancient peoples through multiple methods would have discerned Earth's sphericity leave little doubt that the astronomers they employed knew Earth could not be a flat disk.

ANE Measurements of Distance and Size
Ancient records show that astronomers' eclipse studies also enabled them to determine the approximate size of the Sun and Moon and the distances of each from Earth.[12] For example, they could see that when the Moon is partially eclipsed by Earth's shadow, the curved shape of its shadow yields the Earth's diameter relative to the Moon's. They could obtain a measure of the angular diameter of Earth's shadow on the Moon by measuring how long it takes for Earth's shadow to fully encompass the Moon and how long the Moon remains completely within Earth's shadow during a total lunar eclipse. Thus, a measurement of Earth's diameter provided a value for the Moon's diameter. The observed angular size of the Moon in the sky then allowed them to measure the distance to the Moon. By similar means, ancient astronomers were able to make rough measurements of the Sun's diameter and distance.

These measurements were supplemented by observations of the Moon's phases. At exactly the first and third quarters of the Moon's phases, when the Sun's light is reflected by half of the Moon's face (from the vantage point of Earth), the line between the light half and the dark half of the Moon is perfectly straight. If the Sun were infinitely distant from Earth, the triangle from the

Sun to the Earth to the Moon would be exactly 90 degrees. However, because the Sun is not infinitely distant from Earth, the observed triangle from Earth's surface is less than 90 degrees. The true value is 89 degrees 50 minutes. Ancient astronomers, using naked-eye observations, determined that the value must be greater than 87 degrees. On this basis, they determined that the Sun must be at least 19 times more distant from Earth than the Moon is.[13] Further, given that the Sun and the Moon have nearly equal apparent diameters as seen from Earth, the Sun's diameter must be at least 19 times greater than the Moon's and at least 6 times greater than Earth's.

Realization that the Sun must be much larger than Earth persuaded ancient astronomers that the Earth and other planets revolved around the Sun.[14] Although Copernicus (1473–1543) often receives credit for discovering the heliocentricity of the solar system, his "discovery" came from a visit to Italian libraries, where the manuscripts of ancient Egyptian and Greek astronomers were archived. These manuscripts from about two millennia earlier explained why Earth and the planets must revolve around the Sun.

Because ancient astronomers lacked algebra, however, they were unable to calculate the future positions of the Sun, Moon, and planets from a heliocentric perspective. Nevertheless, their mathematics did permit such predictions from a geocentric perspective. The Egyptian astronomer Ptolemy (AD 100–170) demonstrated how accurately future positions of the Sun, Moon, and planets could be calculated by assuming, arbitrarily, a geocentric perspective. Even today, his mathematical approach still delivers remarkably accurate predictions.

Ancient astronomers attempted to determine distances to the stars by measuring stars' movements relative to other stars in the celestial sky as Earth orbited around the Sun. However, the movements of the stars relative to one another remained undiscernible to them. From this inability to detect any relative movements they came to understand that the stars must be far more distant from Earth than the Sun.

The oldest surviving written records by ancient astronomers citing their measurements of the sizes and distances of the Sun, Moon, and stars are those by Egyptian and Greek astronomers of the seventh to the third centuries BC. However, given how intensely the ancients studied astronomy and how straightforwardly the relevant observations could be made and simple geometry applied, one may reasonably assume that ancient astronomers around the world, not just in the Near East, had determined at least rough estimates of the shapes, sizes, and distances of the Sun, Moon, and Earth by the time—or perhaps long before—the Bible was written.

ANE Astronomy Serves Modern Astronomy

Evidence of the ancient astronomers' expertise comes from its helpfulness to today's researchers. One example is the refinement of stellar burning models. A team of Finnish astronomers used the Cairo Calendar, a stellar almanac dated to 1271–1163 BC, to determine the rate of mass transfer from one star to the other in the binary star system known as Algol.[15]

Algol, the second brightest star in the Perseus constellation, was called "the raging one" by ancient Egyptians and "Rosh ha Satan" (Satan's head) by ancient Hebrews. Its variation in brightness results from its binary structure, given that one of its two stars briefly eclipses the other at a regular rate. Through nightly observations of Algol over a hundred-year span, ancient Egyptian astronomers recorded in the Cairo Calendar that Algol's period or eclipse rate was 2.850 days. At present, Algol's period is 2.867328 days. This change in Algol's period over some 3,250 years tells us that the rate of mass transfer from one of Algol's stars to the other equals 2.2×10^{-7} solar masses per year. This value provided confirmation of modern astronomers' best stellar burning models for Algol and similar binary star systems.

A Case for Human Intellectual Evolution?

Countless books and articles published in the twenty-first century convey the notion that we humans are becoming more intellectually advanced through an ongoing naturalistic evolutionary process. If that were the case, it would make sense to conclude that ancient peoples were either intellectually inferior to us or lacking in intellectual motivation. To me, this idea is an example of twenty-first-century hubris.

Even the brief content presented in this chapter and the previous one would seem adequate to counter the claim that we moderns are intellectually superior to ancient peoples. Readers wanting a more thorough treatment of the topic will want to consider books by Karl Butzer, Marshall Clagett, J. L. E. Dreyer, Christine Garwood, Helge Kragh, and Jeffrey Russell. Even these scholars, however, may have overlooked a significant factor in their assessment of early humans' intelligence.

During the last ice age, the global mean temperature varied by ±8°C on timescales of a few centuries.[16] Such extreme climate instability explains why people living during that period struggled to devote significant resources toward the advancement and scaling up of their technology: they were struggling to survive. This struggle for survival was exacerbated by the much lower atmospheric carbon dioxide levels during the last ice age. With atmospheric carbon dioxide levels of 180–190 parts per million,[17] photosynthesis and, hence, crop productivity would have been seriously hindered.

From 9,500 to about 75 years ago, the global mean temperature varied by no more than ±0.65°C.[18] Such climate stability made possible the Neolithic Revolution—the scaling up of agriculture, manufacturing, city building, and transportation systems. Then, from AD 1000 to 1950, the global mean temperature stabilized to within ±0.06°C.[19] This astounding climate stability contributed significantly to the development of universities during the Middle Ages, then to the Renaissance, and more recently to the industrial, scientific, and technological revolutions.

While the ANE peoples, including ancient Hebrews, lacked the wealth, technology, climate stability, and leisure time that later eras made possible, we must also acknowledge that most of their scientific achievements have been lost. The fire that destroyed the great library in Alexandria, for example, eradicated much of the record of ANE science. However, even the ancient literature we do possess, once we separate out the religious, astrological, and sociopolitical stories, leaves little doubt that these peoples were just as intelligent, just as curious about the workings of the natural realm, and just as committed to scholarly research as people today.

Biblical Evidence of ANE Interest in Science

I would add that even a cursory reading of the Old Testament adequately refutes the claim that ancient Hebrews and their ANE contemporaries cared little and understood little about science. In 1 Kings 4:33–34 we read about the knowledge of Israel's King Solomon:

> He spoke about plant life, from the cedar of Lebanon to the hyssop that grows out of walls. He also spoke about animals and birds, reptiles, and fish. From all nations people came to listen to Solomon's wisdom, sent by all the kings of the world, who had heard of his wisdom.

According to 1 Kings 4:32, Solomon also "spoke three thousand proverbs." Even the much smaller collection of Solomon's sayings recorded in Proverbs and Ecclesiastes leaves no doubt about the magnitude of interest in science and the availability of many accurate assessments of the natural realm.

The Bible makes it clear that the Israelites were not ignorant of the scientific achievements made by neighboring nations. Acts 7:22 reminds us that "Moses was educated in all the wisdom of the Egyptians and was powerful in speech and action." The book of Daniel tells us that Hananiah, Mishael, and Azariah, along with Daniel himself, were educated in "the language and literature of the Babylonians" and gained "knowledge and understanding of all kinds of literature and learning."[20] Daniel's intellectual and executive abilities were so great that he rose from captive slave to prime minister, first of the Babylonian empire and later of the Medo-Persian empire.

In reading through the books and articles of twenty-first-century Christian theologians who have become advocates for rejection or redefinition of the ICBI doctrine of biblical inerrancy, I could not help but notice that all, or nearly all, come from a young-earth creationist background. This background seems to have influenced their belief that a commitment to dual revelation forces a young-earth interpretation of the biblical creation texts. If so, I can easily understand their reasons for advocating a change. The next chapter offers a biblical assessment of this interpretation, including what prompted it and where it violates accepted hermeneutical principles.

Chapter 14

Biblical Cues to Earth's Age

Previous chapters speak of my lack of religious belief, Christian or otherwise, during my Canadian upbringing. By today's labels, I would have been included with the "nones," people who self-identify as having no religious affiliation. Some of my Christian friends tell me, based on their experiences with church, that my background may have been an advantage, at least with respect to my intense interest in science and my tendency to ask questions.

When I did pick up the Bible and begin reading it, I can honestly say that it never occurred to me to view the Genesis creation days as 24-hour periods. In fact, over the following decade, both before and after I committed my life to Christ, I encountered no one, Christian or non-Christian, who interpreted the text that way. And I had *many* conversations about Genesis. After all, the first chapter grabbed my attention and drew me into the rest of the Bible, carrying me all the way to acceptance of its redemptive message.

Eleven years later, I stood before a Southern California audience and shared my personal story, including the Genesis-and-science connection and its impact on me. The audience's mixed reaction caught me off guard. Some people joyfully thanked me, others expressed anger. This was my first encounter with people who thought God created the Earth and all its life in one week, roughly 6,000–10,000 years ago. At the time, I naively thought the 24-hour view must be an obscure one that would soon disappear.

More than four decades later, the young-earth creationist interpretation of Genesis 1 persists—and is far from obscure. Instead, it has remained a divisive controversy across the US and has spread to Christians in many other parts of the world. As I mentioned in the preceding chapter, many or most of the twenty-first-century conservative theologians who now advocate for a nonhistorical interpretation of the Bible's major creation texts come from a young-earth creationist background. I could have been among them had I been taught what they were taught in their churches.

A historically and scientifically accurate interpretation of the Bible's creation passages is impossible from a young-earth perspective. Even if history and science are ignored and only biblical and theological concerns are considered, this interpretive lens leads to conflicts within the biblical text. I have addressed these issues and arguments in prior books and articles.[1] What follows is a brief summary of the basis for understanding each of the creation days, taken literally, as something more than one 24-hour period.

Clear Textual Clues

The Bible that the Gideons provided me was the King James Version. Here, the Hebrew word *yôm* is translated "day" each time it appears in Genesis 1:1–2:4. Thus, even in a first reading of this passage, one can see that the word for "day" in the original Hebrew must be at least as flexible in usage as the English word *day*. *Yôm* can refer to part or all of the daylight hours (Genesis 1:3–5), to a calendar day (Genesis 1:14), or to an extended period of time (Genesis 2:4). In Genesis 2:4, this same Hebrew word refers to the entire span of God's creative activity.

Each of the first six creation days is accompanied by the statement "and there was evening, and there was morning" and an ordinal number. These details seem to communicate that the days are arranged in chronological order. Repeated expressions, including "and God said" and "it was good," affirm the chronological order and express the creative power of God's words, as well as God's pleasure in what his words brought forth.

This pattern leads to anticipation of an "evening-morning" tag to go along with the seventh day, but it does not appear there. Its omission must be intentional, and it certainly piques the curiosity of a first-time reader. Those familiar with the entire Bible would recognize the seventh day, the day of "rest" or cessation, from references to it in other passages of Scripture, such as Psalm 95 and Hebrews 4. In these texts, God's rest from his "work" of creation still continues, and we're invited to enter into his rest from working to save ourselves. In fact, Hebrews mentions that "today," the time to repent and turn to the Lord, continues to this day.

Exegetical support for the meaning of God's rest is abundant, as it is for the notion that God's "work" still continues, but in a very different way since Genesis 1. Exodus 20:11 has been used to assert that "day" must mean calendar day, but this claim is based on the assumption that a "Sabbath" can only and will always mean 24 hours. However, Leviticus 25:2–5 declares a year-long Sabbath for agricultural land. In each case, the Sabbath rest for humans and agricultural land serves biological needs and limitations—things not applicable to God.

God's ongoing seventh day answers a major fossil record enigma. It explains why new phyla, classes, orders, and families of life appear frequently before the advent of humanity and cease after the appearance of the first humans. The physical realm, created for the unfolding drama of human redemption, is complete.

Hosea 6:2 and Zechariah 14:7 show that a day, even a numbered day, can refer to a time span other than 24 hours. But perhaps the clearest indication of this point comes from biblical elaboration (much of it in Genesis 2) on the events of the sixth day. That was a very full day of activity—so full that it is unlikely Adam could have accomplished it all in a single 24-hour day.

Genesis 1 says that God created humans, male and female, on creation day six. According to the details provided in Genesis 2, God created Adam outside the garden and then placed him in the garden, where he introduced Adam to its beauty. Adam observed the trees of Eden growing. God had Adam tend the garden and "watch over it." Then God noted that Adam was alone and that it was "not good for the man to be alone" (Genesis 2:18). Next, God brought Adam various birds and mammals to observe and name. Finally, God put Adam into a sound sleep and created Eve (from a tissue biopsy taken from Adam's side). During this sequence of events, Adam had time to observe the difference between the world outside of Eden and the world within. He had time to learn the wonderful yet limited satisfaction that comes from gardening. He also had time and opportunity to learn about animal life and how soulish creatures (*nephesh*, in Hebrew) related to one another as well as to him. Finally, he had time to realize his own aloneness, his lack of a "like" partner.

According to the text, the exclamation that came from Adam's lips when he first saw Eve was, in Hebrew, "*happa'am*." This expression is translated in Genesis 30:20 as "now at last" and in Genesis 46:30 as "now finally." The *Theological Wordbook of the Old Testament* translates this term in Genesis 2:23 as "at last."[2] The *Brown-Driver-Briggs Hebrew and English Lexicon* translates it in the same passage as "now at length."[3]

Some young-earth creationists argue that Adam, before he sinned, "was much more intelligent than we can even imagine today"[4] and thus could have accomplished all these tasks and discoveries in a few hours. However, while the correlation between IQ and speed may be evident in a few problem-solving scenarios, in physical work or relational situations, the correlation seems more likely inverse. For example, I observed that the scientists with the highest IQs at Caltech were the ones that needed more time to accomplish manual labor tasks and to maintain their interpersonal relationships.

Theologian C. John Collins has explained that the wording and structure of Genesis 1:1–3 allows for a significant gap in time between the creation of the universe (Genesis 1:1) and development of the conditions on Earth described in Genesis 1:2.[5] Another time period of unspecified duration is possible between the state of Earth in Genesis 1:2 and the appearance of light on Earth's surface, described in Genesis 1:3.[6] On this basis, Genesis 1:1–3 would permit, if taken as history, the passage of some billions of years between the creation of the universe and the creation events thereafter. On this basis, Christians who interpret the Genesis creation week as a 144-hour time span could still accept the scientifically established ages of the universe and Earth. They need not reject the astronomical evidence for an ancient universe, nor do they need to accuse astronomers of deceit.

The "Plain Reading" Argument

Young-earth creationists frequently assert that the one and only "plain" reading of Genesis 1 supports their view that the creation days are six consecutive 24-hour periods. They suggest, without evidence, that if Genesis 1 were placed in front of 10,000 people who've not been exposed to modern science, all or nearly all of them would conclude that creation was completed in just 144 hours, from start to finish.[7] Perhaps the greatest weakness of this argument lies in its assumption that people gain a sense of Earth's great age only or primarily from science textbooks.

The book of nature and the whole of Scripture point to Earth's great antiquity. We see the effects of both slow and rapid processes, such as erosion and eruptions, all around us. So did the authors of the Old Testament. We read in passages such as Genesis 49:26, Habakkuk 3:6, Judges 5:21, and Micah 6:2, among many others, about "ancient" mountains, "age-old" rivers, and "enduring" foundations of the earth. These age indicators are evident to all people living at all times in all places.

The "plain reading" assertion seemingly has two additional problems. For one, the first chapter of Genesis was never intended to be read in isolation from the second chapter. Chapter breaks were not part of the original Hebrew text but were first developed by Stephen Langton, Archbishop of Canterbury, around AD 1227. As many Bible scholars have noted, a chapter break after

Genesis 2:4 would be more appropriate than the chapter break after Genesis 1:31. It would reduce the confusion over the relationship between the creation overview with its concluding statement (2:4) and the rest of the chapter's focus on the development of relationships—God with humans, humans with the created realm, humans with each other, humans with self, and humans with idolatry.

The other major problem with the "plain reading" assertion is our English-language bias. Word choice in English exceeds that of biblical Hebrew by roughly a thousand times. In large-vocabulary languages such as English, words can be more precisely wielded to produce clarity, just as a fine paintbrush can help produce a more detailed illustration. In small-vocabulary languages such as Hebrew, words must do double, triple, and quadruple duty. Thus, the Hebrew word *yôm* does not always mean "day" but rather has multiple "literal" definitions (as discussed earlier in this chapter). Context, both internal and external, serves as an essential aid for discerning the meaning of written communication. It seems no accident that the debate over the biblical and scientific timescale of Earth's and life's history is most intense among Christians who speak English, which is by far the largest-vocabulary language yet known.

Church Fathers' Interpretations

Roughly 2,000 pages of the early church fathers' commentary on Genesis 1 that predates 500 AD survives. However, only two of those pages have any relevance to the timing of creation or the duration of the creation days. In his writings, Irenaeus reasoned that because the "day" Adam and Eve ate the forbidden fruit was also said by God to be the "day" of their death, a "day" must be nearly a thousand years long, given that Adam lived 930 years.[8]

Augustine wrote, "At least we know that it [the Genesis creation day] is different from the ordinary day with which we are familiar."[9] He later added, "These days [Earth's days] indeed recall the days of creation, but without in any way being really similar to them."[10] In *Confessions*, Augustine argued that when God sanctified the seventh day, it became an epoch extending onward into eternity.[11] Both Irenaeus and Augustine offered their thoughts on the Genesis days as less than definitive. It seems no wonder, then, that neither the days' duration nor Earth's age "was ever listed as part of the 'rule of faith' (*regula fidei*)" for the early church.[12]

The early church fathers appreciated the mystery that surrounded the timing of creation. They appeared content to wait for further revelation and understanding, given that the creation texts made the most significant message—*who* created and *what* was created—abundantly clear. In this light, modern young-earth creationism did not become "doctrinaire" until the early part of the twentieth century, when Darwin's views began to gain wider attention and acceptance.

Incomplete Genealogies

To support their recent-creation perspective, young-earth creationists claim that the Genesis 5 and 11 genealogies are exhaustively complete.[13] On that basis, a total of 2,023 years would have transpired between the creation of Adam and the call of Abraham. Thus, "mankind is only about 6,000 years old"[14] and "the whole universe is also only about 6,000 years old."[15] But these conclusions again ignore the limited vocabulary of biblical Hebrew.

The Hebrew words for father and son in Genesis 5 and 11 are *'ab* and *ben*, respectively. *'Ab* also can refer to grandfather, great-grandfather, great-great-grandfather, and so forth.[16] It can also mean forefather or ancestor.[17] Similarly, *ben* may mean son, grandson, great-grandson, great-great-grandson, etc., or even a member of a particular group.[18] In other words, *'ab* and *ben* in the Old Testament may not always infer biological lineage. In Daniel 5:10–11, Belshazzar's mother refers to Nebuchadnezzar as Belshazzar's father when, in fact, they were not blood-related and Nebuchadnezzar was followed by two other kings before Belshazzar came to the throne.[19]

This flexibility in usage explains the apparent discrepancies among otherwise parallel genealogies (for example, 1 Chronicles 3, Matthew 1, and Luke 3). Every biblical genealogy provides an abridged listing of a family lineage. Because biblical genealogies are told for theological purposes, some generations may be highlighted and others skipped over.

It is obvious that Genesis 11 omits at least one name. The parallel record in Luke 3 includes the name Cainan (verse 36), which is not listed in Genesis 11.[20] The Genesis author neither totals the ages of the persons listed in chapters 5 and 11 nor offers comment concerning the time elapsed from creation (or from Noah's Flood, for that matter). Other biblical genealogies include such comments,[21] but these two do not.

The notable symmetry of the Genesis 5 and 11 genealogies resembles that of the Matthew 1 genealogy. As Matthew records the genealogy of Jesus in three sets of fourteen names each, Genesis 5 and 11 trace the genealogy of Abraham in two sets of ten names each. None of these genealogies provides a complete list.

Unchanging Laws of Physics

To explain how creation was completed in 144 hours, some young-earth creationists suggest that before sin entered the garden, the laws of thermodynamics operated differently, allowing for reduced entropy.[22] On this basis, trees would grow so rapidly that Adam would be able to observe their growth within a few hours or even minutes. If that were the case, however, Adam would have faced an impossible job in tending the garden. In fact, with entropy that low, the Sun would have been so dim that all life on Earth would have frozen to death.

According to the Bible, the laws of physics, including the thermodynamic laws, are unchanging. In Jeremiah 33, God, speaking through the prophet, contrasts human wavering with his own immutability by referring to the "laws governing the heavens and Earth" (verse 25). Just as they remain "fixed," as in constant and unchanging, so does God. Likewise, Ecclesiastes speaks of the monotonous operation of the natural laws. Paul writes in Romans 8 that the entire universe is subject to the law of decay, a law that will remain in effect until God's redemptive purposes for humanity in this physical realm have been fulfilled.

The biblical declarations of unchanged laws of physics have been exhaustively confirmed by astronomical observations. Because of light's finite velocity, astronomers have direct access to the past. Technologically advanced telescopes allow them to measure the operation of the laws of physics from about 1.4 seconds ago (when the Moon's light left the lunar surface) to 13.5 billion years ago (when the most distant star clusters merged to form the first galaxies). Observations make clear that any changes in the laws of physics from the cosmic beginning till now must be imperceptibly small, smaller than one part in ten quadrillion per year, to be exact.[23]

What few people may realize is that everything from human digestion to the shining of the Sun, Moon, and stars is extremely sensitive to even the tiniest change in the laws of physics. Young-earth creationism faces an insurmountable challenge for the simple reason that such models critically depend on radically altered laws of physics—laws altered not by a factor of 5 or 10 times, but by a factor of millions to billions at both the fall of Adam and the Flood of Noah. But the Bible and the book of nature explicitly affirm that the laws of physics have remained unchanged throughout the universe's history.

To their credit, some young-earth creationists, especially those with science and engineering backgrounds, have acknowledged this problem. The authors of *Radioisotopes and the Age of the Earth* have written, with honesty and multiple times, that if the laws and constants of physics have not changed in any significant way over the universe's and Earth's past, then both the universe and Earth must be billions of years old.[24] They concede, "Either accelerated radioactive decay accounts for the large daughter isotope residues in a short period of time, or a large amount of decay occurred at conventional rates and the earth is old."[25] For this reason, they appeal to vastly accelerated nuclear decay. For example, they assert, "All these products of nuclear decay were indeed produced by nuclear decay! But the amounts of those products we observe are much greater than thousands of years could produce—at today's rates."[26] They add, "A change in the decay constant of the order of 10^9 may be required, if the accelerated decay is restricted to the one year period of the Genesis Flood. . . . A one year episode of accelerated decay at the time of the Flood may not be enough. Other episodes during Creation week or during the Fall may also be necessary."[27]

However, if nuclear decay were occurring at an accelerated rate at any time in cosmic history, the spectra of stars and galaxies would reveal it. They do not. Adding to this lack is the problem that such accelerated nuclear decay would immediately vaporize all life and water on Earth.

Over the past four decades, I have met most of the scientists and engineers who hold to a young-earth creationist perspective. Not one of those I have met came to their belief in a young age for the Earth based on science. Nor could they name even one scientist or engineer who, without any reference to a particular Bible interpretation, had.[28]

My experience with young-earth creationists, both those with doctoral degrees in science and those lacking advanced study of science, tells me that they view nature's record as an unreliable revelation. They view the entirety of the natural realm as having been corrupted by Adam and Eve's sin from the moment sin occurred. On the other hand, they rightly consider the Bible utterly trustworthy in its capacity to reveal truth. Thus, discussions of biblical hermeneutics seem the most productive way to approach our disagreement and seek resolution.

Death before Adam

A more fundamental divide than creation's timing stands between young-earth creationists and other creationists: the issue of physical death before sin entered the world. Knowing that God is wholly good, loving, and powerful, young-earth creationists conclude that no death of any kind could have occurred until Adam sinned. They further state that God introduced death to teach Adam and

Eve the horrible consequences of disobedience. Young-earth creationists find the idea of millions of years of plant and animal death before Adam's sin deeply problematic. They view such a claim as tantamount to accusing God of cruelty and brutality, or at best, weakness and confusion.[29]

The New Testament sheds decisive light on what resulted from Adam's sin. In Romans 5:12, Paul writes, "Sin entered the world through one man, and death through sin, and in this way death came to all *people*, because all sinned" (emphasis added). An exhaustive search of Scripture further clarifies that only humans are capable of sin. Only humans make moral and spiritual choices. The death Adam experienced is carefully qualified in the text as being visited on people—with no reference to Earth's plants or animals (Romans 5:12, 18–19).

According to 1 Corinthians 15:21, the death that "came through a man" came to humans alone, not to humans *and* animals. And 1 Corinthians 15:22–23 explains, "As in Adam all die, so in Christ all will be made alive. But each in his own turn: Christ, the first fruits; then, when he comes, those who belong to him." According to Genesis, God gave Earth's plants and animals to humanity. The only creatures who belong to Christ through acceptance of his redeeming love are the ones made expressly for eternal relationship with him: humans. Only spiritual beings are "made alive" in Christ. Romans 5 and 1 Corinthians 15 are the only Bible passages that explicitly address the death brought by Adam's sin. Neither provides a compelling reason to suggest that physical death of plants and animals could not have occurred prior to Adam's sin—or that the physical death of plants and animals necessarily impugns God's character.

Young-earth creationists assume that physical death in any and all contexts is evil, an enemy of humanity. I trust they will consider that in several contexts, the death of plants and animals is a friend. Our food supply, our technology, our ability to harvest biodeposits from Earth's crust to develop and sustain civilization—these blessings and more are available thanks to the death of plants and animals that came before us. Our ability to print and disseminate Scripture comes from this same source.

The dispute over creation's timing results not from interpreting the Bible as truthful but from failing to integrate all the truth it reveals. Each passage must be understood in a way that is consistent, both internally and externally. Human limitations, even with the help and guidance of the Holy Spirit, make accurate and authoritative interpretation of Scripture a lifelong challenge. But as Christians who accept God's Word as a revelatory gift, we do not give up or discredit it. However, when faced with similar difficulties in interpreting God's other revelatory gift, the natural world, some Christians are tempted to give up, on the pretext that science is "ever-changing." The next chapter addresses the degree to which science can be considered settled, and to what degree it remains a work in progress.

Chapter 15

Science in Continual Flux?

Christians who oppose attempts to link scientific findings with biblical revelation in a concordant way typically do so for one of two reasons. One side states that scientists are motivated to undermine belief in the Bible's message (as discussed in the preceding chapter). The other side claims that science is always changing and is thus an unreliable source of truth.

According to proponents of the latter view, the science of today is likely to be overturned by the science of tomorrow, which makes efforts to connect its facts with the biblical text pointless or, worse, problematic. I have been warned by some theologians that using science to demonstrate the Bible's truth and trustworthiness is both dangerous and potentially damaging. If I gave this warning even the slightest credence, I would most certainly and swiftly alter at least one of my approaches to evangelism. However, I am glad to say there is no need for that.

Claims of Instability

In *The Lost World of Genesis One*, John Walton makes this claim: "If we were to say that God's revelation corresponds to 'true science' we adopt an idea contrary to the very nature of science. What is accepted as true today, may not be accepted as true tomorrow."[1] He goes on to argue that "divine intention must not be held hostage to the ebb and flow of scientific theory."[2] Evidently, he sees this ebb and flow as pervasive and ongoing, for he says, "All scientific frameworks are dynamic and subject to change."[3] Walton strongly warns against wedding the Bible to big bang cosmology in particular.[4]

Cornelis Van Dam goes so far as to say that science cannot tell us with any precision how Earth came to be as it is. In his words, "We do not know in a scientific way how God brought the present creation into being. We have no idea what processes were set in motion."[5] Perhaps Van Dam, Walton, and other twenty-first-century theologians whose work has been quoted in previous chapters take philosopher of science Thomas Kuhn's message about "paradigm shifts" to an extreme. Kuhn, however, never implies that paradigm shifts in science mean that science is untrustworthy. Rather, he exhorts scientists to be humble enough to admit they do not have all the answers and to thus remain open to paradigm shifts that add new knowledge and insight to what is already well established.[6]

Perspicuity of Scripture
The doctrine of biblical perspicuity is a basic tenet of Protestant evangelicalism that simply means the central and most important messages of the Bible are clear and comprehensible. It affirms that the Bible can be understood in a normal, literal sense by all Bible readers independent of church authority or tradition. It means that the Bible is sufficiently clear in communicating what people need to know in regard to their sinful state, their need for redemption, and the means of redemption through faith in what Jesus Christ accomplished in his sinless life, his atoning death, and his bodily resurrection.

The Westminster Confession of Faith describes the perspicuity of Scripture in this way:[7]

> All things in Scripture are not alike plain in themselves, nor alike clear unto all: yet those things that are necessary to be known, believed, and observed for salvation are so clearly propounded, and opened in some place of Scripture or another, that not only the learned, but the unlearned, in a due use of the ordinary means, may attain unto a sufficient understanding of them.

Many Bible passages serve as the direct basis for this doctrine. For example, Psalm 19:7 proclaims that "the statutes of the Lord are trustworthy, making wise the simple." Psalm 119:130 states that "the unfolding of [God's] words . . . gives understanding to the simple."

The Bible's perspicuity does not mean that every passage is perfectly clear. Peter acknowledges that Scripture contains "some things that are hard to understand."[8] Many Bible passages require thoughtful, thorough, scholarly study and exposition. Even then, full comprehension and understanding is beyond our finite minds. God declares in Isaiah, "As the heavens are higher than the earth, so are my ways higher than your ways and my thoughts than your thoughts."[9] Scripture is clear, certainly, but it is not exhaustively clear. To be exhaustive, it would need to overflow all the libraries of the world combined, and then some. For this reason, among others, God's provision of a second source of divine revelation has great value.

Human sin can and does impact comprehension of the Bible's clear meaning. Therefore, the doctrine of Scripture's perspicuity must be coupled with the doctrine of Holy Spirit illumination. Jesus encourages his disciples with the message that the Holy Spirit will guide and illumine their minds, leading them to grasp what is true. This promise would apply to anyone who is open to hearing, embracing, and submitting to Scripture's message.

Perspicuity of Nature

Just as the most important message in Scripture is abundantly clear, well established, and beyond reasonable doubt, so, too, much of nature's record is abundantly and increasingly clear, firmly established, and beyond reasonable dispute. An example already presented is that of the physical laws. Both a careful reading of Scripture and extensive observational validation confirm that the laws of nature are fixed and unchanging.

The constancy of the laws of physics is clear to anyone, ancient or modern, who gives close attention to nature's realm. Because of this fixity, all peoples, both ancient and modern, have been able to trust their investigation of nature to reveal what is real and true in the physical sense. All investigators could be confident that nature itself is neither capricious nor deceptive, even when it seems mystifying. The fixity of the laws and constants of physics also means that ongoing investigation of nature's realms will, through time, accumulate thoroughly tested and secure knowledge, a firm foundation for further investigation and discovery. Two examples may be seen in the scientific disciplines of dynamics and mechanics.

Galileo Galilei's experimental work on the motions of bodies laid a foundation for classical mechanics. He discovered that the rate at which gravity draws massive bodies toward Earth's center is independent of the body's mass. He established that the laws of physics are the same in any system moving at a constant speed in a straight line, regardless of speed or direction. He demonstrated that motion and rest will always be relative to one another and not absolute.

Galileo's principles of dynamics provided the foundational framework for Isaac Newton's recognition of the laws of motion. Newton's laws of motion provided the foundation for the scientific disciplines of classical mechanics and celestial mechanics, and a straightforward pathway for the development of

Albert Einstein's theory of special relativity. More challenging, however, was Einstein's development of the theory of general relativity. Minuscule discrepancies in Newtonian mechanics indicated the need for further refinement. In particular, a century's worth of observations by astronomers revealed that the point in Mercury's orbit where Mercury is closest to the Sun is advancing several arcseconds (1 arcsecond = 0.0000007716 of a circle) faster per century than could be explained by Newtonian mechanics alone. General relativity perfectly explained this extra advance and predicted additional properties of gravity, such as a slight bending of light when it passes near extremely massive bodies.

Newton did not overthrow Galilean dynamics. Nor did Einstein overthrow Newtonian mechanics. Both Galilean dynamics and Newtonian mechanics are still valid. They are still taught in physics textbooks and should continue to be taught. The possibility of their being further refined does not make them "fragile" or "volatile" or "in a state of flux" or "continually and always changing," as Walton, Johnny Miller, John Soden, and Brent Sandy claim.[10] Passengers on aircraft, trains, and automobiles need not worry that a possible failure in Galilean dynamics or Newtonian mechanics will cause them harm. Even when NASA sends a spacecraft to Pluto, the science team need not bother to factor in the relativistic corrections to the flightpath because these corrections are known, and they are much too tiny to be of concern. Likewise, for macro bodies and macro systems, quantum mechanical adjustments are much too minuscule to be of concern.

What is true of Newtonian mechanics also is true of James Clerk Maxwell's theory of electromagnetism. It is taught in physics textbooks and always should be, despite the need for minuscule adjustments to it based on quantum mechanics. These adjustments do not overthrow the theory of electromagnetism. They merely refine it. Or to put it another way, they extend it.

Physics is not the only discipline where this level of solidity and security of knowledge can be observed. Every discipline of science possesses a foundation of knowledge and understanding that remains inviolable, indisputable. That foundational knowledge continues to grow. Rather than being fluid and subject to change, most scientific frameworks are totally stable and *growing* in their range of applicability.

On this point, a fundamental difference between Scripture and God's book of nature becomes obvious. For Scripture, the biblical canon is essentially closed— given the unlikely possibility, for example, that one of Paul's as-yet-uncovered epistles, such as his letter to the church at Laodicea mentioned in Colossians 4:16, will somehow turn up. The Bible is comprised of 66 books. Based on what is written in these books, no one reasonably anticipates that another will be added,[11] and what is written in the 66 books is not subject to change.

Meanwhile the "canon" of nature's revelatory "book" remains open. Although God has ceased from preparing his creation for life and creating that life, scientists are daily adding to the databases undergirding all the scientific disciplines. In my discipline of astrophysics, that database roughly doubles every five years. Only in this sense is science dynamic and ever-changing. Science is continually advancing, yes, but it is not in the state of flux some theologians seem to think.

What Science Is Debatable?

Let me be clear that not *all* points of scientific understanding are stable and secure. Just as theologians continue to wrestle and debate over the meaning of various biblical texts, scientists still wrestle and debate over details in nature's record. The characteristics, operations, and theoretical underpinnings of certain phenomena are still being explored and are still not fully understood. Debate is most prevalent along the frontiers of scientific research.

The job of all scientists is to advance our knowledge and understanding of nature's record and workings. The initial extension of a scientific frontier typically produces measurements with large statistical and systematic errors. (*Statistical errors*, also known as random errors, refer to imprecision in making measurements; *systematic errors* refer to environmental and instrumental factors that could shift *all* the measurements either up or down in value.) Both kinds of errors sometimes produce discordant results. Even when the results are in agreement with previous measurements, probable systematic errors and the possibility of unknown systematic factors often generate debate among scientists.

It takes many repeated experiments and observations and more advanced instruments to transition from frontier science to foundational science. Non-scientists may struggle to distinguish the one from the other. This struggle seems all the more difficult because the typical time for frontier research to become foundational knowledge can vary widely from one discipline to another and even within a discipline.

Certain practices and guidelines can help facilitate the process, however. Many or most scientists by their very nature seem quick to challenge, question, and debate scientific hypotheses, models, and theories. If there is any substantive basis for speculation or doubt, they *will* express it. Therefore, checking the most widely respected journal archives, such as PubMed.gov in the life and medical sciences and the NASA archive at ui.adsabs.harvard.edu in the physical sciences, for articles that challenge a particular theory or model can help readers discern its level of scientific certainty. If challenges appear plentiful and clearly substantive, the theory or model has yet to make the transition from frontier to foundational.

A thorough scan of the NASA archive for published research challenging the Earth's shape may lead to an article or two about its degree of variance from perfect sphericity. However, there will not be any papers proposing the Earth is flat. Earth's shape is settled science. Likewise, one can search the archive for published research challenging the age of the Earth. One or more papers may propose slight adjustments to the currently accepted 4.5662 ± 0.0001 billion years. However, no paper offering evidence for an Earth younger than four billion years old will be found. Earth's age, too, is settled science.

While Earth's shape and age may be among the most extreme examples, at least they remind us that much of science is secure, stable, foundational, and not subject to change. In some cases, the science is firmly settled but communication about it may be slow to trickle down to the general public and to school textbooks.

Big Bang?

The theoretical model for the origin of the universe, called the big bang model, remained hotly contested from the time of the first evidence for it was observed in the 1920s until 1964. That is when researchers discovered the radiation remaining from the cosmic creation event. From 1964 until the beginning of the twenty-first century, a handful of research astronomers continued to challenge the model. Some of them I knew, including Geoffrey Burbidge, longtime chair of the astronomy department and founder of the physics department at the University of California, San Diego. When the COBE satellite discovered tiny temperature ripples in the cosmic background radiation as predicted by the big bang,[12] Burbidge, an atheist, complained to a *Toronto Globe and Mail* journalist that his fellow astronomers were rushing off to join "the First Church of Christ of the Big Bang."[13]

Today, in this third decade of the twenty-first century, the scientific evidence for big bang cosmology is so comprehensive and firmly established[14] that the astronomical community no longer debates its validity. Debate has shifted to what *kind* of big bang model best describes the observed features and history of the universe. More precisely, debate has narrowed to what kind of ΛCDM hot big bang model is most accurate. (According to this set of models, the universe begins near-infinitely hot, and its dominant and second-most dominant components are dark energy, Λ, and cold dark matter, CDM, respectively).

The scientific debate has shifted from the big bang model to a subset of a subset of the big bang model. Such a shift of debate from a model as a whole to the layers below it serves as a measure of the model's security and stability. On this basis alone, one can see how secure, stable, and beyond reasonable doubt the big bang model has become. But does this mean it will no longer be challenged?

Will scientific debate over *any* scientific model ever end? Only when scientists learn everything that can be learned about the model. Given that scientists, as all other humans, are still constrained by the space-time dimensions of the cosmos, that time will never come. Nevertheless, ongoing debate, if below the level of the model as a whole, gives no cause for doubt about anything other than the model's details.

Evolution?

One of the great ironies this book addresses is the readiness of certain Christian theologians to express doubt about settled scientific findings and to express certainty about matters that are far from settled. Some examples of the latter carry far-reaching implications for the biblical doctrine of dual revelation (and biblical inerrancy). These include claims that (1) naturalistic biological processes are sufficient to explain the origin and entire history of life; (2) humans are descended from an ancestor in common with Neanderthals, *Homo erectus*, and chimpanzees; (3) the progenitor of present-day humans is a population much larger than the biblical two; and (4) humans possess no exceptional attributes, no features that distinguish us from Neanderthals, Denisovans, *Homo erectus*, and *Homo heidelbergensis*.

Later chapters will show that scientific breakthroughs in anthropology, genetics, paleontology, atmospheric chemistry, and solar physics, among others, indicate that something beyond strictly natural process and coincidence is involved in the origin and history of Earth's life and of humanity. These same scientific breakthroughs demonstrate close concordance with the biblical accounts of the origin and history of life (including human life).

The next two chapters offer, first, a biblical defense and, second, a scientific defense of the historicity of Genesis 1–11. A response to the recent attempt by some theologians to accommodate naturalistic evolution by altering the lexicon and historic wordbooks of biblical Hebrew appears in an appendix. These chapters attempt to show that the scholarly work of Hebrew language specialists from past centuries is still on the mark.

Chapter 16

The Historicity of Genesis 1–11

Among the many books written by twenty-first-century theologians analyzing and critiquing the biblical creation account from a variety of perspectives, one common denominator stands out. All seem to approach the text with an "either-or" interpretive lens that does not allow for a mixture of miracles and natural processes. How ironic does it seem that scholars devoted to unpacking layer upon layer of meaning in the pages of Scripture would take such a stance? How ironic that Christians, whose faith stands or falls on a miraculous event, would deny the miraculous.

In commenting on Genesis 1–11 as a historically accurate account of what God did to set the stage for the unfolding drama of redemption, I make no claim to present the one and only reading of these chapters. The Bible is a revelation of realities beyond human capacity, expressed in a book that can be held in just one human hand. All who embrace Scripture must return to its pages again and again for further insight. It always has more to tell us than we have yet grasped. This has been my experience in studying Genesis over the past several decades. Every time I return to it, I gain new insights.

In studying Genesis, some scholars of ancient literature notice elements of myth genre. Some experts in Hebrew poetry notice certain poetic elements. Other scholars are struck by the multiple ways Genesis stands out over and against the myths of the ancient Near East.[1] Philosophical physicalists see distortions of reality. As a scientist, I see a straightforward summary of Earth's history, a history I have studied in some depth.

Theologians and others who embrace belief in biblical inerrancy—not blindly but on the basis of their own study—are asking what "facts" disallow a historical reading of Genesis 1–11. What "facts" has the narrative presented out of order or described inaccurately? What parts of the narrative are disproven by "the scientific data"?[2]

The fourth creation day is the most commonly cited reason for rejecting a literal, chronological description of creation events in Genesis 1. I address that issue and other challenges to the historicity of Genesis 1–11 in my book *Navigating Genesis*.[3] What follows here is a brief overview. Many theologians, pastors, and laypeople believe that a literal interpretation of this passage implies that God created the Sun, Moon, and stars after, not before, the creation and development of vegetation on Earth's landmasses. Their confusion is understandable because, whatever timescale one adopts for the six creation days, vegetation cannot exist on Earth's landmasses without the Sun's heat, light, and gravity.

The Frame of Reference in Genesis 1
The problem here is rather obvious, and yet it goes without notice, time and again. Countless books devoted to Genesis 1, including those written by twenty-first-century authors, fail to recognize that the point of view, or *frame of reference*, from which the creation narrative unfolds is *not* out in the heavens looking down on planet Earth. Rather, as Genesis 1:2 makes clear, the story is told from the vantage point of an observer hovering just above Earth's surface, below Earth's primordial atmosphere. To miss this context is fatal to an accurate reading of the chronology (see figure 16.1). Correcting this one mistake can transform Genesis from a scientific embarrassment into one of the most potent demonstrations that the Bible is scientifically accurate in everything it communicates about the natural realm.

Job 38:9 affirms this frame of reference by explaining why darkness covered the surface of Earth's waters: "I [God] made the clouds its [the sea's] garment and wrapped it in thick darkness." Evidently, the darkness on Earth's surface was the result of Earth's primordial clouds blocking visible light from passing through. (See the next chapter for scientific corroboration of this statement.) God allows the Sun's light to penetrate the clouds and thick haze on creation day one, when he says, "Let there be light." This explains how vegetation could have existed before creation day 4.

The Accurate Chronology of Genesis 1
In terms of sequence and descriptions, Genesis 1 highlights the most significant events in Earth's history, and it does so in the correct order. As for the duration of the creation days, a literal, consistent reading of Genesis 1 and 2

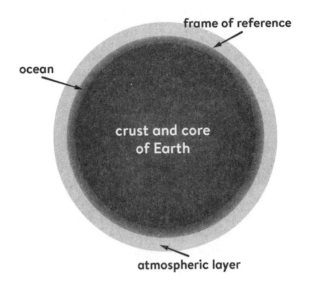

Figure 16.1: Frame of Reference for Genesis 1:3–31
The events of the six creation days are described from the vantage point of Earth's water-covered surface, underneath Earth's cloud cover, as Genesis 1:2 and Job 38:8–9 indicate.
Credit: Hugh Ross

(as described in chapter 14) and more than two dozen other biblical passages on creation makes clear that God's creation activity occurred over six consecutive long periods of time.[4] This conclusion permits two distinct interpretations of the creation days. One is that the days are long time periods, and the other is that each *day* represents the introduction of a long epoch of God's creative activity. Either way, there is no conflict with the established scientific record for the ages of the universe, Earth, and Earth's life.

Genesis 1:2 describes what Earth was like before the events of the six creation days. It states that the initial conditions of the primordial Earth were (1) water existed everywhere on Earth's surface; (2) it was dark everywhere on Earth's surface; (3) Earth was formless; and (4) Earth was void. Given that the context of the six creation days is God's transformation of Earth to make it fit for life and filled with life, the third and fourth initial conditions imply that Earth began unfit for life and empty of life.

It is important to recognize that Genesis 1 is not the only biblical description of God's physical creation activities. Job 37–39, Psalm 104, and Proverbs 8 provide parallel descriptions that add much scientific detail. These three passages plus dozens of briefer biblical creation texts clarify the historical and scientific message of Genesis 1.

Here is a brief overview of what occurred on each creation day:

Creation day 1: Genesis 1:3 says, "Let there be light." Genesis 1:1 and Hebrews 11:3 imply that God had created the universe of matter, energy, space, and time previous to creation day 1. So, light existed in the universe prior to the six creation days, but on the first creation day Earth's atmosphere transitions from opaque to translucent (a thick haze). For the first time, visible light from the Sun, Moon, planets, and stars penetrates Earth's atmosphere to illuminate Earth's surface. On creation day 1, photosynthesis becomes possible.

Creation day 2: Earth's water cycle is established. Water cycles from the waters below (oceans, lakes, rivers, springs, aquifers) to the waters above (clouds in the atmosphere) and back to the waters below through rain, mist, fog, dew, snow, hail, and frost. Genesis 1 offers a very brief description of the water cycle (water above the expanse and water below). Job 37–38 provides extensive details of Earth's water cycle.

Creation day 3: Earth dramatically changes from a water world, entirely covered by an ocean, to a world containing both surface oceans and landmasses. These landmasses then begin to sprout with *deshe*—green vegetation, that is, photosynthetic life.[5] Three out of many examples of this vegetation are listed: *zera'* (also used for semen, but here a reference to the embryos of vegetation),[6] *ets* (any plant containing woody fiber or cellulose),[7] and *peri* (food and/or edible embryonic life produced by a living thing).[8]

Creation day 4: Earth's atmosphere is again transformed, this time from translucent to transparent. Genesis 1:14 refers to the time when the sources of light—the Sun, Moon, and stars—became clearly visible from Earth's surface. For the first time, animals could see objects in the sky that "serve as signs to mark seasons and days and years." Their visibility now plays a vital role in the life cycle of creatures who critically depend on the awareness of these objects' relative positions in the sky to regulate their biological clocks. Genesis 1:16 declares to readers that the Sun, Moon, and stars are not "gods" to be worshipped, as many of the peoples in nations bordering Israel believed, but, rather, material objects that God had made to serve their needs and, through them, the needs of all Earth's life.

Creation day 5: God acts so that Earth's oceans now swarm with *sheres*, teeming sea animals. This is the first mention of animals. Then, God creates birds and sea mammals. The text does not indicate whether birds preceded sea mammals. Nor does it mention the creation of the first land mammals. The text refers to the birds and sea mammals as *nephesh* (soulish) animals. *Nephesh* animals are endowed with intelligence, volition, and emotion and, thus, the capacity to bond with one another and with a (future) higher species, humans.

Creation day 6: Three subcategories of land mammals gain the spotlight: the *remes* (short-legged land mammals), *behemah* (long-legged herbivorous land mammals), and *hayya* (long-legged carnivorous land mammals). This specificity seems to serve as a reminder of Job 38–39, which describes how certain mammals in these categories fulfill crucial roles in the development of human civilization. Even apart from knowledge of the book of Job, the text hints that these three types of land mammals are somehow particularly important for what comes next.

Finally, after all these preparatory events, humans appear on the terrestrial scene. Of all Earth's life, only humans are said to be created in the image of God. Only humans, among all earthly creatures, have the ability to know and relate to the personal God.

This reading of Genesis, based on the frame of reference and Earth's initial conditions provided in the text (Genesis 1:2), is neither contrived nor uniquely mine. One need not understand it fully to grasp its primary message. It does not depend on twenty-first-century scientific hindsight.

Long before scientists gained clear understanding of the historical events described and sequenced in this passage, Christian scholars such as Isaac Newton (1642–1727),[9] Thomas Chalmers (1780–1847),[10] and Hugh Miller (1802–1856)[11] discerned an outline of this same description and sequence of events from the Genesis 1 text alone. During my time at Trinity Evangelical Divinity School (TEDS) for the Kenneth S. Kantzer Lecture Series in 1991, professor of Old Testament and semitics Gleason Archer told me, in the presence of several colleagues, that in 1955 he had written a paper on Genesis 1. Based on his analysis of the structure, grammar, and wording of the original Hebrew text, he had developed an interpretation virtually identical to the one I had presented, but he had never submitted his paper for publication in a theology journal. When asked why not, he explained that he felt he was not sufficiently trained in science to be confident that his analysis of the text would withstand scientific critique.

Archer told the group he was glad to be assured that his exegesis of Genesis 1 was scientifically credible. In turn, I let him know how grateful I was to hear from a Hebrew scholar of his caliber that my interpretation of the Genesis 1 text was a valid one.[12] The next chapter shows how well the text has fared through the subsequent years of scientific advance. Many of its highlighted events can now be understood and scientifically affirmed in remarkable detail.

The Question of Vegetarianism

William Lane Craig includes vegetarianism as a "fantastic element" (see "More Inerrancy 'Disclaimers' Follow" in chapter 3) in the Genesis 1 creation account.[13] Craig's concern came from this statement in Genesis 1:30: "To all the beasts of the earth and all the birds of the air and all the creatures that move on the ground—everything that has the breath of life in it—I give every green plant for food." Craig is aware, of course, that certain animals, such as the felines, cannot survive on a strict vegetarian diet.

Humans, however, can survive on a vegetarian diet. In Genesis 1:29, God places humans on a vegetarian diet. Indeed, such a diet is essential for humans potentially living much longer than the limit of about 120 years God imposed in Genesis 6:3. Animal tissue contains ten to ten thousand times the concentrations of heavy metals as does plant tissue. This difference poses little health risk for humans younger than 120 years, but a substantial risk for humans living well beyond 120 years.

The vegetarian diet restriction was lifted in Genesis 9:2–3, but only humans are mentioned as being granted a wider diet. Therefore, it is fair to assume that God's statement in Genesis 1:30 is in the larger context of humanity's responsibility to manage Earth's resources for the benefit of all life (Genesis 1:28–30). In this context, God exhorts humanity to take special care of Earth's green vegetation. Green vegetation are the base of the food chain. Without green vegetation nobody gets to eat, neither herbivores nor carnivores.

Integrating Genesis 1 and 2

Twenty-first-century theologians are not the first to contend that Genesis 1 and 2 offer contradictory accounts of creation. This argument first appeared in a commentary by Jean Astruc (1684–1766), a French physician. Astruc attempted to disparage the veracity of the Bible by arguing, as Johnny Miller, John Soden, and many of their peers do, that the two chapters represent different and contradictory accounts, presumably by two different authors.[14] Here, again, I am reminded of Galileo's assertion that the biggest mistake one can make in Bible interpretation is to misidentify the frame of reference. I am also reminded that in hermeneutics, context is everything.

Genesis 2:4–25 does indeed tell a separate story about creation. It provides a close-up view of a crucially important part of the larger story. Whereas the focus in Genesis 1:1–2:3 is on the physical creation, culminating in the creation of humans, the focus of Genesis 2:4–25 turns to crucial nonphysical elements of creation. This chapter sets forth God's assignment of human authority and responsibility for management of Earth's resources, including life.

The perceived contradiction between Genesis 1:1–2:3 and Genesis 2:4–25 lies in the apparent mismatch of chronology. Genesis 1 ends with the creation of humans, male and female. Genesis 2 begins with a focus on the first man alone. Genesis 2 may seem to imply that there was no vegetation, rain, or animal life prior to Adam's creation.

The apparent mismatch disappears if we recognize that Genesis 2:5–6 and 2:19 serve as a brief summary, or partial review, of God's creation acts described in Genesis 1:1–2:3. Genesis 2:4–25 includes no indication that the few physical details mentioned are intended to convey a chronology. The shrubs, plants, rain, and man introduced in Genesis 2:5 appear without reference to time sequence. Rather, they form a list, in no particular order, of familiar things that once did not exist. The same is true for the beasts and birds mentioned in Genesis 2:19. By contrast with Genesis 1:1–2:3, no textual clues appear in Genesis 2:4–25 to suggest that the few physical events mentioned there are intended to be understood in chronological order.

A different kind of chronology *can* be seen in Genesis 2:4–25, however. God introduces the man he has created to the three distinct categories of creation, in order. First, God introduces Adam to the physical creation. He brings Adam into Eden (from outside this wondrous garden) and assigns him responsibility for managing its plants and trees. Next, God introduces Adam to the *nephesh* (soulish) animals and assigns him responsibility for examining and naming the *nephesh* kinds. Thus, God allows Adam the opportunity to discover what relationships among and with these creatures are like.

No doubt Adam enjoys much more fulfillment in relating to these animals than he does in tending to Eden's plants and trees. In this process, however, Adam has an opportunity to recognize that he is missing something these creatures possess, a "like" counterpart. God sees that Adam can now comprehend his "aloneness," even with God so near (Genesis 2:18). At this just-right moment, God creates a creature like Adam, a physical, soulish, and spiritual partner.

Genesis 1:1–2:3 provides a physical perspective on creation, whereas Genesis 2:4–25 offers a spiritual perspective on creation. The spiritual perspective carries vital importance. Human responsibility and authority include a physical component, a soulish component, and a spiritual component. To succeed as managers of Earth's physical, soulish, and spiritual resources, humans would need to keep all three components of creation continually in balance, a task that only God's wisdom and guidance could make possible. (This need seems as evident today as ever.)

Robert Boyle, considered the father of modern experimental chemistry, made this statement in 1674: "I see no sound reason to embrace some people's opinion that would so turn the first two chapters of Genesis into an allegory as to overthrow their literal and historical sense."[15] The advance of knowledge since that day gives me no sound reason to disagree with Boyle.

The Biblical Account of Noah's Flood

As controversial as the Genesis 1 and 2 narratives may be, the account of the Flood event, Genesis 6–9, stirs even more historical skepticism. The major concern is with the extent of the Flood. Many Bible interpreters have pictured it as a global deluge. However, a different scenario emerges from integration of all the relevant passages. This integrative analysis shows that the Flood, while utterly destructive to all humans and their domesticated animals outside the ark, most certainly was not a global event.

2 Peter 2:5 says, "He [God] brought a flood upon the world of the ungodly" (ESV). 2 Peter 3:6 refers to "the world that then existed" (ESV) as the world that was flooded. In both cases the Greek word for "world," *kosmos*, is qualified—in the former case, as the place where ungodly people lived, and in the latter, as the world of that time. The Greek expression here, *kosmos tote*, distinguishes the world of Noah from the world of, say, Rome, a world that encompasses significantly less than the entirety of Earth's surface. In both time frames, that of Noah and Peter, "world" more commonly referred to people than to the planet.

The historical context of the Flood, given in Genesis 10–11, implies that the humans of Noah's era had not yet spread out to all regions of the earth. With no people or domesticated animals (*basar* in Genesis 6:19; 7:15–16, 21; 8:17) occupying distant continents, and certainly not Antarctica or Greenland, no need would exist for God to flood those regions. Psalm 104, the most extensive of the creation psalms, clearly rules out a globally extensive Flood. Verses 6–8 reflect on creation day 3, when God transforms Earth from the water world described in Genesis 1:2 to a world with both oceans and landmasses:

You covered it with the watery depths as with a garment;
　　the waters stood above the mountains.
But at your rebuke the waters fled,
　　at the sound of your thunder they took to flight;
they flowed over the mountains,
　　they went down into the valleys,
　　to the place you assigned for them.

Verse 9 then adds,

You set a boundary they cannot cross;
　　never again will they cover the earth.

The guarantee here is that once God has established Earth's landmasses, water will never again cover the whole of Earth. Both Job 38:8–11 and Proverbs 8:22–29 also allude to this promise.

Genesis 7:19, the passage [in English translations] most often cited as proof that the Flood was global, says that as the water rose, "all the high mountains under the entire heavens were covered." This same Hebrew expression appears in the Genesis 8 depiction of the receding of the floodwaters. Verse 9 says, "The dove could find nowhere to perch because there was water over all the surface of the earth." However, Genesis 8:5 tells us that Noah could already see, from his higher perspective at the top of the ark, the peaks of distant mountains. The use of this same Hebrew expression in both contexts implies that "under the entire heavens" refers to the view from one horizon to another, as far as the eye can see. The Flood certainly must have been extensive, but the text does not imply global proportions.

In a weekend-long debate among theologians and me on the scale of Noah's Flood, advocates for a global Flood pointed out that among all the biblical Hebrew nouns for earth and land, three—*haraba, yabbasha,* and *sayon*—are used specifically in reference to a portion of Earth's surface, never to its entirety. They asserted that the absence of these nouns in Genesis 6–8 serves as evidence for a global Flood. However, their assertion was incorrect. *Haraba* does, in fact, appear in the Hebrew text of Genesis 7:22.

Genesis 8 records that the floodwaters required nearly a full year to recede. This time period indicates that Noah's Flood most likely occurred sometime during the most recent ice age. For the floodwaters, without ongoing rainfall, to take that long to flow back into the oceans, especially with the assistance of a strong wind (Genesis 8:1), large quantities of meltwater from snow and ice on the surrounding hills and mountains must have added to that flow of floodwater.

If Noah's Flood occurred sometime during the last ice age, its extent would have been much greater than had it occurred during the current interglacial period. Its extent and intensity would have been large enough to guarantee that no humans or domesticated animals existing outside Noah's ark would survive. A map of its likely extent (more than a half-million square miles) appears in *Navigating Genesis*.[16] The next chapter offers a closer look at some of the scientific corroboration, some only recently added by ongoing research, for a historical interpretation of Genesis 1–11.

Chapter 17

Recent Scientific Corroboration

Many books give a thorough defense of the historical accuracy of Genesis 1–11 from a scientific perspective. Some have been written by other authors[1] and some by me.[2] Rather than attempt to summarize their extensive content, I will use this chapter to illustrate what I see as a core principle of the dual revelation doctrine: the more we learn from the book of nature, the more evidence accumulates for the divine inspiration and accuracy of the book of Scripture.

Four of the many examples of this principle come from recent discoveries related specifically to events described in Genesis 1. That chapter is a primary target for questioning and rejection by twenty-first-century Christian theologians and scholars. What did or didn't occur on the fourth day seems to be the issue of most significant concern. So, let's start there.

Hazy Early Earth Aligns with Creation Day 4

Those who lived in the vicinity of Los Angeles during the 1950s and '60s can speak with conviction about haze that seriously limits visibility. Those who travel to other cities of the world where population is dense and inversion layers hold down exhaust from industry and vehicles can also testify to the visibility issues. When one of my flights touched down in a major Asian city, I encountered a haze so thick I could barely see the buildings just a mile or so from the airport. That night I could not see a single star in the sky.

An interdisciplinary team of scientists led by Sarah Hörst, a planetary astronomer, affirmed that a thick haze surrounded Earth during its early history.[3] This haze would have permitted light from the Sun to pass through Earth's atmosphere, but the Sun would not have been visible from Earth's surface. In other words, the sky would have been translucent, not transparent, prior to the events of the fourth day. This is confirmed by Genesis 1 when it states that God created light on the first day. The research study by Hörst's team demonstrated, through a series of experiments, just how Earth's atmospheric cloudiness and haziness eventually decreased enough that Earth's atmosphere could transition from zero transparency to nearly complete transparency.

Throughout Earth's history, the amount of methane and carbon dioxide in Earth's atmosphere has been declining at a near-exponential rate.[4] The much greater quantity of these gases in Earth's early atmosphere would have produced more clouds. Therefore, early in Earth's history these clouds may have covered the sky so thickly that creatures on Earth's surface would have been prohibited from seeing the Sun, Moon, and stars.

Hörst's team found an additional cause of early Earth's lack of atmospheric transparency—a low level of oxygen. They performed laboratory experiments on gas mixtures of molecular nitrogen, carbon dioxide, methane, and molecular oxygen designed to mimic the composition of Earth's atmosphere during its first four billion years. They noted that oxygen concentrations greater than twenty parts per million "resulted in a decrease in aerosol production rate with increasing O_2 concentration."[5] That is, the more O_2 in Earth's atmosphere, the less haze from aerosols; the less O_2, the greater the haze-producing aerosols.

As figure 17.1 reveals, the oxygen content in Earth's atmosphere was not high enough to clear the pervasive haze until 580 million years ago. Until that time, creatures on Earth's surface would have been unable to see the Sun, Moon, and stars. The team further explained that atmospheric haze contributes to cloud condensation.[6] Therefore, the denser the atmospheric haze, the thicker the cloud cover.

This circumstance poses no problems for life previous to 580 million years ago since such life-forms (microbes, algae, fungi, bryophytes, and tiny marine animals) need no awareness of the positions of the Sun, Moon, and stars in order to thrive and reproduce. Later animal life-forms do. Even a moderate haze is sufficient to obscure the positions of these celestial bodies from the view of animals who depend on them to regulate their life-critical biological clocks.

What this study affirms is that Earth's atmosphere transitioned from translucent to sufficiently transparent just prior to the introduction of Earth's first large-bodied animals, about 575 million years ago. This corroborates the description and chronology of creation day 4 in Genesis and shows how these events helped set the stage for later creation activity.

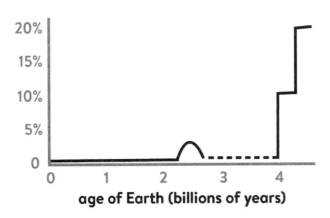

Figure 17.1: Atmospheric Oxygen Levels throughout Earth's History
Diagram credit: Hugh Ross

Atmospheric Oxygen and Carbon Dioxide Aligns with Creation Day 5

As figure 17.1 indicates, Earth's atmosphere has undergone protracted oxygenation, a process that dramatically impacts Earth's capacity for life support. Some microbial species can flourish without any atmospheric oxygen, and others can thrive with atmospheric oxygen below 1%. A few animal species with individual body sizes no larger than about a millimeter across or with slightly larger bodies but very low metabolic requirements can survive in atmospheric oxygen at only a few percent.[7] However, animals with individual body sizes of a few centimeters or more and typical energetic and nutritional needs require atmospheric oxygen levels of at least 8%.

Geochemists have determined Earth's atmospheric oxygen history through measurements of isotope ratios and isotope abundances that serve as proxies for the atmospheric oxygen level. The dotted line in figure 17.1 shows the part of Earth's history for which geochemists lack undisputed proxies. The best available measurements were of cerium abundance levels and chromium isotope ratios in marine sediments. Cerium is preferentially scavenged from seawater when atmospheric oxygen levels are high.[8] However, given that cerium oxidation kinetics are poorly constrained, scientific debate over the oxidative pathway continues.[9] Consequently, atmospheric oxygen level estimates for the era from 2.5 to 4.0 billion years after Earth's formation, based on cerium abundances, range from 0.02 to 0.2%.[10]

Oxidative weathering of continental landmasses delivers fractionated chromium to seawater. Thus, chromium isotope ratios in marine sediments yield a more reliable measure of atmospheric oxygen content. Chromium isotope measurements of atmospheric oxygen in that era yielded the same result, levels of 0.02–0.2%.[11] However, two other studies produced values ten times higher.[12] This wide variance in results explains the dotted line in figure 17.1. It also explains the degree of speculation that once prevailed over what kind of plants and animals may have existed 2.5–4.0 billion years after Earth's formation.

A dozen geophysicists and geochemists have more recently imposed severe constraints on these speculations. They developed a new proxy for determining the atmospheric oxygen level: iron isotope ratios in iron-rich sedimentary rocks deposited on continental shelves.[13] The team discovered that whatever the source of Fe-II (ionized iron), partial Fe-II oxidation in such rocks requires low oxygen levels in shallow marine waters. These levels are linked to low levels of oxygen in the atmosphere. Because iron is ubiquitous and abundant in marine sedimentary rocks, iron isotope ratios proved a powerful, reliable proxy for atmospheric oxygen levels. Thus, for the first time, scientists have been able to develop an accurate and virtually complete record of Earth's atmospheric oxygen levels. No longer is there a dotted line in the graph (see figure 17.2).

This team of geoscientists established that from 2.1 to 0.9 billion years ago, Earth's atmospheric oxygen level remained below 0.2%. Sometime between 900 and 750 million years ago, the atmospheric oxygen level began to slowly rise.

The most recent measurement made by the team shows that the atmospheric oxygen level 750 million years ago was about 1%. That level at that time coincides with the first appearance of eukaryotic predation—tiny primitive animals that feed on even tinier animals. These creatures require a minimum atmospheric oxygen level of 1%. Not until the Avalon explosion 575 million years ago do animals requiring at least 8% atmospheric oxygen show up in the fossil record.

The team's paper concludes with this statement: "Surface O_2 levels were changing *in step* with eukaryotic evolution in the Proterozoic"[14] (italics added). In other words, the moment the atmospheric oxygen rose to a level suitable for animals requiring at least that level of atmospheric oxygen, those animals

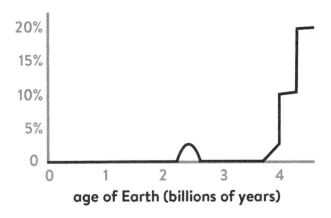

Figure 17.2: New Measure of Historic Atmospheric Oxygen Levels
Diagram credit: Hugh Ross

appeared. Researchers observed no drawn-out evolutionary process. The animals appeared as soon as oxygen conditions permitted their existence.

Meanwhile, animals also require low levels of atmospheric carbon dioxide. High concentrations of carbon dioxide produce acidosis (low pH) in oceans, lakes, and rivers, and in aquatic animal tissues and body fluids. This acidosis proves damaging to the long-term health of all aquatic animals and also to the short-term health of aquatic animals with high metabolic rates.[15] In air-breathing animals, elevated carbon dioxide levels disrupt respiration and the autoregulation of blood supply, causing cognitive and respiratory failure and circulatory arrest.[16]

Researchers have found that three "slushball" events (ice ages during which more than half of Earth's surface is covered with thick ice) must have occurred to bring the atmospheric carbon dioxide level down to the level at which large-bodied animals could survive.[17] These three events were the Sturtian (715–680 million years ago), Marinoan (650–635 million years ago), and Gaskiers (579.9–579.6 million years ago) glaciations. Shortly after the Gaskiers glaciation, Earth's atmospheric carbon dioxide finally decreased to a level that would allow for large-bodied animals to exist. The first Avalon explosion, 575 million years ago, marks the first appearance of large-bodied animals on Earth.

These animals appeared rapidly—as soon as physical and chemical conditions permitted. And the fossil record evidence shows that phyla proliferated *before* the proliferation of species and genera. These two facts combined present an enormous challenge to belief that naturalistic processes completely explain the history of Earth's life. Naturalistic processes—natural selection, gene exchange, and epigenetics—all require long time periods to produce significant, noncatastrophic changes. What is more, all of these processes predict a bottom-up development of taxonomic hierarchy. That is, they predict that naturalistic processes will first produce a proliferation of species, which, in more time, will produce a proliferation of genera. The last of all to appear would be new phyla. However, as paleontologists Douglas Erwin, James Valentine, and John Sepkoski have observed with respect to the Avalon and Cambrian explosions, "The major pulse of diversification of phyla occurs before that of classes, classes before that of orders, and orders before that of families."[18]

The Cambrian explosion refers to the sudden appearance, 538.79 ± 0.21 million years ago,[19] of animals with digestive tracts, circulatory systems, skeletons, and internal and external organs. These animals require a minimum atmospheric oxygen level of 10%, and they appear in the record at the very moment that level is reached. As paleontologists Kevin Peterson, Michael Dietrich, and Mark McPeek state in a review paper, "Elucidating the materialistic basis for the Cambrian explosion has become more elusive, not less, the more we know about the event itself."[20] The latest scientific findings strongly suggest what a historical interpretation of the biblical creation texts reveals, that God is the Author and Creator of Earth's life.

Landmass Emergence Aligns with Creation Day 3
When I was in high school, textbooks taught that Earth's continental landmasses have been present for virtually all Earth's history. When I first read Genesis 1, I encountered a different story. Two years later, I took a geophysics course taught by Jack Jacobs and Don Russell, two of the founders of plate tectonics theory. In that course I learned of emerging evidence that Earth has had a long history of plate tectonic activity that gave rise to continents, mountain ranges, and volcanoes.[21] I recognized that this model of Earth's history was at least broadly consistent with the biblical description of creation.

Genesis 1, however, seemed to imply that the majority of continental

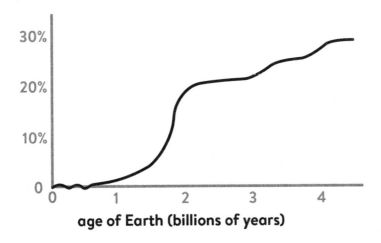

Figure 17.3: Growth of Continents as a Percentage of Earth's Surface Based on O_{18}/O_{16} Ratios
Diagram credit: Hugh Ross

landmass growth occurred within a relatively short period, when Earth was about half or slightly less than half its present age (corresponding with the first part of creation day 3). I wondered whether future geophysical research would align (or conflict) with the biblical claim.

In 1982, geoscientists used chemical analysis of fine-grained sedimentary rock consisting of clay or silt particles or both to infer that much of Earth's continental landmass formation occurred 2.1–2.5 billion years ago.[22] In 2016, geoscientists used radiometric dating and oxygen-18 to oxygen-16 (O_{18}/O_{16}) isotope ratios of shale deposits around the world to more accurately affirm that, indeed, the bulk of continental landmass formation occurred around 2.5 billion years ago.[23] Figure 17.3 shows the continental landmass growth as a percentage of Earth's total surface area, based on these O_{18}/O_{16} ratios.

In 2018, another team of geologists and geophysicists provided the most accurate data to date on the emergence of continents over the past 3.7 billion years. This team was the first to use triple-oxygen isotope ratio analysis on shale deposits from every continent.[24] Shales are useful for this research because they are the dominant sedimentary rock on Earth—the product of chemical and

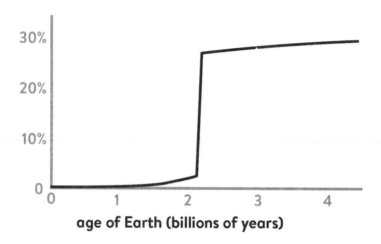

Figure 17.4: Growth of Continents as a Percentage of Earth's Surface Based on O_{18}/O_{16} and O_{17}/O_{16} Ratios
Diagram credit: Hugh Ross

physical weathering of the landmasses. Thus, shales serve as an excellent proxy for determining how much of Earth's surface was comprised of landmasses in times past.

This team analyzed both O_{18}/O_{16} and O_{17}/O_{16} ratios in shale deposits. They also used the most extensive sample of shale deposits yet: 278 outcrops and drill holes from all seven continents. The combined use of two oxygen isotope ratios enabled the team to determine exactly how the shale deposits were formed. This knowledge allowed them to accurately reconstruct Earth's past surface conditions. Figure 17.4 shows the growth history of Earth's continental landmasses based on data presented in the team's paper.

Geophysical research over the past half century demonstrates that the more accurately geophysicists unearth the history of continental landmass growth, the more consistently that history aligns with the Genesis 1:9 implication that nearly all continents arose within a short period close to the midpoint of Earth's current age.

Solar Burning History Impacts Evolutionary Theory

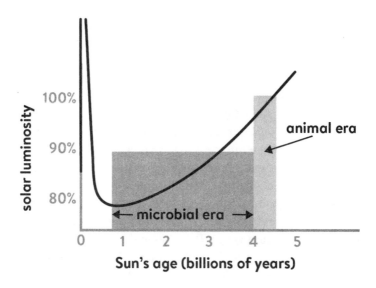

Figure 17.5: Sun's Luminosity History
Diagram credit: Hugh Ross

Today, the Sun burns 19–24% more brightly than it did at the time of life's origin 3.8 billion years ago (see figure 17.5).[25] It will continue to brighten as its nuclear furnace fuses hydrogen into helium. (The fusion of hydrogen into helium in the Sun's core increases the core density, which increases the efficiency of the Sun's nuclear furnace. The increasing efficiency of the Sun's nuclear furnace causes the Sun to shine more brightly.)

Under normal circumstances, even a 2% change in solar luminosity would lead to the extinction of all life on Earth, either through the runaway freezing or runaway evaporation of Earth's surface water. A 1% change would mean the end of advanced plants and animals.

So, how has Earth avoided such a catastrophe? A perfectly timed and proportioned drawdown of Earth's greenhouse gases in combination with a perfectly timed and proportioned alteration of Earth's albedo (reflectivity) prevented it. As the Sun increasingly brightened, the quantity of greenhouse gases in Earth's atmosphere proportionately decreased and Earth's reflectivity adjusted appropriately, keeping Earth's surface temperature continuously suitable for life.

By far the largest factor in compensating for the Sun's increasing luminosity is the reduction of atmospheric greenhouse gases. That reduction occurs through two processes: the silicate-carbonate cycle and the burial of organic carbon. The silicate-carbonate cycle involves rain and dew acting as a catalyst as it falls on exposed silicates (the continents are predominantly silicate rock). This moisture generates a chemical reaction that converts carbon dioxide and silicates from the atmosphere into carbonates and sand.[26]

Various life-forms regulate how much silicate rock is exposed to falling rain and dew, how much dew forms, and how much rain falls from clouds. For example, the root systems of shrubs and trees are capable of penetrating the upper 6 meters (20 feet) of bedrock.[27] This process greatly expands the silicate surface area exposed to liquid water. These same shrubs and trees access water stored in bedrock, converting most of this water into vapor through transpiration (exhalation of water into the atmosphere through their stomata). This transpiration increases rates of precipitation, and the increased precipitation, in turn, accelerates the silicate-carbonate cycle, drawing more carbon dioxide from the atmosphere.

Microbes, plants, and animals all play a part in pulling carbon dioxide from the atmosphere, either directly or indirectly, to produce organic carbon compounds. The burial of these organisms by floods, landslides, volcanic eruptions, or other tectonic events serves to prevent the decay of their bodies and the resultant release of carbon dioxide into the atmosphere.

Only if the diversity and abundance of life exists on Earth at just-right times and places will the appropriate quantity of greenhouse gases be removed from Earth's atmosphere, at the just-right rate, to compensate for the Sun's increasing luminosity. The abundance of life on Earth's surface also substantially affects Earth's cloud cover and the reflectivity of Earth's surface. In four specific and interrelated ways, Earth's life manages to compensate for the Sun's increasing luminosity: (1) by regulating the silicate-carbonate cycle, (2) by altering the organic carbon burial rate, (3) by changing the atmospheric chemistry and cloud cover, and (4) by changing Earth's reflectivity.

Just as the Sun's luminosity changes over time, so do its radiation and flaring activity. These changes impact what and when various kinds of life can survive and thrive on Earth. Such variability poses an immense challenge to ensuring that just-right life is present on Earth to compensate for the Sun's increasing luminosity. Unless all four of life's compensating factors remain at just-right levels at all times throughout the past 3.8 billion years, the Sun's increasing luminosity and other variations would prevent life from thriving and potentially drive it to extinction.

As amazing as natural processes may be in effecting change and enabling Earth's life to adapt, natural selection, mutations, gene exchange, and epigenetics possess no inherent capacity to anticipate the future physics of the Sun. It seems reasonable to infer that an intelligent, powerful, purposeful Agent with awareness of the changing physics of the Sun would know which life must be present on Earth at which times for the good of future humanity. For Earth's life to persist for 3.8 billion years through radical solar changes and avoid complete annihilation requires skillful and precise orchestration. Certain life-forms that can no longer compensate for the solar changes must be replaced by life-forms that can—at just-right times in the just-right abundance, diversity, and location.

Given the pace at which the Sun's luminosity is increasing, extinction events that are followed quickly by speciation events must occur at a rate of about every 30–35 million years. The fossil record bears witness that mass-extinction and mass-speciation events have, in fact, occurred at this rate.[28] This timing happens to match the rate at which the Sun passes through the galactic plane as it makes its 250-million-year orbit about the center of the Milky Way Galaxy.[29]

Psalm 104, a creation psalm written roughly three millennia ago, makes mention of a process that reflects the extinction and speciation we observe. Verses 27–30 provide this picture:

> All creatures look to you [God]
> to give them their food at the proper time.
> When you give it to them,
> they gather it up;
> when you open your hand,
> they are satisfied with good things.
> When you hide your face,
> they are terrified;
> when you take away their breath,
> they die and return to the dust.
> When you send your Spirit,
> they are created,
> and you renew the face of the ground.

These verses do seem consistent with the fossil record's extinction and speciation cycle, but I also recognize that they may simply refer to nature's pattern of regeneration, with the death of one generation of creatures making way for the next generation. Perhaps this passage refers to both.

Integration as an Essential to Interpretation

As we have seen, knowledge of the Sun's increasing luminosity and of the variations in its flaring activity and radiation output have profound implications for evolutionary theory. But a lack of dialogue between and among the science disciplines has led to what now appears to be, certainly from a scientific standpoint, an untenable theoretical model for the naturalistic origin and history of life. Integration is as much a core element in the development of realistic scientific theories and models as it is in the accurate interpretation of the Scriptures.

For too long, debates over the creation and evolution of Earth's life have focused almost exclusively on paleontology and genetics. This chapter demonstrates the importance of including physics, geology, chemistry, mathematics, and astronomy in analysis of the data. It also reminds us that we must integrate all relevant biblical texts on creation, not just those in Genesis. Only through a comprehensive examination of both the scientific data and the biblical data does a fuller picture of God's supernatural handiwork come to light.

A comprehensive and integrative approach seems the only hope for resolving one of the most controversial and consequential points in the twenty-first-century debate over dual revelation and biblical inerrancy: human origins. Does the Bible really say that all humans are descended from one human pair? Is there a solid biblical basis for the doctrine of original sin? What do the sciences have to say about these issues? These questions are addressed in the next two chapters.

Chapter 18

The Original Human Pair and Original Sin

In the millennia since God's "special" (written) revelation of himself first became available, those who have embraced it as true and trustworthy have held a sure sense of their identity. From the ancient Hebrews to the *ekklesia* (assemblies of Christians), we have known who we are in relation to all other life: the epitome of God's creative work, the unique bearers of his image, the sons and daughters of Adam and Eve. Arguably, the primary driver behind the twenty-first-century movement to discard or revise the doctrine of biblical inerrancy is the loss of certainty about who we are.

Many reputable scientists have spoken: belief in Adam and Eve as the sole progenitors of all humans is no longer defensible. These facts, they say, are based on genomics research. They have convinced a number of twenty-first-century theologians, most of them widely considered biblically conservative or evangelical, that our ancestral population numbered in the thousands *and* was descended from a common ancestor with Neanderthals, Denisovans, *Homo erectus*, and chimpanzees. This theological capitulation poses major problems for the doctrine of original sin.

Theologians React

Peter Enns, an early adopter of the claims coming from these scientists, appears to be leading the charge for other theologians to do the same. He devoted an entire book, *The Evolution of Adam* (2012), to convincing his peers of this point: "The Human Genome Project, completed in 2003, has shown beyond any reasonable scientific doubt that humans and primates share common ancestry."[1] Throughout the book he makes assertions such as these:

- Without question, evolution requires us to revisit how the Bible thinks of human origins.[2]
- There is no 'Adam' to be found in an evolutionary scheme.[3]
- Attributing the cause of universal sin and death to a historical Adam is not necessary.[4]
- "Original sin," where Adam's disobedience is the cause . . . does not find clear—if any—biblical support.[5]
- The role that Paul assigns to Adam in this passage [Romans 5:12–21] is largely unique to Paul.[6]
- I do not think that Romans is a primer for systematic theology.[7]

Enns's reference to Paul and the book of Romans takes me back to a private conversation I had with a group of scientists and theologians influenced by statements such as these. As we discussed my biblical concerns about their view, they were honest in acknowledging, "Romans is our biggest problem."

John Walton followed Enns with a book of his own, *The Lost World of Adam and Eve* (2015), organized as a set of propositions rather than chapters, along with comments from N. T. Wright. According to Proposition 19, "Paul's use of Adam is more interested in the effects of sin on the cosmos than in the effect of sin on humanity and has nothing to say about human origins."[8] Proposition 20 says, "It is not essential that all people descended from Adam and Eve."[9] N. T. Wright adds, *"God chose one pair from the rest of early hominids for a special, strange, demanding vocation. This pair* (call them Adam and Eve if you like) *were to be representatives of the whole human race"* (emphasis in the original).[10]

Two years later, Dennis Venema and Scot McKnight added support to the scientific claims of these earlier authors in their book, *Adam and the Genome* (2017). In their words, "To insist that our DNA comes from two humans, Adam and Eve, is intentionally to run contrary to what science now teaches."[11] Therefore, they argue, "Any talk of the 'historical Adam' is steeped in the theological conversation about original sin,"[12] a conversation based on what they consider a misinterpretation of Romans 5 and 1 Corinthians 15. Concerning these two chapters, they write, "Paul's Adam is the *literary* Adam of Genesis filtered through the Jewish tradition of interpreting Adam as the *archetypal, moral, and exemplary* Adam" (italics in the original).[13] While they acknowledge, of course, that "Paul believed in the Bible"[14] and viewed it "in some ways as 'scientific,'"[15] they state that "he *could* not have and therefore *did* not know better" (italics in the original).[16]

Biblical Dates for Adam and Eve and the Flood

The Bible provides only a few hints at the timing of two major events described in the early chapters of Genesis: the creation of Adam and Eve and the Flood of Noah's era. The clues with respect to Adam and Eve are found in a geographic reference. The text mentions that the Tigris, Euphrates, Pishon, and Gihon rivers all came close together in the Garden of Eden.

The rivers are easy to identify given that Genesis 2 identifies the regions from which each river flows. The Tigris and Euphrates still flow today through Asshur (Genesis 2:14), fed by melting snow and ice on the mountains of Ararat. The Pishon and Gihon are dry today but would have been flowing during the last ice age, when snow and ice were abundant on the mountains of Havilah (Genesis 2:11) and Cush (Genesis 2:13). Today, these mountains are recognized as the Hejaz and Najd mountains of western Arabia and the Sarat al Yemen and Ethiopian highlands of southwestern Arabia and eastern Africa, respectively. (During an ice age, a land bridge would have connected southwestern Arabia to eastern Africa.) The one location where the four rivers likely flowed near each other currently sits more than two hundred feet below sea level in the southeastern portion of what is now the Persian Gulf.

During an ice age, this location would have been above sea level. (Sea levels were as much as 390 feet lower during the previous two ice ages.) Two recent epochs when this region would have been above sea level extend from 13,000 to 120,000 years ago and from 132,000 to 230,000 years ago. During the more recent of these ice ages, several time windows a few thousand years in length would have permitted an easy migration route joining the Persian Gulf region to eastern Africa.[17] Such a route would help explain why some of the earliest artifacts indisputably attributed to humans have been found in eastern Africa.

If the origin of the human race occurred during one of the two most recent ice ages, the biblical clues would align well with the best scientific estimates. Due to the limitations of our dating technology, only rough estimates are possible. Carbon-14 dating tells us that humans have been present on Earth for at least the last 45,000 years, but the methods used for dating human remains and artifacts between 45,000 and 250,000 years ago are all indirect and hindered by large systematic uncertainties.[18] The most accurate date scientists can provide for the origin of anatomically modern humans is sometime between 45,000 and 250,000 years ago.

From biblical details we can gather that Noah's Flood also must have been an ice age event. The text says that the floodwaters took 335 days to recede.[19] For the receding process to take so long, huge quantities of ice and snow must have been melting off the mountains and hills surrounding the flooded region. Genesis 10–11 indicates that the spread of humanity from just one geographical area into all of Earth's habitable landmasses occurred after Noah's Flood. The carbon-14 dating and genetic signatures both date this human dispersal and colonization to about 45,000 years ago. Based on events mentioned in Genesis 10:21–25 and 11:1–17, Noah's Flood must have occurred at least some generations prior to this date.

Other prominent twenty-first-century theologians have also come to accept these assertions about human origins. Tremper Longman III writes, "The mapping of the human genome . . . testifies to the persuasiveness of the theory presented by Darwin."[20] William Lane Craig now envisions "an initial population of, say, five thousand hominins" and that "out of this population, God selects two and furnishes them with intellects by renovating their brains and endowing them with rational souls."[21] Craig's Adam and Eve are members of the *Homo heidelbergensis* population that "lived sometime between 1 mya to 750 kya."[22] This proposed date seems to seriously mismatch a number of time indicators in Genesis 1–11 (see sidebar, "Biblical Dates for Adam and Eve and the Flood").

Biblical Case for an Original Human Pair

How clearly, we must ask, does the Bible claim that we "modern humans," often referred to as *Homo sapiens sapiens*, are the biological progeny of an original pair, referred to in the Bible (and elsewhere) as Adam and Eve? To begin, Genesis 1–2 uses three Hebrew verbs, *bara*, *asa*, and *yatsar*, to describe God's creation of Adam and Eve. Despite a few recent attempts to say otherwise (see appendix, The Meaning of *Bara* and *Asa* in Genesis), all three of these verbs imply divine *de novo, ex nihilo* creation, or direct divine manufacture. To interpret Adam and Eve's origin as a long-extended, wholly natural evolutionary process would be to misinterpret these words.

Genesis 2 further challenges the notion that God selected Adam and Eve from a population of hominids. Verse 18 describes Adam as "alone," and in verse 20 we read that among all the creatures with which Adam had contact, "no suitable helper was found." The woman God made for Adam did not, according to Genesis 2, come from a population of hominids, but rather from Adam's biological tissue. While the text mentions "the birds of the air" and "the beasts of the fields" in Adam's environment, it makes no mention of any humanlike creatures.

According to Genesis 3:20, "Adam named his wife Eve, because she would become the mother of all the living." This passage implies that ultimately all humans born into the world are descended from one woman, Eve. In Acts 17:26, Paul tells the gathering of philosophers at the Areopagus, "From one man he made every nation of men, that they should inhabit the whole earth." Again, the Scripture clearly implies that the entire human race is descended from the one man, Adam.

Adam's name appears in not one but three biblical genealogies: Genesis 5:1–3, 1 Chronicles 1:1, and Luke 3:38. The first of these reads, in Genesis 5:1–2, "These are the family records of the descendants of Adam. On the day that God created man, He made him in the likeness of God; He created them male and female. When they were created, He blessed them and called them man" (HCSB). The language used here leaves little doubt that the author of Genesis considered Adam to be a real historical person—the progenitor of all humanity—specially created by God.

Gospel writers Matthew and Mark record Jesus's response when asked about marriage and divorce. In his brief discourse on the topic (Matthew 19:4–6, Mark 10:4–9), Jesus draws directly from the account of creation and quotes, verbatim, Genesis 1:27 and Genesis 2:24. His words make clear that Genesis is an account of the first union between a human man and woman, a union that sets the pattern for all generations to follow. Each couple starts a new family unit.

The apostle Paul leaves no doubt about his belief that Adam and Eve were the original human pair. In Romans 5:12, he explains that "sin entered the world through one man, and death through sin, and in this way death came to all people." As Venema, McKnight, and other theologians have noted, Paul clearly believed that Adam was the earthly father of all humankind. After all, he repeats this belief many times, here in verses 15, 17, and 18 of Romans 5 and then again in his first letter to the church at Corinth. In 1 Corinthians 15:21–22, Paul says again that the trespass of the one man, Adam, brought condemnation to all humans. Then, in 15:45, he cites Genesis 2: "So it is written: 'The first man Adam became a living being.'" Paul's comparison and contrast of the one man, Adam, to the one man, Jesus, strongly suggest that Adam, like Jesus, must be a single individual, not a population.

The twenty-first-century theologians who deny Adam as the progenitor of all humans must conclude, and do conclude, that on this point, at least, Paul was simply wrong.[23] However, this conclusion is difficult to sustain, to say the least. In 2 Peter 3:15–16, Peter vouches for Paul's letters as divinely inspired Scripture. The doctrines Paul addresses in Romans 5 and 1 Corinthians 15 are not theologically peripheral. These are doctrines that directly pertain to our fundamental need for deliverance from sin, our incapacity to deliver ourselves, and how God, alone, made a way for us to be delivered and to enter into an eternal loving relationship with him, along with others who put their faith in him. These doctrines are presented in the Christian creeds and confessions as part of the very definition of our Christian faith.

Biblical Case for Original Sin

King David says in Psalm 51:5, "Surely I was sinful at birth, sinful from the time my mother conceived me." The apostle Paul affirms this doctrine of original sin most extensively and explicitly in Romans (2–3; 5:12–19; 6:17) and 1 Corinthians (15:20–22). Original sin is the doctrine that sin originated from Adam and was passed on to all humans. Scripture does not state that we were born innocent and become sinners. Rather, we enter this world as sinners in need of redemption.

Some theologians have challenged the centrality of the doctrine of original sin on the grounds that the Orthodox branch of the church does not officially endorse it. While it is true that the Orthodox Church does not require its adherents to believe that the sin of Adam was imputed to all his descendants, it does require belief that Adam's sin morally corrupted human nature in such a way that the corruption was transmitted to all his offspring.

This doctrine requires a historical Adam and Eve, an original human pair. According to the treatise that was considered essential reading in Christian seminaries for the better part of the twentieth century, "The rejection of the Genesis story as a myth, tends to the rejection of the Gospel of salvation. One of the chief corner stones of the Christian doctrine is removed, if the historical reality of Adam and Eve is abandoned, for the fall will ever remain as the starting point of special revelation, of salvation by grace, and of the need of personal regeneration."[24]

The majority of theologians up to and throughout the twentieth century have consistently believed in these core doctrines, which have stood firm through twenty centuries of theological testing. Thus, it seems highly presumptuous to argue that Christian scholars and lay readers of the Bible have been mistaken for more than two millennia in their view of human origins. Would not it be reasonable to first question the scientific assertion on which this supposed doctrinal error is based? The following chapter shows that human descent from an ancestor in common with chimpanzees, bipedal primates, and various populations of humanlike or *Homo* species is not as scientifically unassailable as many twenty-first-century theologians consider it to be.

Chapter 19

Scientific Defense of an Original Human Pair

When I say that I majored in simple science and my colleague Fazale "Fuz" Rana majored in complex science, people think I am joking, but I am not. The complexity of the life sciences is orders of magnitude greater than that of the physical sciences. For this reason alone, the progression from frontier science to settled science takes even longer in the life sciences than in the physical sciences. What further complicates this progression is the lack of interdisciplinary research and dialogue within the various life sciences as well as between them and the various physical sciences—virtually all of which have some bearing on the origin and history of life on Earth, including human life.

The fact that evolutionary sciences have only a minuscule sampling of Earth's past life to work with complicates the situation still further. So, my purpose in addressing any topic within the life sciences is to stimulate further engagement, further dialogue and debate, and not to disparage or discredit. I am not anti-evolution. Change can and does occur over time. The question is whether or not natural process, alone, can account for the magnitude and rapidity of the change.

Over the past several years, biochemist Fazale Rana and I have published two editions of a book titled *Who Was Adam?* In it we present what we see as the best scientific indicators for special creation of a single human pair made uniquely in God's image and from whom all humans who have ever lived are descended.[1] Rana was the major author of both editions. What prompted the writing of the second edition was the availability of additional data with which to explore the question of human origins and identity. Since the publication of that material, even more evidence has come to light.

Rather than attempt to summarize a nearly 500-page book, my aim in this chapter is to highlight discoveries published since the release of that second edition, discoveries relevant to the question of how settled the science is and whether there is basis for upholding scientifically credible belief that an exceptional human pair gave rise to all humanity. Let's consider how well the latest science aligns with the biblical account. Are we truly forced by the facts of science to reject or revise historic Christian doctrines?

Nephesh Exceptionalism

The Hebrew word for create, *bara*, appears three times in Genesis 1: first, in reference to God's bringing the physical realm into existence (verse 1); second, in reference to God's introduction of *nephesh*, animals that are both physical and "soulish" (verse 21); and third, in reference to God's crafting humans, who are physical, soulish, and spiritual beings (verse 27).

Nephesh, like so many Hebrew words, has a broad range of meaning. The *Brown-Driver-Briggs Hebrew and English Lexicon* defines *nephesh* as "soul, living being, life, self, person, desire, appetite, emotion, and passion."[2] The *Theological Wordbook of the Old Testament* defines *nephesh* as "life, soul, creature, person, appetite, and mind."[3] When used to refer to nonhuman animals, *nephesh* are animals with intellectual, relational, and nurturing capacities. All birds and mammals and a handful of reptilian species can be classified as *nephesh* creatures.

Field observations and experiments establish that *nephesh* animals possess emotions and mental attributes not seen in bacteria, plants, insects, amphibians, and fish.[4] Other experiments show that the human mind (spirit) exhibits capacities never seen in any bird or nonhuman mammal.[5]

Nephesh are observed to form relationships—with each other and with humans. They show and express some degree of understanding, choice, and emotion. Unlike other animals, *nephesh* can be tamed by humans. When tamed, they will submit to commands and instructions from humans. Humans can train them to perform tasks irrelevant to their survival. They are capable of forming strong, enduring emotional bonds with humans.

These creatures are clearly exceptional when compared and contrasted with other nonhuman life—so much so that we humans often anthropomorphize, attributing characteristics to them that they do not really possess. In doing so, we fail to appreciate just how exceptional we humans are.

Smartest Nonhuman Animals

Standard evolutionary trees show humans as descended from a common ancestor with chimpanzees. Chimpanzees, we are told, are the closest living relatives to humans. It seems obvious in terms of morphology that chimpanzees come closest to looking like us. From a naturalistic evolutionary perspective, they would be expected to most closely resemble us in their intellectual properties as well. As biologist Johan Bolhuis and psychologist Clive Wynne report in their *Nature* article, "In taking an evolutionary approach, biologists have tended to assume that species with shared ancestry will have similar cognitive abilities."[6] However, this assumption proves incorrect.

Repeated studies have demonstrated that the intellectual capabilities of ravens and New Caledonian crows most closely match those of humans. As Bolhuis and Wynne note, "Caledonian crows outperform monkeys in their ability to retrieve food from a trap tube—from which food can be accessed only at one end. The crows can also work out how to use one tool to obtain a second with which they can retrieve food, a skill that monkeys and apes struggle to master."[7] Another research team reported, "The New Caledonian crow is the only non-human animal known to craft hooks in the wild."[8] It does so using a multi-step process: (1) detaching a twig from a tree or bush, (2) sculpting a terminal hook from a nodal joint, (3) length trimming, (4) bark stripping, (5) shaft bending, and (6) shaft twisting.[9] Multiple other research field studies establish that the capacity for tool manufacture, tool use, and problem solving exhibited by New Caledonian crows and ravens exceeds by a considerable margin that of chimpanzees, orangutans, and gorillas.[10] This video clip shows a crow executing a complex eight-step process to recover a food treat: youtube.com/watch?v=AVaITA7eBZE.

Despite their clear intellectual prowess, New Caledonian crows and ravens possess a brain structure distinct from that of both humans and the great apes. Like humans, but unlike the great apes, these birds possess larger forebrains, telencephala (cerebra), perineuronal glial clusters, and hippocampi relative to their body size.[11] Unlike humans and the great apes, these birds lack a cerebral cortex.[12] This combination of like and unlike characteristics argues strongly against the possibility of common descent of humans from either the apes or the birds.

Some evolutionary biologists argue that *convergence* explains why some bird and marine mammal species more closely resemble the intelligence of humans than do the great apes.[13] This term refers to the widely observed tendency of organisms that are unrelated (used here in the naturalistic evolutionary sense, without reference to lineage) to manifest nearly identical genetic, anatomical, physiological, or behavioral characteristics. If natural processes are responsible for life's diversity, though, one would expect convergence to be extremely rare. But it is not.

Evolutionary biologist Simon Conway Morris documents dozens of examples of convergence among Earth's life.[14] Other scholars, including my colleague Rana, have documented hundreds more.[15] Some examples of shared features are seen in organisms living under radically different environmental pressures.[16] One particular feature is observed in life-forms across eight different phyla![17] As Bolhuis writes in the journal *Behavioural Processes*, "Evolution cannot explain how minds work."[18]

Advantage of Bonding to a Human

Many scientists, among others, cite the amazing achievements of nonhuman animals as evidence that humans differ only in degree, not in kind, from previously existing life-forms. On this basis they argue for naturalistic descent of humans from LUCA (the last universal common ancestor). Given that language capability represents a prime example of human exceptionalism, people often refer to Koko the gorilla and African grey parrots as evidence in favor of natural descent and against humans' linguistic exceptional capacity.

Koko's story is familiar. She spent her entire life in captivity, and her closest companion was her human trainer, Francine Patterson. Over a 20-year period, Patterson put Koko through intense vocabulary training. In that time, Koko learned to "speak" through sign language over 200 words. Remarkably, Koko's vocabulary has been bested by a few African grey parrots with vocabulary lists as long as 800–1,000 words.[19]

Vocabulary, however, is not the same as language capability. Nonhuman animals are unable to use grammar or syntax. They cannot compose sentences or paragraphs. They cannot create stories. Their "language capability" is based entirely on mimicking what they hear from human trainers. Only through long-term bonding with—and intensive training by—a human caregiver can a primate or parrot perform at such a level as these two. In the wild, animals can and do communicate with each another, some in complex ways, but language is not one of those ways.

Only humans invent and use symbols to communicate. Only humans can read and understand written signs and symbols. Only humans are capable of composing complex narratives, stories, legends, instruction manuals, and scientific treatises. As three research neuropsychologists have concluded,

> There is a significant discontinuity in the degree to which human and nonhuman animals are able to approximate the higher order, systematic, relational capabilities of a physical symbol system. We show that this symbol relational discontinuity pervades nearly every domain of cognition and runs much deeper than even the spectacular scaffolding provided by language or culture alone can explain.[20]

Humans have the unique ability to create words for abstract thought, mathematical terms, and terminology far outside our immediate environment—beyond even our planet and the material universe. The language capabilities developed by Koko and African grey parrots demonstrate that when a mammal or bird is strongly bonded to a human, it will far outperform its formerly wild self and its wild counterparts. Scientists have documented this distinction in numerous animals-in-captivity experiments.[21]

The Question of Neanderthal "Humanness"

One inference on which nearly all young-earth creationists, theistic evolutionists, naturalistic evolutionists, evolutionary creationists, and intelligent design proponents seem to agree is that Neanderthals were fully human. If that inference were true, then the anatomical, behavioral, and other differences between Neanderthals and modern humans could be attributed to the operation of natural-process evolution over a relatively brief time. This would directly challenge the biblical account of human origins as an act of creation.

While Neanderthals obviously share certain features in common with modern humans (bipedalism and tool use, for example), these features are essentially the same features modern humans share with chimpanzees. A brief survey of the differences—anatomical, genetic, behavioral, societal, intellectual, and inventive—between Neanderthals and modern humans argues against their shared lineage.

At a 2020 workshop on human origins sponsored by Reasons to Believe, a number of Christian scholars who support the view of Neanderthals as humans presented papers and cited other scholars to assert that Neanderthals were capable of starting and controlling fires, distilling birch sap to make adhesives, hafting chiseled stone points with wooden spears, and manufacturing shell beads.[22] William Lane Craig considered one of the Shöningen spears (ca. 300,000 years old) so similar to an Olympic javelin that he felt compelled to conclude that Neanderthals were no less advanced than humans today.[23]

Soon after the conference, a paper published by Bruce Hardy and five colleagues in France and Spain claimed Neanderthals had mastered the weaving of fibers and, therefore, had likely been capable of making ropes, bags, nets, clothing, mats, and boats.[24] Hardy's team proposed that such weaving ability demonstrated Neanderthals' language ability and "mathematical understanding of pairs, sets, and numbers."[25] The paper concludes with this bold assertion: "The idea that Neanderthals were cognitively inferior to modern humans is becoming increasingly untenable."[26] The paper's claims instantly catapulted Hardy to national headlines.[27]

Upon further investigation, the team's claims appear increasingly untenable. The so-called evidence for "Neanderthal weaving" is a 6-millimeter-long thread that closely resembles fibers found in the inner bark of conifers. At the base of the thread is a tangle of three fibers measuring about 1 millimeter across. The thread and its "knot" were found on the lower surface of a stone flake measuring 60 millimeters in length (see figure 19.1). The stone flake and its 3-ply knot were found in a collapsed cave, Abri du Maras, near a tributary of the Rhône River in France. The stone flake was recovered from a layer that has been dated by the uranium-thorium differential precipitation and the electron spin resonance methods to be 41,000 ± 2,000; 46,000 ± 5,000; and 52,000 ± 2,000 years old.[28] The error bars include probable statistical errors but not the probable systematic errors. The latter errors could be as large as ± 50,000 years.[29] Since it is known that modern humans entered the Rhône Valley at least that long ago (in calibrated radiocarbon years),[30] the claim that the knot must have been tied by Neanderthals rather than by modern humans seems more than slightly suspect.

More likely, the knot had nothing to do with either Neanderthals or modern humans. Many bird species have the brain capacity and eye-beak coordination to weave fibers, as their nests reveal. Yet no scientists attribute advanced mathematical understanding to birds on the basis of their weaving accomplishments. What is more, thermodynamics alone can cause fibers to appear woven. Stringy fibers from the inner bark of conifers, once expelled from the bark, frequently twist themselves into knots as complex as the one found by Hardy's team. No intelligent agency is needed.

To date, no undisputed evidence for Neanderthals' manufacture of ropes, bags, nets, clothing, mats, or boats has come to light. If these creatures had truly mastered such weaving technology, abundant and unequivocal archaeological evidence for such technology would have been discovered. As for the Schöningen spear Craig found so convincing, the resemblance is rough, at best.

While the spear's length and weight approximate the features of a javelin, its initial straightness cannot be determined. The spear is a single piece of wood, possibly a slender trunk or branch of spruce or pine with its bark stripped off and a sharpened tip. It only vaguely resembled the precisely engineered Olympic javelin. (Olympic javelins have a machine-sharpened metal tip and a metal shaft.)

It should be noted that chimpanzees in the wild have been observed to use spears to hunt bush babies.[31] The spears they manufacture closely resemble the Schöningen spears presumably used by Neantherthals. Chimpanzees will break off an appropriately sized tree branch, strip away its bark, and use their incisors to sharpen its end to a point. Trial and error apparently taught them which of their spears prove most effective in hunting.

The fact that Neanderthals exploited fire is not a matter of debate. The hotly contested claim is that they started fires from scratch and controlled them for warmth, cooking, and manufacture of tools rather than exploiting them opportunistically, as chimpanzees do.[32] Three anthropologists observed microwear patterns on bifacial flint rocks found at sites where Neanderthals were known to live.[33] These patterns appeared roughly consistent with those on rocks the anthropologists had repeatedly struck with pyrite to start fires. Based on this observation, the three anthropologists concluded that Neanderthals had mastery over fire, that they could start and control fires at will.

The anthropologists failed to consider that the wear patterns may have nothing to do with attempts to start fires. They could have resulted from the use of rocks for animal butchery, use of the rocks on other rocks to produce basic tools, or simply natural abrasion. Furthermore, whereas flint rocks recovered from ancient human sites show evidence of pyrite, not even a trace amount of pyrite was found on these bifacial flint rocks.

Oddly, paleoclimate data reveal that Neanderthals' use of fire was restricted to warm climate conditions.[34] Natural wildfires occur under warm climate conditions, not cold ones. If Neanderthals had indeed mastered fire, evidence of such mastery would more likely be found under predominantly cold climate conditions. Meanwhile, despite having the most cold-adapted anatomy among all the hominid species,[35] Neanderthals failed to survive the two severe cold-dry episodes that chilled Europe 44,300–43,300 and 40,800–40,200 years ago, while modern humans did.[36] Modern humans survived because, unlike Neanderthals, they could control fire, and they were also able to manufacture warm clothing. Bone needles and the skins of weasels and wolverines have been found at ancient human sites, but these items are absent from Neanderthal sites. Apparently, Neanderthal clothing was limited to occasional use of large animal hides as capes.[37]

Control of fire gave early humans yet another survival advantage over Neanderthals: they could cook. Cooked food yields more calories per pound than raw food. The lack of regularly cooked food likely played a significant role in Neanderthals' extinction.[38]

Early humans not only cooked their food, they processed it for easier consumption. Several studies show, for example, that as early as 32,600 years ago, humans were roasting and grinding grains and using roasted ground grains to bake bread.[39]

Another study shows that humans, in spite of their greater energy needs, enjoy a huge chewing advantage over present and past nonhuman primates.[40] The daily chewing time for humans today is low, ranging from 7.2–75.7 minutes, with a mean of 35 minutes.[41] The daily chewing time for chimpanzees and bonobos is 4.5 hours.[42] For orangutans it is 6.6 hours.[43] As a research team led by Adam van Casteren noted, the energy and time that extinct hominin species spent chewing food must have been similar to that spent by the great apes.[44] The same team showed that early modern humans' ability to grind, roast, process, and cook their food liberated them from energy-intensive chewing and lengthy daily chewing time. The researchers also pointed out that humans possess a unique anatomy designed to take advantage of easier-to-chew food sources.

Many anthropologists and several theologians have interpreted "birch tar production" by Neanderthals, apparently used for attaching flint spearheads to wooden spear shafts, as evidence that Neanderthals possessed levels of cognition, intelligence, and cultural transmission equivalent to those of modern humans. This interpretation is based on discovery of stone flakes partly covered in birch-bark tar or in other organic residues resembling birch-bark-tar at Neanderthal sites.[45] No actual hafted tools have been recovered at these or any other sites.

Because production of this tarry substance was thought to involve a heating process based on sophisticated planning, preparation, and control, anthropologists inferred that Neanderthals also may have possessed the cognitive skills required for the manufacture of ceramics. However, a team of eight researchers—anthropologists, archaeologists, and engineers—has demonstrated that production of birch-bark tar requires no cognitive or intellectual sophistication.[46] It can be produced naturally.

When a wildfire burns birch adjacent to and above stone, birch-bark tar drips naturally onto the stone. Such tar can easily be scraped off the rock and attached to a flint flake, or can land directly onto a flint flake. It also could be naturally deposited as a drop or drops falling on a flint flake, as anyone who has hiked through boreal forests of birch and pine has observed. The eight researchers concluded, "The presence of birch tar alone cannot indicate the presence of modern cognition and/or cultural behaviors in Neanderthals."[47] It should also be noted that no ceramics have been found at Neanderthal sites.

Neanderthal tool technology is marginally more advanced than chimpanzee tool technology. Neanderthals and chimpanzees use stone tools and use rocks as hammers to manufacture stone flakes for cutting and scraping.[48] Chimpanzees make and use spears in hunting prey. They and other apes use plants for medicinal purposes.[49] They gather woodland vegetation to construct insect-repellent nests and beds.[50] They congregate to mourn their dead. They use caves as refuges for family groups.[51] As amazing as this chimpanzee technology is, and as similar as it seems to that of Neanderthals, no anthropologist denies that an enormous gulf separates the cognitive, intellectual, and technological capabilities of chimpanzees from those of modern humans.

Neanderthal "jewelry" has also been cited as evidence for their symbolic capability and, thus, of humanness. Discovery of ocher and perforated marine shells at a site in southeast Spain known to have been inhabited by Neanderthals led to this jewelry-making inference.[52] It appeared that the ocher might have been used to paint the shells and the perforated shells might have been strung together to make necklaces and bracelets. The attribution of this jewelry-making to Neanderthals, rather than to modern humans who later inhabited the area, came as the result of a dating technique called uranium-thorium differential precipitation. By this means, the ocher and shells were dated to 115,000–200,000 years ago.[53] However, as demonstrated in multiple studies[54] and in an article explaining how these studies work,[55] this dating method yields systematic errors as great as ±100%.

Carbon–14 dating of shells from the same site yielded dates of 45,000–50,000 years ago. Statistical errors in the carbon–14 method at such an early date can be significant. In this particular case, the probable error is at least ±5,000 years. Nevertheless, because the carbon-14 method is free of the large systematic effects that plague the uranium-thorium differential precipitation method, its result is more reliable. Given that carbon-14 dating shows that modern humans arrived in Spain 45,000–40,000 years ago,[56] it is possible the ocher and perforated shells are modern human, rather than Neanderthal, artifacts. This possibility is all the more likely given that fossils of modern humans in France's Rhône Valley date even earlier.[57]

Another possibility is that the ocher and perforated shells are not artifacts at all. Ocher is iron oxide, which *can* be used for artistic expression, but it is a common mineral, naturally found throughout the world and especially abundant in southern Spain. As for the perforated shells, predatory mollusks cause identical perforations at identical locations in similar seashells.[58]

Neanderthals apparently lived in southern and central Europe and southwestern Asia from ~400,000 until 40,200 years ago.[59] Researchers see no undisputed evidence of Neanderthal technological advance during this entire ~360,000-year period. By contrast, technological advance is a hallmark of modern humans. Humans are compulsively inventive and innovative. Even the earliest of modern humans left evidence of harvesting, roasting, and grinding grains and constructing hearths to transform processed grains (flour) into baked products.[60] In just 200 years, modern human transportation progressed from horse-driven carriages to landing on the Moon.

Neanderthals are distinct from modern humans anatomically, as well. The difference is especially pronounced in brain structure, and it would explain Neanderthals' lack of technological advance. Computational neuroanatomy of four Neanderthal and four modern human skulls, all roughly the same age, reveals the following differences:[61]

1. The human cerebellum is larger in both hemispheres and projected more to the interior.
2. The left and right sides of the human cerebellum are the same size, whereas the right side of the Neanderthal cerebellum is much smaller than the left.
3. The human brain is globular in shape. The Neanderthal brain is elongated.
4. The human parietal lobe is larger than the Neanderthal parietal lobe, especially in the superior medial and lateral areas.

With a smaller right cerebellum providing only limited connections to the prefrontal lobes, Neanderthals would have lacked language processing capability. Modern humans' larger cerebellum endows them with "a larger capacity for cognitive information processing"[62] and for "episodic and working memory capacity."[63] The much larger superior medial part of the human parietal lobe gives humans the ability to engage in "highly integrated tasks, including visuospatial imagery, episodic memory and self-related mental representations."[64] The larger superior lateral portion of the human parietal lobe allows for humans' "integration and coordination between the self and the external space, generation of body image and sense of agency."[65]

Neanderthals' smaller parietal lobe indicates that Neanderthals lacked the kind of hand-eye coordination and mental visualization capability that modern humans manifest.[66] This lack explains Neanderthals' more limited prey, the absence of Neanderthal representative art, and the absence of stitched Neanderthal clothing. Thus, it also refutes the hypothesis that Neanderthals could have engaged in weaving.

Is Common Descent Physically Viable?

Studies confirm that the populations of the various bipedal primate species preceding modern humans were relatively small. Independent analyses of Neanderthal DNA, fossils, tools, and artifacts yield estimates of Neanderthals' maximum population size throughout the ~360,000 years of their existence. These estimates range from 1,000 to 70,000 individuals.[67]

Estimates above 10,000 are based on the number of tools and artifacts. These estimates, however, assume that all the recovered tools and artifacts were manufactured by Neanderthals and that the sample size of recovered tools and artifacts is largely incomplete.

Anthropologists have found most of these tools and artifacts in or near caves. Given that Neanderthals lived in small, isolated groups and sought caves for shelter, the sample size of recovered tools and artifacts may be more complete than estimated. Many of the "tools and artifacts" may have been natural, not manufactured at all. And some may, in fact, have been made by modern humans. Therefore, the estimates based on tools and artifacts likely represent overestimates.

Analysis of Neanderthal DNA reveals certain telltale features: (1) pervasive inbreeding; (2) "Allee effects" (diminished cooperative hunting and tool manufacture as well as random, large variations in sex ratios that make finding a mate difficult); and (3) "stochasticity" (without a predictable pattern, likely due to environmental catastrophes).[68] Such inbreeding, Allee effects, and stochasticity indicate that the total Neanderthal population rarely exceeded 10,000 individuals, never exceeded 15,000 individuals, and was typically divided into small, isolated, inbred groups widely separated from one another.[69]

A measure of the degree of inbreeding occurring among Neanderthals and Denisovans is their low level of heterozygosity. For both species, only 2 of every 10,000 nucleotides differ between two copies of a chromosome. Such a low level of heterozygosity implies effective populations (individuals capable of breeding) no greater than 5,000.[70]

The effective population of Neanderthals appears to have remained low throughout their ~360,000-year history. A team of 18 geneticists and anthropologists concluded, "Patterns of mtDNA protein evolution are consistent with the notion that the effective population size of Neandertals was small and not only among late Neanderthals but over a longer period of their existence."[71]

Neanderthal fossils range from Britain to Gibraltar, Siberia to Mesopotamia. Their habitat encompassed about 26 million square kilometers (10 million square miles), which translates to a population density of about 0.0002 individuals per square kilometer (0.0005 per square mile). For comparison, in the least densely populated independent nation today, Mongolia, the density measures 2.07 humans per square kilometer (5.4 humans per square mile).

The only reliable DNA data for a hominin species that predates the Neanderthals and the Denisovans is a single, almost complete mitochondrial (but no nuclear) genome sequence. It comes from a hominin dated to about 400,000 years ago that is closely similar to the Denisovan mitochondrial genomes.[72] However, the fossils and artifacts attributable to this species indicate that their effective population sizes were likely even smaller than those of Neanderthals and Denisovans.

Population size is significant because the probability for evolutionary change within a mammalian species is proportional to the species' long-term effective population size. The probability is inversely proportional to the species' average adult body mass, average generation time (time between birth and reproduction for an individual), and reproductive rate.[73] With long-term effective population sizes of less than 10,000, body sizes in the tens of kilograms, generation times of several years, and only a few progeny per female, the possibility of prehuman hominid species experiencing significant natural-process morphological or genomic change before going extinct drops to zero.

This finding correlates with the lack of any significant observable change in the fossils of these species over time. The oldest Neanderthal fossils look nearly identical to the most recent. Likewise, the oldest *Homo erectus* fossils look virtually the same as the most recent. Given that the hominid species predating modern humans show no substantial natural evolutionary change, the hypothesis that modern humans, Neanderthals, Denisovans, *Homo erectus*, and the other hominid species are descended from a common ancestor warrants reconsideration. The evidence tells us that naturalistic bipedal primate evolution did not happen.

Possible Purpose for Hominins' Existence

If neither modern humans nor the hominin species were produced by common descent, this question arises: Why would God create so many hominin species over the past 6 million years? One answer may come from a review of the history of mammalian life. We see a stark difference in that record between continents where hominid species are known to have lived and continents where they did not.

Across the entirety of the Cenozoic era (66 million years ago to now), with the exception of the last 100,000 years, "body mass was rarely significantly associated with the probability of extinction."[74] Throughout the Cenozoic, "neither small nor large mammals were more vulnerable to extinction during times of high climate variability."[75] Over the past 100,000 years, however, the mean body mass of terrestrial mammals has plummeted. The average body mass of mammalian extinction victims is more than a hundred times greater than the average body mass of surviving mammals.[76]

Many anthropologists have long held that premodern hominins drove the extinction of high-body-mass terrestrial animals. However, an analysis of eastern African herbivore populations spanning the past 7 million years has now refuted this hypothesis.[77] Even though eastern Africa held the greatest number of known hominin species, and even though these hominins did hunt large-bodied mammals, their presence and hunting seems to have had no significant negative impact on the survival of Africa's megaherbivores.

A species-level macroscale analysis at high geographical resolution shows that modern humans were clearly the primary drivers of worldwide megafauna extinctions.[78] While anthropologists have yet to recover any fossil evidence of hominin species predating the arrival of modern humans in Australia, North America, or South America, the arrival of modern humans on these continents resulted in the extinction of 88%, 72%, and 83% of large-bodied (44+ kilograms adult body weight) mammal genera, respectively.[79] Australia also lost all 7 of its terrestrial large-bodied bird and reptile genera.[80] Meanwhile, the extinction rate of large-bodied mammal genera in Africa and Eurasia amounted to only 18% and 36%, respectively.[81]

With respect to the launch and maintenance of civilization, North and South America and Australia lost nearly all the mammal genera that could have been domesticated for agricultural purposes. Meanwhile, Eurasia and Africa lost none. One likely inference from this data is that long-term exposure to several species of hominin hunters with rocks, spears, and javelins prevented the loss of agriculturally important mammals in these regions. Over time, large-bodied mammals learned to avoid or flee from bipedal primates with implements in their hands. In Eurasia and Africa, these mammals survived the arrival of the superpredator, modern humans, but in North and South America and Australia, they did not. The absence of these large mammals constrained humans in North and South America and Australia to a stone-age-level culture and a limited population until Europeans arrived with agriculturally crucial animals.

A potential scenario consistent with Christian theology comes to mind in light of these observations: God knew that humans would sin and, consequently, struggle to fulfill their assignment to manage Earth's resources for the benefit of all life. They would fail even to the point of nearly wiping out the specific animals they needed to launch and sustain civilization. Perhaps God created a sequence of hominins to allow agriculturally vital mammals to develop a cautious response to modern humans, resulting in human flourishing. This hypothesis would seem to align with God's common grace.

Original Human Pair and Genetics

When Francis Collins claimed in his book *The Language of God* that humanity's ancestral population must have consisted of at least 10,000 individuals,[82] it seemed to end all questioning on the matter. Geneticists quickly agreed that the genetic diversity of humans is too great to have come from a single primordial couple, the biblical Adam and Eve. Because Collins is a brilliant scholar and a respected Christian, I can understand why theologians readily accepted his word as the final verdict, especially given the complexities of the science involved.

Geneticists use three methods for determining humanity's initial population: (1) estimates of mutation rate; (2) incidence of linkage disequilibrium (nonrandom association of gene variants at different positions along a chromosome); and (3) incidence of incomplete-lineage sorting (retention of different gene variants at a particular chromosome position within a population). What is troubling about the use of these methods is that all three fundamentally depend on the assumption that humans, Neanderthals, *Homo erectus*, and the great apes have naturally descended from a relatively recent common ancestor, an assumption that does not fit the evidence.

Mutation rates throughout humanity's history are impossible to determine with any accuracy. Likewise, the location of mutations along the genome at different times in humanity's history are difficult to ascertain. Consequently, evolutionary estimates of humanity's initial population based on mutation rates range from the high hundreds to ten thousand.[83]

All three methods also critically depend on a chosen mathematical model. Different mathematical models yield different initial population numbers. Meanwhile, linkage disequilibrium is subject to uncertainties in natural selection, mating cultures and practices, genetic drift, genetic linkage, genetic recombination, mutation rates, tribal divisions, and tribal structures. In addition, the incomplete-lineage sorting method typically yields different results depending on which genes are selected for use in the calculation.

Field studies performed on eight animal species—Mouflon sheep,[84] gray whales,[85] blue whales,[86] Przewalski's horses,[87] copper redhorse,[88] common toad,[89] white-tailed deer,[90] and white-tailed eagles[91]—with known initial populations consistently demonstrate that all three methods greatly overestimate ancestral populations. This overestimation is most strongly correlated with the species' generation time.[92]

Among Earth's mammalian species, past and present, modern humans hold the record, by a wide margin, for length of generation time. Therefore, overestimation will be the most dramatic for modern humans. In a *Nature News* article, Joseph Milton quotes a statement by evolutionary geneticist William Amos that seems crucially relevant to Collins's assertion. Amos says, "We don't fully understand the relationship between genetic diversity and population size."[93]

Genetics is, indeed, an extremely complex science. Factors generating genetic change are fraught with uncertainties. Further, not all genetic change factors have yet been identified. So, any claim of a past genetic status or outcome is subject to significant statistical and even greater systematic uncertainties. Thus, genetics offers no "indisputable" refutation of the biblical account of all humans as descended from Adam and Eve.

Geneticists who argue against the descent of all humanity from the biblical couple also overlook, or disregard, the supernatural factor. Genesis and Romans explicitly state, and other biblical texts imply, that the origin of Adam and Eve was an act of God. These Bible passages tell us that God directly intervened to create, *de novo*, the first human male and female. I am convinced that Jesus had this event in mind as he used mud in miraculously giving sight to the man born blind (John 9).

God clearly intended to minimize humans' genetic defects and diseases, which would explain why, in Leviticus, he instructed God's people to forgo sexual union between close relatives. However, for the first few generations of humanity, at least, such unions would be inevitable. One way God could ensure the genetic health of the first few generations of people would be to endow Eve with genetically diverse eggs. In this hypothetical scenario, Eve could be "the mother of all the living" (Genesis 3:20) without risking the propagation of genetic defects and diseases early on. If God did endow Eve with such eggs, then regardless of present-day genetic diversity among humans, no genetic contradiction exists for the descent of all humans from a single human couple.

Human Exceptionalism and the Case for Special Creation

As wondrous, capable, and humanlike as various animal species may be, the gulf between humans and the most intelligent, perceptive, communicative, and relational of them is wide. Compared with all other life on Earth, past and present, humans stand apart, not just in degree but also—and more importantly—in kind. Only humans possess the unique capacity and motivation needed to launch, sustain, and technologically advance their civilization. And only humans manifest pervasive awareness of moral-ethical boundaries. Even though moral values may vary from person to person and group to group, the sense that some actions and attitudes are right and others are wrong is universal.

The following tables highlight at least some of the characteristic qualities that differentiate humans from all other creatures on Earth.

Table 19.1 Behavioral Attributes Unique to Humans

1. capacity for symbolic expression and comprehension
2. ability to invent and manipulate symbols
3. capacity to generate complex music, literature, and abstract art
4. ability to invent and manufacture complex tools
5. ability to manufacture and propensity to wear clothing
6. ability to invent, use, and learn complex languages/codes
7. capacity to form highly complex social structures
8. capacity for abstract thought
9. ability to invent and implement complex trade and transportation systems
10. capacity and motivation for technological advance
11. ability to engage in complex mathematics
12. ability to tame, domesticate, and train various animals
13. ability to simultaneously engage in complex thought and complex body movements[94]
14. hyperomnivory and prey-switching ability[95]
15. curiosity about the natural realm beyond habitat and survival needs

---

Table 19.2 Exceptional Human Morphology and Development

1. globular skull of appropriate size to accommodate a uniquely large parietal lobe
2. brain circuitry to facilitate rapid language acquisition and multilingual capability
3. hand-eye coordination and manual dexterity for complex function (e.g., typing, performing surgery, playing piano)
4. uniquely high sustained metabolic rate throughout an exceptionally long average lifespan
5. unique cancer and tumor suppression in the context of high metabolic output
6. long infant and adolescent development times
7. relatively tall, slender skeletal frame with long, muscular legs
8. limited body hair
9. twisted birth canal[96]
10. efficient cooling system
11. energy efficiency that allows for fast, long-distance ambulation[97]
12. eyeballs with large contrasting whites, enabling silent, complex interpersonal signaling
13. enduring high-resolution eyesight[98]
14. ability to communicate via auditory smiles[99]
15. hunting-gathering capability that delivers more calories/nutrients per unit of time[100]
16. complex physiology in multiple organs, making possible the utterance of a vast range of distinct complex sounds at a rapid pace
17. capacity for selective attention, e.g., "cocktail party listening"[101]

Table 19.3 Exceptional Human Spiritual Qualities

1. awareness of self
2. theory of mind (ability to discern other humans' thoughts)
3. ability to distinguish between good and bad, noble and evil
4. ability to conceptualize time—past, present, and future
5. curiosity about life beyond earthly life
6. capacity to contemplate death
7. ability to imagine and to express imagination
8. compulsion to worship
9. curiosity about what lies beyond the universe

The next chapter explains the benefits of taking a "testable model" approach to resolving apparent conflicts between what science experts and theology experts say about origins, especially human origins. As we examine and evaluate how well competing models perform with respect to the ongoing advance of knowledge, we will let the evidence speak for itself. A comparison of creation and evolution models reveals clearly that conflict has arisen not from the data but from the interpretation of the data—and what presuppositions are impacting that interpretation. A testable model that accounts for the data and reasonably explains it means that Christians worldwide *can* use the book of nature to build trust in the book of Scripture and point people toward a personal, eternal relationship with God, our Creator and Redeemer.

Chapter 20

The Benefit of a Model Approach

In science, the term "model" refers to the schematic description of a physical or living system, or combined set of systems, that accounts for its origin and operation. A model is more than an idea, inference, method, hypothesis, or rudimentary theory. It is a reasonable and well-developed attempt to explain the entire scope of a particular system, as well as that system's relationship to other phenomena.

Theologians assemble models, too. For example, systematic theologians compile all biblical passages relevant to a particular theme or topic and construct from this compilation a scenario that offers a consistent, comprehensive, and coherent perspective on that topic, whether it be marriage, end times, the sacraments, or another matter of theological importance.

Using a model approach supplies researchers and Bible scholars with a sufficiently detailed outline to assist in further study. It portrays how, when, where, and why a phenomenon, or a set of phenomena, takes place. It anticipates future discoveries or biblical insights that could either verify or falsify the model's explanation. In science, the best models also yield specific recommendations for future research that could potentially improve understanding of the systems or phenomena they attempt to explain.

Given that neither scientists nor theologians can know everything about any particular system, no model can offer a perfect explanation. However, as different models are compared and contrasted and more thoroughly tested, scientific and theological understanding advances. Models with the best record for anticipating future findings or for integrating the widest range of current knowledge are recognized as the most accurate. Such models are kept for further development and refinement while others are either greatly revised, set aside for future research, or rejected. The most successful models are those that require progressively less refinement and less significant adjustment through ongoing research and testing. In other words, the gaps in such models are shrinking rather than expanding.

What many people do not realize, however, is that scientists will typically retain a model with widening or important weaknesses, or gaps, until a more successful or comprehensive model emerges to take its place. For this reason, it is not helpful for Christians to do no more than to point out flaws and failures in evolutionists' models for the origin and history of life. Most evolutionists are aware of their models' shortcomings. Nevertheless, they will not abandon their models until they first see a superior, more comprehensive one. Since "evolution bashing" is unhelpful, Christian scholars would do well to focus efforts on developing a positive case for creation through a detailed, comprehensive, and predictive model, one that integrates both the biblical and scientific data. The goal for such a model is to demonstrate greater success than competing models in predicting future scientific discoveries and offering a more comprehensive and detailed explanation of nature's record.

During the past few decades, many Christians have pursued a "bottom-up" approach—a grassroots or political approach—to challenging and overturning the standard evolutionary model for the origin and history of life. Unfortunately, such approaches serve only to heighten resistance. Most research scientists consider the subject so complex and the data so deep that to make a significant, model-based contribution requires extensive science education and research experience.

God- or Nature-of-the-Gaps?

Nontheistic scientists enjoy pointing out past instances where "God" was inserted to fill the gaps in natural explanation, only to be overcome by future research and greater knowledge. Many such instances exist. For example, millennia ago, people of many faiths believed that lightning and solar and lunar eclipses were directly caused by the hand of God.

Beginning with Gottfried Leibniz, many nontheistic scientists accused Isaac Newton of committing a god-of-the-gaps fallacy when he credited the orderliness of the orbits of celestial bodies to God. However, Newton was simply extolling God's skill in setting up the laws of physics and designing the universe so that orderly orbits of celestial bodies would result.[1]

A classic response to valid instances of god-of-the-gaps fallacies is to assert that absence of evidence is not evidence of absence. However, it does not necessarily follow, as some insist, that every failure to provide a natural explanation will eventually be overcome through ongoing scientific discovery and understanding. Such a priori insistence assumes, but does not prove, that God has not, does not, nor ever will intervene in the natural order of things.

But the god-of-the-gaps response is not the only or most frequent reaction to gaps in our knowledge and understanding. Today, the nature-of-the-gaps argument seems more prevalent. The inability to explain a phenomenon often leads to the conclusion that an undiscovered or unknown natural process, or combination of natural processes, must be responsible. The logical fallacy here is the presumption that gaps in our knowledge and understanding can *only* imply hidden naturalistic causes, never supernatural ones.

An appeal to God may not necessarily be a god-of-the-gaps argument unless we blindly accept that the physical universe is all there is or ever was or ever will be—thus, completely self-caused and self-explanatory.

To word it another way, an appeal to God is not a god-of-the-gaps argument if the evidence points to a supernatural cause. It is only a god-of-the-gaps argument when we appeal to God despite the evidence.

Gaps in our understanding and knowledge represent opportunities to test competing explanatory models. If a biblical creation model delivers a more comprehensive and consistent explanation of nature as our gaps in knowledge and understanding grow smaller, fewer, and less problematic, then the veracity of that creation model is sustained. Such a model earns yet more respect if and when gaps in nontheistic models grow larger, more numerous, and more problematic as research advances.

Observing what happens to gaps as we learn more requires a shift from nonempirical appeals into the arena of the empirical. It moves appeals to the unknown into the realm of the known. It encourages nontheists to base their case on what is known, knowable, and reasonable rather than on what is unknown, unknowable, and unreasonable. Just before being martyred for his faith in Nazi Germany, theologian Dietrich Bonhoeffer wrote, "How wrong it is to use God as a stop-gap for the incompleteness of our knowledge. If in fact the frontiers of knowledge are being pushed further and further back (and that is bound to be the case), then God is being pushed back with them, and is therefore continually in retreat. We are to find God in what we know, not in what we don't know; God wants us to realize his presence, not in unsolved problems but in those that are solved."[2]

The Design Question

All participants in the creation and evolution debates acknowledge that the universe, life, and the molecular machinery of life show characteristics of design. In fact, most acknowledge that the scientific case for design is convincing. The real issue of contention is the *source* of the observed design.

Ironically, by declaring Nature (with a capital N) as the sole source of its observed design, naturalists have, in fact, placed the question of nature's sufficiency as an Agent of its own design squarely on the scientific table. And that's exactly where it needs to be resolved—on the scientific table, by the accepted rules of scientific inquiry, by application of the scientific method.

The way forward in building a biblical creation model for the purpose of engaging scientists and theologians across the spectrum of creation and evolution beliefs begins with identifying and analyzing, in as much detail as possible, the characteristics of observed design. Then we must consider and discuss at least these two key questions: (1) What could be responsible for generating the observed design? and (2) What are some definitive scientific tests or predictions that could serve to distinguish among the proposed possible sources or causes of the design?

These are the questions various scholars, including my Reasons to Believe colleagues and I, have been addressing over the past three decades in our books, articles, courses, and lectures. As we continue to identify and analyze design in nature, we also propose an answer to the question of what could be responsible for generating the observed design. In some cases, we see natural processes at work, but in others, we see the input of a supernatural, purposeful Designer, the God of the Bible. We continue to propose various tests and identify predictions that can help distinguish among proposed design sources, and we enthusiastically encourage others to do the same.

In the process, we have developed a list of questions we regard as essential to ask of any viable model for creation or evolution. Does the proposed model

1. Identify, honestly, the philosophical biases/presuppositions on which it rests?
2. Integrate relevant data from all 66 books of the Bible?
3. Integrate relevant data from all disciplines and subdisciplines of science?
4. Show consistency and/or inconsistency of data from various sources?
5. Use knowledge gaps and data anomalies to develop new tests of validity?

6. Consider complex issues in light of simpler, more clearly understood ones?

7. Strive for more detailed and comprehensive explanations?

8. Treat biblical texts as literal unless context indicates use of figurative language?

9. Distinguish among transcendent, transformative, and sustaining miracles when appealing to supernatural intervention in nature?

10. Identify tests or discoveries that could potentially falsify or alter the model?

11. Include critique from scholars who express reservations or reject the model?

12. Make predictions of future discoveries that are distinct from those arising from competing models and that are likely to be fulfilled or falsified within relatively short time periods?

Corroborating Books

The bottom line is that we must be willing to follow the accumulating evidence wherever it leads, always mindful to subject it to ever more rigorous and more comprehensive tests. Given our Christian belief that all truth is God's truth, followers of Jesus Christ have nothing to fear—and every reason to support—the scientific and theological enterprises.

The diligent pursuit of an ever more detailed and comprehensive biblical creation model has the potential to show the world that the more we learn from and come to understand the book of nature, the more closely it aligns with the book of Scripture. As an additional bonus, the more we learn and understand from both books, the more efficient and successful we will be in deepening our understanding of nature's realm—so we can manage it more effectively for the benefit of all life.

Chapter 21

A Modest Defense of
Biblical Inerrancy

Biblical inerrancy is more than a minor Christian doctrine. It has stood for centuries as a foundational tenet of our faith, confirmed again and again by councils, creeds, and confessions of the church. Most recently it was affirmed again by a body of esteemed theologians who formed the International Council on Biblical Inerrancy. Thus, when influential voices within the church claim that "newly discovered facts" call for a major revision, if not rejection, of this doctrine, their claims demand a response. It's as if the Bible is again on trial, and predominantly among those who are now teaching and training future leaders of the global body of Christ.

Given that the human eyewitnesses—the active participants in the Bible's supernaturally guided authorship—are no longer with us to testify in person, other witnesses to the Bible's veracity must take the stand. Is the long-standing verdict in this case at risk of being overturned by new knowledge? It must be acknowledged that science in the twentieth and twenty-first centuries has brought us an exponential increase in knowledge about the book of nature. In some scientific disciplines, the knowledge base doubles within a single decade. Has this knowledge explosion in the life sciences—specifically with regard to humanity's origin—really compromised the reliability of God's written revelation?

Let us focus on the explanatory models rather than on the individuals making bold claims. Let's consider how these models fare in light of settled science and the latest findings across scientific disciplines. On a multitude of points, primarily data points, the evolutionary model and the creation model agree: Earth began without life, life appeared early, life changed little for a long time, and then life began to multiply, diversify, and become increasingly complex.

The evolutionary model, held by theists and nontheists alike, asserts that this entire process, including emergence of life from nonlife, has unfolded continuously—and is still unfolding—by nature and its processes alone, without supernatural input.

By contrast, the creation model, based on the biblical record, asserts that God made life from nonlife. As solar burning progressed, God intervened to ensure life's survival and diversification. Through life's survival and diversification, God prepared Earth to serve as a long-enduring yet ultimately temporary home for humanity, the one creature designed for and endowed with the capacity for relationship with the Creator.

With respect to humanity, the evolutionary model says modern humans emerge naturally from the same branch chimpanzees and Neanderthals do, despite obvious discontinuities. In this view, we humans today are the progeny of those first humans via a large ancestral population. The creation model, on the other hand, says God intervened to create an exceptional human pair. In this view, we humans today are their progeny, uniquely endowed with God's image that has been marred but not erased by our propensity for autonomy.

The preceding chapters provide only a few of the salient discoveries to show how these models fare in view of established facts and reasonable inferences from them. They also address the fallacy behind assertions that the ancient Hebrews merely echoed their neighbors' mythologies, expressing neither interest in nor understanding of what today we refer to as science. The Hebrews' creation "myth" could well be referred to as what C. S. Lewis called the one "true myth."

As a scientist, I realize that my trust in the truthfulness of the biblical creation account requires belief in the possibility of "miracles," of divine intervention in the physical realm, nature's realm. But this trust is merely consistent with settled scientific evidence that the universe of space-time, matter, and energy came into existence from a transcendent Source. That same Source chose to take on human form, by transcendent means, and in doing so demonstrated his authority and power over the laws of nature he established. Although Jesus kept quiet about this power and authority, he did not hide the evidence of its effects.

The recent explosion of revelation from the book of nature has provided a stunning perspective on God's purpose and plan for humanity. As we examine every major component and event in God's creation, we see how it fits with his intent to make possible the existence—*and* the redemption—of billions of humans.

Through ongoing research in the two books and through the careful, diligent, and thorough integration of all that we find therein, Christians today have an unprecedented opportunity to present God's message of redemption to a greater depth and breadth than at any prior moment in history. Christian theologians can enhance, rather than stultify, scientific advance by encouraging research into purposeful design behind what scientists once considered useless evolutionary artifacts—and then sharing the results in their teaching and writing.

One example of an "artifact" turned into an advance is the 98.5% of the human genome that evolutionary biologists and geneticists presumed was comprised of useless junk DNA. Research on this portion of the genome was abandoned for several decades because research on it was deemed pointless. Then, as a follow-up to the Human Genome Project, the Encode Project published the unexpected finding that at least 80.4% of the human genome is, in fact, functional. Phases III and IV have uncovered yet more functional components. An extrapolation suggests that over 98.5% of the human genome will prove functional. This finding is but one of many examples where scientific advances provide accumulating scientific evidence for a biblical creation model and counter to naturalistic models.[1]

Likewise, Christians in the sciences can help Christian theologians recognize God's handiwork in nature, revealing more about his wisdom, artistry, and other attributes that draw people to seek a relationship with him. A (moderate) concordist approach to teaching on God's revelation can help deepen Christians' trust in the Bible while also drawing skeptics to its message. Such teaching will restore the value of loving the Lord with all our mind, as well as our heart, soul, and strength.

The more fully we who are Christians place our trust in the reliability of God's Word as a revelation of God's works, the more fully our hearts can rejoice in the reality of his goodness, the more firmly we can embrace the hope he offers, the more wisely we can care for the home he gave us, the more freely we can express our worship to him, and the more selflessly we can extend his love to all people.

My prayer is that each of us will eagerly continue to learn, but also to share what we learn, from God's two books. May we respond to both current and future challenges, beyond those addressed in these pages, with full confidence in the one supernatural Source of both books, the one who is Truth, personified. May we eagerly anticipate and invite others to join us in the realm of indescribable beauty and wonder to which these two books reliably point the way.

The Meaning of *Bara* and *Asa*

A few of the twenty-first-century theologians who challenge the credibility of Genesis 1 have argued for a revised translation of certain key words within the Hebrew text. Their particular focus is the meaning of two verbs, *bara* and *asa*, translated as "create" and "make," respectively.

In the *Journal for the Study of the Old Testament*, Ellen van Wolde writes, "The linguistic and textual examination of the seven usages of the verb *bara* in Genesis 1 leads to the conclusion that the verb *bara* in Genesis 1 does not mean 'to create' but 'to separate,'"[1] in the spatial sense. She builds her case on the fact that *bara* in Genesis 1 applies to more than one element of creation at a time. In Genesis 1:1, *bara* is associated with the "heavens" and the "earth"; in 1:21, with the "birds" and "great sea creatures"; and in 1:27, with humans, "male" and "female." On this basis, it could be used to distinguish, or "separate," each of the two things from the other.

The first problem with this conclusion comes from the recognition that "the heavens and the earth" in Genesis 1:1 is not a reference to two separate things. Rather, it is a merism, a phrase used to express completeness. Some common examples are loving someone "heart and soul" or searching "high and low." In Hebrew, this particular merism is used with reference to the entirety of the physical realm of which Earth is a part. Biblical Hebrew has no single word that means "the universe." Therefore, it uses a distinct phrase, in this case "the heavens and the earth," to take on that definition.

A second problem is that Genesis 1 does not read like an account about separation. God did not spatially separate mankind in his own image or spatially separate human males from human females.

Although the *Theological Wordbook of the Old Testament* states that *bara* in the Qal verb form means "create" or "make," it also allows for a slightly different meaning in the Piel verb form: "choose," "cut down," or "dispatch."[2] However, in Genesis 1, *bara* appears only in the Qal form, not in the Piel form.

In his book *The Lost World of Genesis 1*, John Walton asserts that "Genesis 1 was never intended to offer an account of material origins"[3] and therefore "offers no descriptive mechanism for material origins."[4] Walton views Genesis 1 as "an account of functional origins,"[5] and on this basis, he claims that "*bara* is not a material activity but a functional one."[6]

Rather than to say the Hebrew-English lexicons over the past millennium were wrong in their definitions of *bara* and *asa*, Walton suggests that the lexicographers failed to take notice of other components of what *bara* and *asa* can mean. In his words, "It [the functional definition] is simply one they have never considered because their material ontology was a blind presupposition for which no alternative was ever considered."[7] He goes on to say that his alternate definition of *bara* is fitting because "no materials for the creative act are ever mentioned."[8]

In Genesis 1, the verb *bara* is used for the creation of "the heavens and the earth." Given that the universe is, indeed, a material entity, Walton's claim is contradicted in the very first verse.

Where God is acting, *bara* means to create something new and unparalleled that did not exist before.[9] *Asa* means to manufacture or fashion something out of previously existing resources.[10] Thus, the only instance in Genesis 1 where *bara* refers to something physical is in Genesis 1:1, where God creates physical matter and energy. It would be inappropriate to use *bara* for anything physical thereafter. This interpretation fits with Hebrews 11:3, which says, "By faith we understand that the universe was formed at God's command, so that what is seen was not made out of what was visible."

The second of the three uses of *bara* in Genesis 1 denotes God's creation of *nephesh*, the "soulish" birds and sea mammals. The third use refers to creation of the humans, the "spiritual" creatures bearing his image. Creative acts 2 and 3 are simultaneously material and nonmaterial. The creatures in each case have material bodies, but they also have a new and immaterial quality that did not previously exist.

It makes sense, then, that the writer would limit his use of *bara* to only these three creative acts while using the verb *asa* with reference to other acts of creation. From the context alone, it appears that *bara* in this passage refers to creation of something new and unparalleled that did not previously exist.

The verb *bara* in the Qal form occurs 48 times in the Old Testament. In every instance, God is the subject or implied subject of the verb. In all 48 appearances, *bara* is in the masculine singular form. The masculine pronoun he is implied, a peculiarity of this verb used only of God. This exclusivity indicates that *bara* refers to divine activity, beyond what humans are capable of performing. Given that humans can and do assign functions to many material entities, it seems problematic to claim that in Genesis 1, *bara* refers only to the assignment of function.

Concerning *asa*, Walton claims that in Genesis 1 it always means doing and never means making.[11] Such a claim makes for awkward translations of Genesis 1:16, 25, and 26 as "God did two great lights and also did the stars," "God did the wildlife of the earth," and "let us do mankind in our image," respectively. Such translations are not only bizarre but also inconsistent with other Old Testament creation passages.

To see *bara* and *asa* as verbs *either* for assignment of function *or* for creative activity seems more limiting than necessary. After all, everything God has created is functional in that it plays some role in making possible the existence of billions of humans and their opportunity for redemption within a relatively short time (in astronomers' terms).

Finally, if there were any validity to Walton's definitions, one would expect to find support for them in one or more of the several Hebrew-English lexicons. Given that God desires to speak to all generations of humanity through the Bible, to assert that all the lexicons throughout church history have been wrong about the meanings of both of these verbs seems unreasonable.

Notes

Chapter 1: Surprising Theological Developments

1. George Barna, Cultural Research Center, Arizona Christian University, *American Worldview Inventory 2020 #11* (October 6, 2020), arizonachristian.edu/wp-content/uploads/2020/10/CRC_AWVI2020_Release11_Digital_04_20201006.pdf, 5.
2. Barna, *American Worldview Inventory 2020 #11*, 5.
3. Barna, 5.
4. Barna, 5.

Chapter 2: Dual or Dueling Divine Revelation?

1. C. John Collins, "Romans 1:20 – 'From the Creation of the World,' (ἀπὸ κτίσεως κόσμου)," *Presbyterion* 47, no. 2 (Fall 2021): 88–104.

Chapter 3: A New Challenge Arises

1. Ironically, these same individuals seem reluctant to acknowledge that scientific and historical discoveries and models are just as much subject to interpretation as are biblical texts.
2. Harold Lindsell, *The Battle for the Bible: Defending the Inerrancy of Scripture* (Grand Rapids, MI: Zondervan, 1976).
3. Jay Grimstead, quoted in "Records of the International Council on Biblical Inerrancy," Special Collections, Dallas Theological Seminary Mosher and Turpin Libraries, accessed December 12, 2021, library.dts.edu/Pages/TL/Special/ICBI.shtml.
4. International Council on Biblical Inerrancy, *The Chicago Statement on Biblical Inerrancy: Articles of Affirmation and Denial* (November 7, 1978), library.dts.edu/Pages/TL/Special/ICBI-1978-11-07.pdf, accessed December 12, 2021.
5. International Council on Biblical Inerrancy, *The Chicago Statement on Biblical Hermeneutics: Articles of Affirmation and Denial* (November 13, 1982), library.dts.edu/Pages/TL/Special/ICBI_2.pdf, accessed date December 12, 2021.
6. Wayne Grudem, *Systematic Theology: An Introduction to Biblical Doctrine,* 2nd ed. (Grand Rapids, MI: Zondervan Academic, 2020).
7. Wayne Grudem, "Why Has the Chicago Statement Had Such Wide Influence? Reflections by a Participant," (lecture, Evangelical Theological Society 73rd annual meeting, Fort Worth, TX, November 17, 2021).
8. Lucretius, *De Rerum Natura* (ca. 55 BC), two unabridged translations, one by Hugh Munro and the other by Cyril Bailey, are available side by side online without a paywall at

epicureanfriends.com/lucretius/about-lucretius/.

9. Carl Sagan, *Cosmos* (New York: Ballantine Books, 1985), 1.

10. John William Draper, *History of the Conflict between Religion and Science* (New York: D. Appleton, 1875), 363.

11. Robert Green Ingersoll, "Orthodoxy: A Lecture," *The Works of Robert G. Ingersoll*, vol. 2 (New York: Dresden Publishing, 1902; Project Gutenberg), gutenberg.org/files/38802/38802-h/38802-h.htm.

12. Jerry A. Coyne, *Faith Versus Fact: Why Science and Religion Are Incompatible* (New York: Viking, 2015), 2.

13. Richard Dawkins, *The God Delusion* (Boston: Houghton Mifflin Publishing, 2006).

14. Friedrich Schleiermacher, *The Christian Faith*, 2nd ed. trans. H. R. Mackintosh, ed. J. S. Stewart (Berkeley, CA: Apocryphile Press, 2011); Matthias Jakob Schleden, "Schleiermacher, Friedrich Daniel Ernst," *1911 Encyclopaedia Britannica*, vol. 24, en.wikisource.org/wiki/1911_Encyclopædia_Britannica/Schleiermacher,_Friedrich_Daniel_Ernst (in the public domain, accessed December 8, 2021).

15. Johann Gottfried Eichhorn, *Einleitung in das Alte Testament*, 5 vols. (Göttingen, Netherlands: C. E. Rosenbusch, 1823–24).

16. Gunkel, *The Legends of Genesis*, trans. William Herbert Carruth (Chicago: Open Court Publishing, 1901), 7–8, archive.org/details/bub_gb_PgkXAAAAYAAJ_2/page/n7/mode/2up.

17. Gunkel, *The Legends of Genesis*, 7–8.

18. John Shelby Spong, *Rescuing the Bible from Fundamentalism: A Bishop Rethinks the Meaning of Scripture* (San Francisco: Harper, 1991).

19. John Shelby Spong, "A Call for a New Reformation," *The Fourth R* 11, no. 4 (July–August 1998), westarinstitute.org/resources/the-fourth-r/a-call-for-a-new-reformation/.

20. David Tracy, *Blessed Rage for Order: The New Pluralism in Theology* (New York: Seabury, 1975); David Tracy, *The Analogical Imagination: Christian Theology and the Culture of Pluralism* (New York: Crossroad, 1981); Francis Schüssler Fiorenza, "Systematic Theology: Tasks and Methods," in *Systematic Theology: Roman Catholic Perspectives*, 2nd ed., ed. Francis Schüssler Fiorenza and John P. Galvin (Minneapolis: Fortress Press, 2011), 1–78; Anne M. Clifford, "Creation," in *Systematic Theology: Roman Catholic Perspectives*, 2nd ed., ed. Francis Schüssler Fiorenza and John P. Galvin (Minneapolis: Fortress Press, 2011), 201–251.

21. Karl Barth, *The Epistle to the Romans*, 6th ed., trans. Edwyn C. Hoskyns (New York: Oxford University Press, 1968).

22. Karl Barth, *Church Dogmatics*, ed. G. W. Bromiley and T. F. Torrance and trans. G. T. Thomson et al., vol. 1.2, *The Doctrine of the Word of God*, sections 16–18 (Edinburgh: T&T Clark, 1963), 50.

23. Barth, *Church Dogmatics*, 1.2: 518–524.

24. Barth, *Church Dogmatics*, 3.1: 80–84.

25. Colin Brown, "Karl Barth's Doctrine of the Creation," *The Churchman* 76, no. 2 (1962): 101, churchsociety.org/wp-content/uploads/2021/05/Cman_076_2_Brown.pdf.

26. R. Laird Harris, Gleason L. Archer, Jr., and Bruce K. Waltke, eds., *Theological Wordbook of the Old Testament*, 2 vols. (Chicago: Moody Bible Institute of Chicago, 1980).

27. Peter Enns, *Inspiration and Incarnation: Evangelicals and the Problem of the Old Testament* (Grand Rapids, MI: Baker Academic, 2005).

28. Peter Enns, *Inspiration and Incarnation: Evangelicals and the Problem of the Old Testament*, 2nd ed. (Grand Rapids, MI: Baker Academic, 2015), x.

29. Enns, *Inspiration and Incarnation*, 2nd ed., 27.

30. Enns, *Inspiration and Incarnation*, 2nd ed., 56.
31. Enns, *Inspiration and Incarnation*, 2nd ed., 174.
32. Kenton L. Sparks, *God's Word in Human Words: An Evangelical Appropriation of Critical Biblical Scholarship* (Grand Rapids, MI: Baker Academic, 2008): 256.
33. Sparks, *God's Word in Human Words*, 256.
34. Sparks, 55.
35. Sparks, 231.
36. Sparks, 256.
37. Sparks, 361.

Chapter 4: Disturbing Concessions
1. Bruce K. Waltke, "Revisiting *Inspiration and Incarnation*," *Westminster Theological Journal* 71, no. 1 (Spring 2009): 83–85.
2. Waltke, "Revisiting *Inspiration and Incarnation*," 94.
3. PDS_, "Full Transcript of Bruce Waltke Video Clip," *The Design Spectrum* (blog), posted April 10, 2010, accessed December 27, 2021, thedesignspectrum.wordpress.com/2010/04/10/full-transcript-of-bruce-waltke-video-clip/.
4. Peter Enns, "Science, Faith, and the Chicago Statement on Biblical Inerrancy," *The Biologos Forum: Science and Faith in Dialogue* (June 17, 2011), part 1, 2, wp.production.patheos.com/blogs/peterenns/files/2014/08/Science-Faith-and-the-Chicago-Statement-on-Biblical-Inerrancy-Enns-Edited-no-watermark.pdf.
5. Enns, "Science, Faith, and the Chicago Statement," part 1, 2.
6. Enns, "Science, Faith, and the Chicago Statement," (June 21, 2011), part 2, 6.
7. Enns, "Science, Faith, and the Chicago Statement," part 2, 6.
8. Enns, "Science, Faith, and the Chicago Statement," (June 24, 2011), part 3, 9–10.
9. Enns, "Science, Faith, and the Chicago Statement," (July 19, 2011), part 8, 24.
10. Enns, "Science, Faith, and the Chicago Statement," (July 22, 2011), part 9, 26.
11. Enns, "Science, Faith, and the Chicago Statement," (July 26, 2011), part 10, 29.
12. Enns, "Science, Faith, and the Chicago Statement," part 10, 30.
13. Enns, "Science, Faith, and the Chicago Statement," part 10, 30.
14. Enns, "Science, Faith, and the Chicago Statement," (July 29, 2011), part 11, 32–33.
15. Enns, "Science, Faith, and the Chicago Statement," (August 9, 2011), part 13, 39.
16. Enns, "Science, Faith, and the Chicago Statement," (August 17, 2011), part 14, 42.
17. Peter Enns in *Five Views on Biblical Inerrancy*, ed. James R. A. Merrick, Stephen M. Garrett, and Stanley N. Gundry (Grand Rapids, MI: Zondervan, 2013), 83.
18. Peter Enns, "What Is the Bible? A Good Question That Biblical Inerrancy Can't Answer," *The Bible for Normal People* (blog), February 22, 2017, peteenns.com/what-is-the-bible/.
19. Peter Enns, *The Evolution of Adam: What the Bible Does and Doesn't Say about Human Origins* (Grand Rapids, MI: Brazos Press, 2012).
20. Peter Enns and Jared Byas, *Genesis for Normal People: A Guide to the Most Controversial, Misunderstood, and Abused Book of the Bible* (Englewood, CO: Patheos Press, 2012).
21. John H. Walton, *The Lost World of Genesis One* (Downers Grove, IL: InterVarsity Press Academic, 2009).
22. Walton, *The Lost World of Genesis One*, 171.
23. Walton, 84.
24. Walton, 113.
25. Walton, 113.

26. Walton, 107.
27. Walton, 113.
28. Walton, 16.
29. Walton, 20.
30. Walton, 113.
31. Walton, 116.
32. Walton, 127.
33. Walton, 17.
34. Walton, 61.
35. John H. Walton and D. Brent Sandy, *The Lost World of Scripture: Ancient Literary Culture and Biblical Authority* (Downers Grove, IL: InterVarsity Press Academic, 2013).
36. John H. Walton with N. T. Wright, *The Lost World of Adam and Eve: Genesis 2-3 and the Human Origins Debate* (Downers Grove, IL: Intervarsity Press Academic, 2015).
37. John H. Walton and J. Harvey Walton, *The Lost World of the Israelite Conquest: Covenant, Retribution, and the Fate of the Canaanites* (Downers Grove, IL: Intervarsity Press Academic, 2017).
38. Tremper Longman III and John H. Walton with Stephen O. Moshier, *The Lost World of the Flood: Mythology, Theology, and the Deluge Debate* (Downers Grove, IL: InterVarsity Press Academic, 2018).
39. John H. Walton and J. Harvey Walton, *The Lost World of the Torah: Law as Covenant and Wisdom in Ancient Context* (Downers Grove, IL: Intervarsity Press Academic, 2019).
40. Walton and Sandy, *The Lost World of Scripture*, 50.
41. Walton and Sandy, 49.
42. Walton and Sandy, 51.
43. Walton and Sandy, 57.
44. Walton and Sandy, 57.
45. Walton and Sandy, 53–54.
46. Walton and Wright, *The Lost World of Adam and Eve*, 184.
47. Walton and Walton, *The Lost World of the Israelite Conquest*, 239.
48. Walton and Walton, 100.
49. Longman and Walton with Moshier, *The Lost World of the Flood*, 39–41.
50. Genesis 7:21–23; 8:21; 2 Peter 2:5; 2 Peter 3:6.
51. Walton and Walton, *The Lost World of the Torah*, 44.
52. Walton and Walton, 44. For a detailed critique of *The Lost World of the Torah*, see Joseph Miller, globaljournalct.com/wp-content/uploads/2021/03/Global-Journal-17.3-Joseph-Miller-Jesus-in-the-Torah.pdf.
53. Johnny V. Miller and John M. Soden, *In the Beginning . . . We Misunderstood: Interpreting Genesis 1 in Its Original Context* (Grand Rapids, MI: Kregel Publications, 2012).
54. Miller and Soden, *In the Beginning*, 40.
55. Miller and Soden, 152.
56. Miller and Soden, 101.
57. Miller and Soden, 52, 89–91, 120.
58. Miller and Soden, 36, 43–44, 85, 102, 160.
59. Miller and Soden, 18, 21, 184.
60. Miller and Soden, 48, 154.
61. Miller and Soden, 45, 101–102, 147, 160.
62. Miller and Soden, 40.

63. Tremper Longman III, *How to Read Genesis* (Downers Grove, IL: InterVarsity Press, 2005), 104.

64. Tremper Longman III, "What Genesis 1–2 Teaches (and What It Doesn't)," in *Reading Genesis 1–2: An Evangelical Conversation*, ed. J. Daryl Charles (Peabody, MA: Hendrickson, 2013), 103–122.

65. Tremper Longman III, *Job* (Grand Rapids, MI: Baker Academic, 2012), 454. Similar statements are made on pages 426, 441, 445, 455.

66. Longman III, *Job*, 455.

67. Dennis R. Venema and Scot McKnight, *Adam and the Genome: Reading Scripture After Genetic Science* (Grand Rapids, MI: Brazos Press, 2012).

68. Tremper Longman III, in Venema and McKnight, *Adam and the Genome*, vii.

69. Tremper Longman III, *Confronting Old Testament Controversies: Pressing Questions about Evolution, Sexuality, History, and Violence* (Grand Rapids, MI: Baker Books, 2019), 25–71.

70. Venema and McKnight, *Adam and the Genome*, 124.

71. Venema and McKnight, 118.

72. Venema and McKnight, 145.

73. Venema and McKnight, 139.

74. Venema and McKnight, 190–191.

75. Denis Lamoureux, *Evolution: Scripture and Nature Say Yes!* (Grand Rapids, MI: Zondervan, 2016), 27.

76. Denis O. Lamoureux, *The Bible and Ancient Science: Principles of Interpretation* (Tullahoma, TN: McGahan, 2020), 26–31, 155–161, 199–202.

77. Michael S. Heiser, "The Evolution of Adam: Additional Thoughts," *Naked Bible* (June 2, 2012), accessed January 8, 2022, drmsh.com/evolution-adam-additional-thoughts/.

78. Heiser, "The Evolution of Adam."

79. William Lane Craig, *In Quest of the Historical Adam: A Biblical and Scientific Exploration* (Grand Rapids, MI: Eerdmans, 2021), 16.

80. William Lane Craig, "#317 Confused about Concordism," *Reasonable Faith with William Lane Craig* (blog), Reasonable Faith, May 13, 2013, reasonablefaith.org/writings/question-answer/confused-about-concordism; William Lane Craig, "#343 Concordism," *Reasonable Faith with William Lane Craig* (blog), Reasonable Faith, November 11, 2013, reasonable-faith.org/writings/question-answer/concordism.

81. Craig, *In Quest of the Historical Adam*, 152–157, 198–203, 363.

82. William Lane Craig, "The Historical Adam," *First Things*, October 2021, firstthings.com/article/2021/10/the-historical-adam.

83. Craig, "The Historical Adam."

84. Craig, *In Quest of the Historical Adam*, 104–131.

85. Craig, *In Quest of the Historical Adam*, 380; Craig, "The Historical Adam."

86. Craig, *In Quest of the Historical Adam*, 378.

87. Craig, "The Historical Adam"; Craig, *In Quest of the Historical Adam*, 378.

Chapter 5: Dual Revelation and Inerrancy in Church History

1. Jack B. Rogers and Donald K. McKim, *The Authority and Interpretation of the Bible: An Historical Approach* (San Francisco: Harper & Row, 1979).

2. Clement of Alexandria, *The Stromata*, book V: chap. 3, book VI, chap. 8, 10–11 in *Ante-Nicene Fathers, Volume 2: Fathers of the Second Century*, ed. Alexander Roberts and James Donaldson (Peabody, MA: Hendrickson Publishers, July 1999), 448–449, 494–496, 498–

501; Origen, *Against Celsus*, book III, chap. 58 in *Ante-Nicene Fathers, Volume 4: Fathers of the Third Century*, ed. Alexander Roberts and James Donaldson (Peabody, MA: Hendrickson Publishers, July 1999), 487; Ronald E. Heine, "Stoic Logic as Handmaid to Exegesis and Theology in Origen's Commentary on the Gospel of John," *Journal of Theological Studies* 44, no. 1 (April 1993): 90–117.

3.   Tertullian, *On the Resurrection of the Flesh*, trans. Peter Holmes, in *Ante-Nicene Fathers*, vol. 3, ed. Alexander Roberts and James Donaldson (New York: Scribners, 1896–1903), 547.

4.   Irenaeus, *Against Heresies* 2.28.2, trans. Alexander Roberts, in *Ante-Nicene Fathers*, vol. 1, ed. Alexander Roberts and James Donaldson (New York: Scribners, 1896–1903), 399.

5.   Clement of Rome, *First Epistle to the Corinthians* 45, trans. Alexander Roberts and James Donaldson, in *Ante-Nicene Fathers*, vol. 9, 4th ed., ed. Allan Menzies (Peabody, MA: Hendrickson Publishers, 1999), 242.

6.   Tertullian, *A Treatise on the Soul* 21, trans. Peter Holmes, in *Ante-Nicene Fathers*, vol. 3, 202.

7.   Justin Martyr, *Dialogue with Trypho, a Jew* 65, trans. Marcus Dods and George Reith, in *Ante-Nicene Fathers*, vol. 1, 230.

8.   Origen, *Commentary on Matthew* II, trans. John Patrick, in *Ante-Nicene Fathers*, vol. 9, 413.

9.   Basil, *Exegetical Homilies*, trans. Agnes Clare Way, in *The Fathers of the Church*, vol. 46, ed. Roy Joseph Deferrari (Washington, DC: Catholic University of America Press, 1963).

10. Ambrose, *Hexaemeron, Paradise, and Cain and Abel*, trans. John J. Savage, in *The Fathers of the Church*, ed. Thomas P. Halton, vol. 42 (Washington, DC: Catholic University of America Press, 1961).

11. Augustine, *The Literal Meaning of Genesis* 1.19.39, trans. J. H. Taylor, in *Ancient Christian Writers*, vol. 41 (Westminster, MD: Newman Press, 1982), 42–43.

12. Augustine, *Literal Meaning of Genesis* 1.12.25, 33.

13. Augustine, *Literal Meaning of Genesis* 2.11.31, 68–69.

14. Augustine, *Confessions* 13.18 (New York: Barnes and Noble 1992), 326.

15. Athanasius, *Thirty-Ninth Festal Epistle*, in *Nicene and Post-Nicene Fathers*, 2nd ser., *Athanasius: Select Works and Letters*, vol. 4, ed. Philip Schaff and Henry Wace, trans. Archibald Robertson (Peabody, MA: Hendrickson Publishers, 1999), 551.

16. Augustine to St. Jerome 82.3, AD 405, trans. J. G. Cunningham, in *Nicene and Post-Nicene Fathers*, 1st ser., ed. Philip Schaff, vol. 1 (Buffalo, NY: Christian Literature Publishing, 1887), 350, newadvent.org/fathers/1102082.htm.

17. Augustine to St. Jerome 28.3, AD 394 or 395, trans. J. G. Cunningham in *Nicene and Post-Nicene Fathers*, 1st ser., ed. Philip Schaff, vol. 1 (Peabody, MA: Hendrickson Publishing, 1999), 251–252.

18. Anthony of Egypt, in *The Letters of St. Antony the Great*, ed. Derwas J. Chitty (Oxford: SLG Press, 1975), ix.

19. The four books are: *Against Proclus on the Eternity of the World, Against Aristotle on the Eternity of World, On the Creation of the World, On the Contingency of the World.*

20. Anselm, *Cur Deus Homo*, trans. Sidney Norton Deane (Chicago: Open Court Publishing, 1903; Fort Worth, TX: RDMc Publishing, 2005), 137. Citation refers to RDMc edition.

21. Hugh of St. Victor, *Eruditionis Didascalicae* 7 in Jacques-Paul Migne, *Patrologia Latina*, 1841–1855, 176:814b. Also quoted in Peter Harrison, *Territories of Science and Religion* (Chicago: University of Chicago Press, 2015), 60.

22. Thomas Aquinas, *Summa Theologica*, trans. Fathers of the English Dominican Province (Claremont, CA: Coyote Canyon Press, 2018), part 1, question 1, article 10, reply to objection 3.

23. Aquinas, *Summa Theologica*, part 2, question 110, article 3, reply to objection 1.
24. Thomas Aquinas, *Commentary on the Gospel of St. John*, trans. Fabian R. Larcher OP and James A. Weisheipl OP (Albany, NY: Magi Books, 1998), 21.6.2656.
25. Wallace Nelson Pierson, "The Relation of Theology to Natural Sciences in the Thirteenth Century, with a Translation of Part Two of the Opus Maius of Roger Bacon" (master's thesis, University of California, 1921): 62, babel.hathitrust.org/cgi/pt?id=uc1. b5427322&view–1up&seq=7.
26. Richard A. Muller, *Post-Reformation Reformed Dogmatics*, vol. 2: *Holy Scripture* (Grand Rapids, MI: Baker Academic, 2003), 45.
27. Muller, *Post-Reformation Reformed Dogmatics*, 47.
28. Martin Luther, *Works of Luther* 1481, vol. 19, ed. Jaroslav Pelikan (St. Louis: Concordia Publishing House, 1955–1986).
29. Martin Luther, *Works of Luther* 343, vol. 28 (Erlangen, Germany: Erlangen Edition, 1826–1857).
30. Martin Luther, *Works of Luther* 1073, vol .19.
31. Martin Luther, *Works of Luther* 491, vol. 14.
32. Martin Luther, quoted in Johann Michael Rue, *Luther and the Scriptures* (Columbus, OH: Wartburg Press, 1944), 36–37.
33. Martin Luther, quoted in William Hazlitt, trans. and ed., *The Table Talk or Familiar Discourse of Martin Luther* (London: David Bogue, 1848), 341, books.google.com/books?id=G SwHAAAAQAAJ&pg=PR1&source=gbs_selected_pages&cad=2#v=onepage&q&f=false.
34. John Calvin, *Calvin: Institutes of the Christian Religion* 1.5.1, ed. John T. McNeill, trans. Ford Lewis Battles, vol. 1 (Philadelphia: Westminster Press, 1960), 52.
35. Calvin, *Institutes of the Christian Religion* 2.2.15, 273–274.
36. Calvin, 2.2.16, 275.
37. John Calvin, *The Second Epistle of Paul the Apostle to the Corinthians and the Epistles to Timothy, Titus, and Philemon* (Grand Rapids, MI: Eerdmans, 1964), 330.
38. Calvin, *Institutes of the Christian Religion* 3.5.8, 679.
39. Francis Turretin, *Institutes of Elenctic Theology*, vol. 1, ed. James T. Dennison, Jr., trans. George Musgrave Giger (Phillipsburg, NJ: P & R Publishing 1992), 120.
40. Abraham Kuyper, *Lectures on Calvinism* (Peabody, MA: Hendrickson Publishers, 2008), 120–121.
41. Thomas Browne, *Religio Medici* (London: Cassell & Company, 1892), 34, google.com/ books/edition/Religio_Medici/7slNAQAAMAAJ?hl=en&gbpv=1&printsec=frontcover.
42. Browne, *Religio Medici*, 34.
43. Johannes Kepler to Mästlin (April 19, 1597) in "*Carta de Johannes Kepler a Michael Mästlin em Tübingen,*" *Scientiae Studia* 1, no. 2 (June 2003): 207–215, doi:10.1590/S1678-31662003000200006.
44. Robert Boyle, *The Excellence of Theology, Compared with Natural Philosophy* II. 1. (1674), earlymoderntexts.com/assets/pdfs/boyle1674b.pdf, 40.
45. *Catechism of the Catholic Church* 3.2.107, 2nd ed. (Vatican: Libreria Editrice Vaticana, 1997), 31, usccb.org/sites/default/files/flipbooks/catechism/.
46. "I. Of the Holy Scripture," *The Westminster Confession of Faith*, paragraph 10, thewestminsterstandard.org/the-westminster-confession/.
47. Rogers and McKim, *Authority and Interpretation of the Bible*; Mark A. Noll, *Between Faith and Criticism: Evangelicals, Scholarship, and the Bible in America* (San Francisco: Harper & Row, 1986).

48. Norman L. Geisler, "Theology. Review of the Debate about the Bible by Stephen Davis," *Journal of the Evangelical Theological Society* 21, no. 3 (1978): 264.

Chapter 6: Dual Revelation and Inerrancy in the Bible and the Creeds
1. I review all the evidence for the content of the book of Job predating written Scripture in my book *Hidden Treasures in the Book of Job: How the Oldest Book in the Bible Answers Today's Scientific Questions* (Grand Rapids, MI: Baker Books, 2011), 30–32.
2. John 14:17; 15:26; 16:13.
3. Peter Enns, *Inspiration and Incarnation: Evangelicals and the Problem of the Old Testament*, 2nd ed. (Grand Rapids, MI: Baker Academic, 2015), 174.
4. Kenton L. Sparks, *God's Word in Human Words: An Evangelical Appropriation of Critical Biblical Scholarship* (Grand Rapids, MI: Baker Academic, 2008), 48.
5. Christian Reformed Church, *Ecumenical Creeds and Reformed Confessions* (Grand Rapids, MI: CRC Publications, 1988), 79.
6. "*Creeds and Confessions*," Reformed Church Press, rca.org/about/theology/creeds-and-confessions/, accessed October 15, 2022.
7. J. Ligon Duncan III, ed., *The Westminster Confession into the 21st Century* (Ross-shire, Scotland: Christian Focus Publications, 2003).
8. "I. Of the Holy Scripture," *The Westminster Confession of Faith*, paragraphs 4, 5, and 8, thewestminsterstandard.org/the-westminster-confession/.

Chapter 7: Concordism and Science
1. Wiktionary, s.v. "concordism," last modified August 28, 2022, en.wiktionary.org/wiki/concordism.
2. Cambridge Dictionary, s.v. "ism," accessed January 5, 2023, dictionary.cambridge.org/us/dictionary/english/ism.
3. David Schatz, "Is There Science in the Torah? An Assessment of Biblical Concordism," *Tradition* 41, no. 2 (summer 2008): 198–244, traditiononline.org/is-there-science-in-the-bible-an-assessment-of-biblical-concordism/.
4. Bernard Ramm, *The Christian View of Science and Scripture* (Grand Rapids, MI: Eerdmans, 1954), 211–218.
5. Ramm, *Christian View of Science and Scripture*, 213, 218.
6. Denis Lamoureux, *Evolution: Scripture and Nature Say Yes!* (Grand Rapids, MI: Zondervan, 2016): 27.
7. John H. Walton and D. Brent Sandy, *The Lost World of Scripture: Ancient Literary Culture and Biblical Authority* (Downers Grove, IL: InterVarsity Press Academic, 2013), 59.
8. Johnny V. Miller and John M. Soden, *In the Beginning . . . We Misunderstood: Interpreting Genesis 1 in Its Original Context* (Grand Rapids, MI: Kregel, 2012), 35.
9. William Lane Craig, "#343 Concordism," *Questions and Answers with Dr. William Lane Craig* (blog), Reasonable Faith with William Lane Craig, November 11, 2013, reasonablefaith.org/writings/question-answer/concordism.
10. William Lane Craig, "Concordism," *The Good Book Blog*, Talbot School of Theology, October 11, 2019, biola.edu/blogs/good-book-blog/2019/concordism.
11. John Walton, *The Lost World of Genesis One: Ancient Cosmology and the Origins Debate* (Downers Grove, IL: InterVarsity Press Academic, 2009), 127.
12. Walton, *The Lost World of Genesis One*, 135.
13. Walton, *The Lost World of Genesis One*, 91; Peter Enns, *The Evolution of Adam: What the Bi-*

ble Does and Doesn't Say About Human Origins (Grand Rapids, MI: Brazos Press, 2012), xiii.
14. Walton, *The Lost World of Genesis One*, 61.
15. Walton, 17.
16. Walton, 105.
17. Peter Enns, *Evolution of Adam*, xiv.
18. Enns, *Evolution of Adam*, ix.
19. Enns, xiv.
20. Walton and Sandy, *Lost World of Scripture*, 225–232.
21. Walton and Sandy, 229.
22. Stanley L. Jaki, *Science and Creation: From Eternal Cycles to an Oscillating Universe* (Edinburgh: Scottish Academic Press, 1974).
23. James L. Kinneavy, *Greek Rhetorical Origins of Christian Faith: An Inquiry* (Oxford, UK: Oxford University Press, 1987). The Greek word for faith, *pistis*, used in the New Testament, means to fully accept and surrender to that which has been shown to be trustworthy.
24. I describe and document this pervasive immutability of the laws of physics in *A Matter of Days*, 2nd ed. (Covina, CA: RTB Press, 2015), 70. See also: Hugh Ross, "New Evidence Further Affirms Biblical Prediction of Unchanging Physics," *Today's New Reason to Believe* (blog), Reasons to Believe, August 9, 2021, reasons.org/explore/blogs/todays-new-reason-to-believe/more-evidence-for-biblical-prediction-of-unchanging-physics; and Hugh Ross, "More Evidences for Biblical Claim of Unchanging Physics," *Today's New Reason to Believe* (blog), Reasons to Believe, June 22, 2020, reasons.org/explore/blogs/todays-new-reason-to-believe/more-evidences-for-biblical-claim-of-unchanging-physics.
25. Peter Enns, *Inspiration and Incarnation: Evangelicals and the Problem of the Old Testament*, 2nd ed. (Grand Rapids, MI: Baker Academic, 2015), 61–152.
26. Kenton L. Sparks, *God's Word in Human Words: An Evangelical Appropriation of Critical Biblical Scholarship* (Grand Rapids, MI: Baker Academic, 2008), 37–374.
27. Bruce Waltke responded to the most significant of Enns's claims of internal biblical contradictions in "Revisiting *Inspiration and Incarnation*," *Westminster Theological Journal* 71, no. 1 (Spring 2009): 83–95, galaxie.com/article/wtj71-1-04. The following books provide exhaustive responses to claims of contradictions in the Bible: Gleason L. Archer, *Encyclopedia of Bible Difficulties* (Grand Rapids, MI: Regency Reference Library, 1982); Norman L. Geisler and Thomas A. Howe, *When Critics Ask: A Popular Handbook on Bible Difficulties* (Wheaton, IL: Victor Press, 1992); Walter C. Kaiser Jr., Peter H. Davids, F. F. Bruce, and Manfred T. Brauch, *Hard Sayings of the Bible* (Downers Grove, IL: InterVarsity Press Academic, 1996).
28. Atheists United, *136 Contradictions in the Bible* (Redmond, WA: Crusade Publications).
29. Brad McCoy, *136 Bible Contradictions . . . Answered* (1985), jubilee-fellowship.com/documents/136BC.pdf.
30. "List of Bible 'Contradictions'," Defending Inerrancy, accessed February 1, 2022, defendinginerrancy.com/bible-solutions/_list_bible_%22contradictions%22.html.
31. During this meeting at UC Berkeley, I observed Torrance's passion to lead physicists to faith in Jesus Christ. Likewise, he saw my passion to bring theologians to faith in Jesus Christ. He joked that mine was the more difficult task.
32. Thomas F. Torrance, *Theology in Reconstruction* (Grand Rapids, MI: Eerdmans, 1965); Thomas F. Torrance, *Theological Science* (London: Oxford University Press, 1969); Thomas F. Torrance, *Christian Theology and Scientific Culture* (New York: Oxford University Press, 1981); Thomas F. Torrance, *Reality and Scientific Theology* (Edinburgh: Scottish Academic Press, 1985); Thomas

F. Torrance, "Ultimate and Penultimate Beliefs in Science," in *Facets of Faith and Science*, vol. 1, *Historiography and Modes of Interaction*, ed. Jitse M. van der Meer (New York: University Press of America, 1996), 151–176.

Chapter 8: Bible-and-Science Models

1. Ian G. Barbour, *Issues in Science and Religion* (London: SCM Press, 1966).
2. Ian G. Barbour, *When Science Meets Religion: Enemies, Strangers, or Partners?* (San Francisco: HarperOne, 2000).
3. John C. Whitcomb and Donald B. DeYoung, *The Moon: Its Creation, Form, and Significance* (Winona Lake, IN: BMH Books, 1978), 69.
4. Henry M. Morris, *The Long War Against God: The History and Impact of the Creation/Evolution Conflict* (Green Forest, AR: Master Books, 2000).
5. Ken Ham, *The Lie: Evolution/Millions of Years* (Green Forest, AR: Master Books, 1987).
6. Three examples would be: Jonathan Sarfati's book, *Refuting Compromise*, 2nd ed. (Atlanta: Creation Book Publishers, 2011); *The John Ankerberg Debate: Young-Earth vs. Old Earth*, featuring Hugh Ross and Kent Hovind (Pasadena, CA: Reasons to Believe, 2000), DVD; and "Hugh Ross vs. Ken Ham – TBN Debate," Sentinel Apologetics, video, 1:13:41, youtube.com/watch?v=w0ZzU_Y8YD0.
7. Stephen Jay Gould, "Nonoverlapping Magisteria," *Natural History* 106, no. 2 (March 1997): 19, also available at caspar.bgsu.edu/~courses/4510/Classes/48A078B0-8402-4995-9161-A2C418612C75_files/Gould_97.pdf.
8. Gould, "Nonoverlapping Magisteria," 19.
9. Gould, 19–20.
10. John Walton, *The Lost World of Genesis One: Ancient Cosmology and the Origins Debate* (Downers Grove, IL: InterVarsity Press Academic, 2009), 127, 135; John H. Walton and D. Brent Sandy, *The Lost World of Scripture: Ancient Literary Culture and Biblical Authority* (Downers Grove, IL: Intervarsity Press Academic, 2013), 48, 50–51, 53–54, 57.
11. Many view the terms "evolutionary creationist" and "theistic evolutionist" as synonymous. However, every evolutionary creationist I've met, but not every theistic evolutionist, interprets all the claimed New Testament miracles both historically and literally. Evolutionary creationists insist that God is involved in the origin and history of Earth's life; theistic evolutionists do not. However, evolutionary creationists also insist that God's involvement is beyond the capacity of scientists to discover. It is this hidden nature of God's involvement in biology that causes many to conclude that there is no substantial distinction between theistic evolution and evolutionary creationism.
12. For a comprehensive comparison of RTB's model to the model of evolutionary creation organization BioLogos, see Kenneth Keathley, J. B. Stump, and Joe Aguirre, eds., *Old-Earth or Evolutionary Creation?: Discussing Origins with Reasons to Believe and BioLogos* (Downers Grove, IL: InterVarsity Press Academic, 2017).
13. For a comprehensive comparison of RTB's model to the framework view and young-earth creationism, see David G. Hagopian, ed., *The Genesis Debate: Three Views on the Days of Creation* (Mission Viejo, CA: Crux Press, 2001).
14. John Walton, *Lost World of Genesis One*, 120.
15. I describe twelve distinct known purposes for God creating and designing the universe the way that he did in my book *Why the Universe Is the Way It Is* (Grand Rapids, MI: Baker Books, 2008), 154–163. There may be other, as-yet-unknown purposes, as well.
16. Job 16:19–21; 19:25; Proverbs 8:22–30; Matthew 25:34; John 1:1–3; 1 Corinthians 2:7.

17. Hugh Ross, *Designed to the Core* (Covina, CA: RTB Press, 2022); Hugh Ross, *Weathering Climate Change: A Fresh Approach* (Covina, CA: RTB Press, 2020); Hugh Ross, *The Creator and the Cosmos: How the Latest Scientific Discoveries Reveal God*, 4th ed. (Covina, CA: RTB Press, 2018); Hugh Ross, *Improbable Planet: How Earth Became Humanity's Home* (Grand Rapids, MI: Baker Books, 2016); Hugh Ross, *More Than a Theory: Revealing a Testable Model for Creation* (Grand Rapids, MI: Baker Books, 2009); Hugh Ross, *Why the Universe Is the Way It Is* (Grand Rapids, MI: Baker Books, 2008).

Chapter 9: Concordance vs. Concordism

1. So pervasive is this claim that I devoted an entire chapter in one of my books to respond to it: Hugh Ross, *Hidden Treasures in the Book of Job: How the Oldest Book in the Bible Answers Today's Scientific Questions* (Grand Rapids, MI: Baker Books, 2011): 175–185.

2. See, for example, Matthew Henry, *Matthew Henry Commentary on the Whole Bible*, s.v. "Job 40" and "Job 41" (1710; Grand Rapids, MI: Zondervan, 1961), biblestudytools.com/commentaries/matthew-henry-complete/.

3. In 1819, William Buckland, vicar, paleontologist, and Oxford University professor of geology and minerology, dug up bones in Stonesfield, England, that he identified as belonging to a huge carnivorous reptilian species that later was named Megalosaurus. Buckland published his findings in William Buckland, "Notice on the Megalosaurus or Great Fossil Lizard of Stonesfield," *Transactions of the Geological Society* 2.1 (1824): 390–396, biodiversitylibrary.org/page/36238855#page/486/mode/1up.

4. Paul R. Renne et al., "Time Scales of Critical Events Around the Cretaceous-Paleogene Boundary," *Science* 339, no. 6120 (February 8, 2013): 684–687, doi:10.1126/science.1230492; Johan Vellekoop et al., "Evidence for Cretaceous-Paleogene Boundary Bolide 'Impact Winter' Conditions from New Jersey, USA," *Geology* 44 (August 2016): 619–622, doi:10.1130/G37961.1; Hugh Ross, "More Evidence of Mass Extinction Event Challenging Evolutionary Models," *Today's New Reason to Believe* (blog), Reasons to Believe, September 19, 2016, reasons.org/explore/blogs/todays-new-reason-to-believe/more-evidence-of-mass-extinction-event-challenging-evolutionary-models.

5. R. Laird Harris, Gleason L. Archer, and Bruce K. Waltke, *Theological Wordbook of the Old Testament*, vol. 1 (Chicago: Moody Press, 1980), 246.

6. The hippopotamus is the most difficult mammal for humans to tame. However, a few have been tamed where a human rescued and raised a baby hippopotamus after its mother had died giving birth to the baby. The only known reptiles that have been tamed to serve, please, and emotionally bond to humans, beyond merely seeking food and body heat from humans, are crocodiles and alligators. Instances of such taming, however, are extremely rare and where they do occur require continual ongoing human attention and contact from the moment they emerge from their eggs. Dinosaurs are reptiles and there is no known evidence of them behaving in a manner akin to the soulish behavior of mammals and birds.

7. An example is Tremper Longman III, *Job* (Grand Rapids, MI: Baker Academic, 2012): 407–408.

8. An example would be the "fantastic" elements William Lane Craig describes in his book *In Quest of the Historical Adam* (Grand Rapids, MI: Eerdmans, 2021), 101–131. New Testament miracles are rarely challenged by conservative Christian theologians since they are unable to be tested by scientific investigation.

9. I provide multiple documented examples in my book *Designed to the Core* (Covina, CA: RTB Press, 2022).

10. Hugh Ross, *The Creator and the Cosmos*, 4th ed. (Covina, CA: RTB Press, 2018), 85–126.
11. Arthur S. Eddington, "The End of the World: From the Standpoint of Mathematical Physics," *Nature* 127 (March 21, 1931): 450, doi:10.1038/127447a0.
12. John Gribbin, "Oscillating Universe Bounces Back," *Nature* 259 (January 1, 1976): 15, doi:10.1038/259015c0.
13. Ross, *The Creator and the Cosmos*, 25–122.
14. Ross, *The Creator and the Cosmos*, 33–76, 85–122.
15. Ross, *The Creator and the Cosmos*, 45–55.
16. Reasons to Believe Scholar Community, *2022 Workshop on Dual Revelation* (June 24–25, 2022), sites.google.com/view/rtbscholarcommunity/workshops?authuser=0.
17. Hugh Ross, "What Does the Bible Say about the Big Bang," *Today's New Reason to Believe* (blog), Reasons to Believe, February 6, 2023, reasons.org/explore/blogs/todays-new-reason-to-believe/what-does-the-bible-say-about-the-big-bang.

Chapter 10: Concordism in Other Faiths
1. N. Krishnaswamy, *The Rig Veda for the First Time Reader*, Veda Vyasa, A Vidya Vriksah Publication, February 1, 2014, chap. 2, vidyavrikshah.org/THERIGVEDA.pdf.
2. Krishnaswamy, *Rig Veda*, chapter 2.
3. John Gribbin, "Oscillating Universe Bounces Back," *Nature* 259 (January 1, 1976): 16, doi:10.1038/259015c0.
4. I explain and document why oscillating universe models no longer are scientifically viable in two of my books: Hugh Ross, *The Creator and the Cosmos: How the Latest Scientific Discoveries Reveal God*, 4th ed. (Covina, CA: RTB Press, 2018), 97–107; Hugh Ross, *The Fingerprint of God*, comm. ed. (Covina, CA: RTB Press, 2010), 79–86.
5. See Krishnaswamy, *Rig Veda*, chapter 8.
6. *Rig Veda* 1.33.8, trans. H. H. Wilson, Wisdom Library, accessed October 18, 2022, wisdomlib.org/hinduism/book/rig-veda-english-translation/d/doc829288.html.
7. *Rig Veda* 10.58.3, accessed February 4, 2022, wisdomlib.org/hinduism/book/rig-veda-english-translation/d/doc839142.html.
8. *Rig Veda* 10.22.14, accessed October 18, 2022, wisdomlib.org/hinduism/book/rig-veda-english-translation/d/doc838746.html.
9. One example is HariBhakt, "Astronomy, Cosmology Science Is Based on Vedas, Vedic Hindu Texts, Samhitas Written Thousands of Years Ago," accessed January 16, 2023, haribhakt.com/cosmic-science-of-today-is-based-on-vedic-hindu-texts-written-thousands-of-years-ago.
10. Ramesh, "20 Reasons Why Hinduism Is Very Scientific Religion," Detechter, accessed February 4, 2022, detechter.com/20-reasons-why-hinduism-is-very-scientific-religion/.
11. Maurice Bucaille, *The Bible, the Qur'an, and Science*, trans. Alastair D. Pannell and Maurice Bucaille (Indianapolis: North American Trust Publications, 1979).
12. Bucaille, *The Bible, the Qur'an, and Science*, 141.
13. Bucaille, 140.
14. William F. Campbell, *The Qur'an and the Bible in the Light of History and Science* (Upper Darby, PA: Middle East Resources, 1992).
15. Arshul Muhammad, "Pulsars and Black Holes—Miracles from the Qur'an," The Lion of Allah (May 19, 2015), accessed January 12, 2023, thelionofallah.wordpress.com/2015/05/19/pulsars-and-black-holes-%E2%80%95-miracles-from-the-quran/; Magdy Abd Al-Shafy, *Pulsars in the Noble Quran*, accessed January 12, 2023, answering-christianity.com/mahir/pulsar_miracle.htm; Harun Yahya, "Pulsars: Pulsating Stars," Miracles of the Qur'an (2004), accessed January

12, 2023, archive.wikiislam.net/wiki/Quran_Predicted_Black_Holes_And_Pulsars; The Last Dialogue, "Mention of Pulsars in The Quran," *Quran on Pulsars* (2022), accessed January 12, 2023, thelastdialogue.org/article/pulsars-mentioned-in-quran/.

16. *Qur'an in English—Clear, Pure, Easy to Read* 86:1–3, trans. Talal Itani, accessed February 3, 2022, clearquran.com/086.html.

17. By itself, the globular cluster 47 Tucanae contains 25 known pulsars. In spite of a lack of an all-sky survey for pulsars, astronomers have discovered over 2,000 pulsars in our Milky Way Galaxy.

18. *Qur'an in English* 55:33, accessed February 3, 2022, clearquran.com/055.html.

19. *Qur'an in English* 17:1, accessed February 3, 2022, clearquran.com/017.html.

20. Sally Tyler, "The False, but Persistent, Rumor That Neil Armstrong Converted to Islam," *Washington Post*, October 12, 2018, washingtonpost.com/outlook/2018/10/12/false-persistent-rumor-that-neil-armstrong-converted-islam/.

21. "Quran on the Moon Landing—What Are the Odds," Answering Islamic Skeptics, accessed February 4, 2022, answeringislamicskeptics.com/moon-landing.html.

22. Martin J. Verhoeven, "Science through Buddhist Eyes: On the Imperfect Harmonizing of Buddhism with Science," *New Atlantis*, no. 39 (Summer 2013): 107–118, thenewatlantis.com/publications/science-through-buddhist-eyes.

23. Paul David Numrich, *The Boundaries of Knowledge in Buddhism, Christianity, and Science* (Göttingen, Germany: Vandenhoeck & Ruprecht, 2008), 35–36.

24. Evan Thompson, *Why I Am Not a Buddhist* (New Haven, CT: Yale University Press, 2020), 36.

25. Tensin Gyatso, *The Universe in a Single Atom: The Convergence of Science and Spirituality* (New York: Morgan Road, 2005), 2.

26. Jehovah's Witnesses, "Does Science Agree with the Bible?: Are there Scientific Errors in the Bible?," Jehovah's Witnesses, accessed February 5, 2022, jw.org/en/bible-teachings/questions/science-and-the-bible/; "What Does Genesis Say?," in *Life—How Did It Get Here? By Evolution or by Creation?* (New York: Watch Tower Bible and Tract Society, 2006), 25–37, Watchtower Online Library, wol.jw.org/en/wol/d/r1/lp-e/1101985013?q=Genesis+1&p=par.

27. Jehovah's Witnesses, "Does Science Agree with the Bible?"; "What Does Genesis Say?," *Life—How Did It Get Here?*, chap. 3; Hugh Ross, *Genesis One: A Scientific Perspective*, 4th ed. (Covina, CA: RTB Press, 2006); Hugh Ross, *The Genesis Question: Scientific Advances and the Accuracy of Genesis*, 2nd ed. (Colorado Springs, CO: NavPress, 2001); Hugh Ross, *Navigating Genesis: A Scientist's Journey through Genesis 1–11* (Covina, CA: RTB Press, 2014).

28. Anthony A. Hoekema, *The Four Major Cults: Christian Science; Jehovah's Witnesses, Mormonism, Seventh-day Adventism* (Grand Rapids, MI: Eerdmans, 1963), 208–209; Robert Countess, *The Jehovah's Witnesses' New Testament: A Critical Analysis of the New World Translation of the Christian Greek Scriptures* (Phillipsburg, NJ: Presbyterian & Reformed, 1982), 91–93.

29. Thomas W. Murphy, "Simply Implausible: DNA and a Mesoamerican Setting for the Book of Mormon," *Dialogue: A Journal of Mormon Thought* 36, no. 4 (Winter 2003b): 109–131, dialoguejournal.com/wp-content/uploads/sbi/articles/Dialogue_V36N04_129.pdf.

30. *Pearl of Great Price*, Abraham 4:1; *Doctrines and Covenants* 93:33, 131:7. See also Richard Lyman Bushman, *Mormonism: A Very Short Introduction* (New York: Oxford University Press, 2008), 71.

31. *Doctrines and Covenants*, Abraham 3:2.

32. In 1994, I wrote a short paper—Hugh Ross, *KOLOB, the Mormon Master Planet* (Covina, CA: RTB Press, 1994), P9401—in which I explained as an astronomer why the description of Kolob in Abraham 3 ruled out the possibility that it could be inhabited by any physical

001b

life-form, let alone the equivalent of human life. I soon thereafter got a letter from Mormon headquarters in Salt Lake City, Utah, written on official LDS stationery. The author complained that I had interpreted Abraham 3 literally when the text, in fact, had been intended to be interpreted figuratively. I sent a letter back stating that my copy of *Doctrines and Covenants* included a facing page to Abraham 3 that encouraged readers to interpret Abraham 3 literally. I wrote that if the Mormon church has changed its position on Abraham 3 or has come out with a new edition of *Doctrines and Covenants* that provides a substantially different description of Kolob, I would issue a public statement to that effect. I never heard from the author again or from anyone else at Mormon headquarters.

33. Matthew 28:18–20; Acts 1:8.

Chapter 11: The Great Genre Debate

1. Michael S. Heiser, *Faithful Study Bible*, ed. John D. Berry et al. (Bellingham, WA: Logos Bible Software, 2012), 2, moreunseenrealm.com/wp-content/uploads/2014/12/Heiser-Genesis-and-Ancient-Near-Eastern-Cosmology-FSB.pdf.
2. William Lane Craig, "The Historical Adam," *First Things* (October 2021), p. 2 of 14, firstthings.com/article/2021/10/the-historical-adam.
3. Peter Enns, *Inspiration and Incarnation: Evangelicals and the Problem of the Old Testament*, 2nd ed. (Grand Rapids, MI: Baker Academic, 2015), 43.
4. Peter Enns, *The Evolution of Adam: What the Bible Does and Doesn't Say about Human Origins* (Grand Rapids, MI: Brazos Press, 2012), 58.
5. Johnny V. Miller and John M. Soden, *In the Beginning . . . We Misunderstood: Interpreting Genesis 1 in Its Original Context* (Grand Rapids, MI: Kregel Publications, 2012), 73.
6. Miller and Soden, *In the Beginning*, 138.
7. Kenton Sparks, *God's Word in Human Words: An Evangelical Appropriation of Critical Biblical Scholarship* (Grand Rapids, MI: Baker Academic, 2008), 213.
8. Dennis R. Venema and Scot McKnight, *Adam and the Genome: Reading Scripture after Genetic Science* (Grand Rapids, MI: Brazos Press, 2017), 97.
9. Bruce K. Waltke, "Myth, History, and the Bible," in *The Enduring Authority of the Christian Scriptures*, ed. D. A. Carson (Grand Rapids, MI: Eerdmans, 2016), 569.
10. John H. Walton, *The Lost World of Genesis One: Ancient Cosmology and the Origins Debate* (Downers Grove, IL: InterVarsity Press Academic, 2009), 12.
11. Tremper Longman III, "What Genesis 1–2 Teaches," in J. Daryl Charles, ed., *Reading Genesis 1–2: An Evangelical Conversation* (Peabody, MA: Henrickson, 2013), 103–128.
12. Bernard F. Batto, *In the Beginning: Essays on Creation Motifs in the Ancient Near East and the Bible* (Winona Lake, IN: Eisenbrauns, 2013); Christopher B. Hays, *Hidden Riches: A Source Book for the Comparative Study of the Hebrew Bible and Ancient Near East* (Louisville, KY: Westminster John Knox Press, 2014); Kenton L. Sparks, *Ancient Texts for the Study of the Hebrew Bible: A Guide to the Background Literature* (Grand Rapids, MI: Baker Academic, 2005); John H. Walton, *Ancient Near Eastern Thought and the Old Testament: Introducing the Conceptual World of the Hebrew Bible* (Grand Rapids, MI: Baker Academic, 2006).
13. Enns, *Inspiration and Incarnation*, 160.
14. John 1:3; 1 Corinthians 8:6; Colossians 1:16–17.
15. Enns, *Inspiration and Incarnation*, 39, 50.
16. William Lane Craig, *In Quest of the Historical Adam: A Biblical and Scientific Exploration* (Grand Rapids, MI: Eerdmans, 2021); Craig, "The Historical Adam," firstthings.com/article/2021/10/the-historical-adam.

17. Joshua 24.
18. Gerhard F. Hasel, "The Polemic Nature of the Genesis Cosmology," *Evangelical Quarterly* 46 (1974): 91.
19. C. S. Lewis, *Of Other Worlds: Essays and Stories*, ed. Walter Hooper (New York: Harcourt, Brace, and Company, 1994), 427.
20. "'Thus Says the Lord' in the Bible," Knowing Jesus, accessed February 12, 2022, bible.knowing-jesus.com/phrases/Thus-Says-the-Lord?page=5.
21. Job 16:19–21; 19:25; Proverbs 8:22–30; Matthew 25:34; John 1:1–3; 1 Corinthians 2:7; 2 Timothy 1:9; Titus 1:2; 1 Peter 1:18–20.
22. I have demonstrated this design for redemption in my books *Designed to the Core* (Covina, CA: RTB Press, 2022); *Improbable Planet* (Grand Rapids, MI: Baker Books, 2016); and *Why the Universe Is the Way It Is* (Grand Rapids, MI: Baker Books, 2008).
23. Peter Enns, *The Evolution of Adam: What the Bible Does and Doesn't Say About Human Origins* (Grand Rapids, MI: Brazos Press, 2012), ix.
24. Francis S. Collins, *The Language of God: A Scientist Presents Evidence for Belief* (New York: Free Press, 2007).
25. See for example Peter Enns, *Inspiration and Incarnation: Evangelicals and the Problem of the Old Testament* (Grand Rapids, MI: Baker, 2005): 43–44.

Chapter 12: Debunking the Dome Myth

1. Ronald L. Ecker, *Dictionary of Science and Creationism* (Buffalo: Prometheus Books, 1990), 56; William D. Reyburn and Euan McG Fry, *A Handbook on Genesis* (Miami: United Bible Societies, 1997), 27; Paul H. Seely, "The Firmament and the Water Above, Part I: The Meaning of Raqia in Gen. 1:6–8," *Westminster Theological Journal* 53, no. 2 (1991): 227–240; John Pye-Smith, *On the Relation between the Holy Scriptures and Some Parts of Geological Science* (London: Jackson and Walford, 1839), 271–273; Andrew Dickson White, *A History of the Warfare of Science and Theology in Christendom*, vol. 1 (New York: Appleton, 1896), 89–91; Harry Emerson Fosdick, *The Modern Use of the Bible* (New York: MacMillan, 1958), 46–47.
2. John H. Walton and D. Brent Sandy, *The Lost World of Scripture: Ancient Literary Culture and Biblical Authority* (Downers Grove, IL: InterVarsity Press Academic, 2013), 57.
3. Walton and Sandy, *Lost World of Scripture*, 53–54.
4. Johnny V. Miller and John M. Soden, *In the Beginning . . . We Misunderstood: Interpreting Genesis 1 in Its Original Context* (Grand Rapids, MI: Kregel Publications, 2012), 102.
5. Miller and Soden, *In the Beginning . . . We Misunderstood*, 160.
6. Peter Enns, *Inspiration and Incarnation: Evangelicals and the Problem of the Old Testament*, 2nd ed. (Grand Rapids, MI: Baker Academic, 2015), 43.
7. Michael S. Heiser, "Genesis and Ancient Near Eastern Cosmology," in *Faithful Study Bible*, ed. John D. Barry et al. (Bellingham, WA: Logos Bible Software, 2012), 2, also available at moreunseenrealm.com/wp-content/uploads/2014/12/Genesis-and-Ancient-Near-Eastern-Cosmology.pdf.
8. Dennis R. Venema and Scot McKnight, *Adam and the Genome: Reading Scripture after Genetic Science* (Grand Rapids, MI: Brazos Press, 2017), 96.
9. Othmar Keel and Silvia Schroer, *Creation: Biblical Theologies in the Context of the Ancient Near East*, trans. Peter T. Daniels (Winona Lake, IN: Eisenbrauns, 2015), 83.
10. Wilfred G. Lambert, "The Cosmology of Sumer and Babylon," in *Ancient Cosmologies*, ed. Carmen Blacker and Michael Loewe (London: George Allen & Unwin, 1975), 42–65.
11. Wayne Horowitz, *Mesopotamian Cosmic Geography* (Winona Lake, IN: Eisenbrauns, 1998).

12. Karl W. Butzer, "Early Hydraulic Civilization in Egypt: A Study in Cultural Ecology" in *Prehistoric Archeology and Ecology*, ed. Karl W. Butzer and Leslie G. Freeman (Chicago: University of Chicago Press, 1976), 39–56, also available at oi.uchicago.edu/sites/oi.uchicago.edu/files/uploads/shared/docs/early_hydraulic.pdf.

13. Carlton T. Lewis and Charles Short, *A Latin Dictionary* (Oxford: Clarendon Press, 1879), s.v. "firmāmentum," also available at perseus.tufts.edu/hopper/text?doc=Perseus:text:1999.04.005 9:entry=firmamentum.

14. Lewis and Short, *Latin Dictionary*.

15. R. Laird Harris, Gleason L. Archer, and Bruce K. Waltke, eds., *Theological Wordbook of the Old Testament*, vol. 2 (Chicago, Moody Press, 1980), 862.

16. Harris, Archer, and Waltke, *Theological Wordbook of the Old Testament*, 862.

17. The first to do so in a scholarly publication was Paul H. Seely, "The Three-Storied Universe," *Journal of the American Scientific Affiliation: Science in Christian Perspective* 21 (March 1969): 18–22.

18. Paul J. Kissling, *Genesis*, vol. 1 (Joplin, MO: College Press Publishing, 2004), 102.

19. Basil, *Hexameron* 3.7, in *Nicene and Post-Nicene Fathers*, ed. Philip Schaff and Henry Wace, trans. Blomfield Jackson, vol. 8, 2nd series (Peabody, MA: Hendrickson, 1999), 69.

20. Thomas Aquinas, *Summa Theologica* 1.5.68, trans. Fathers of the English Dominican Province, rev. Daniel J. Sullivan in *Great Books of the Western World*, ed. Robert Maynard Hutchins, vol. 19 (Chicago: Encyclopaedia Britannica, 1952), 355.

21. 2 Corinthians 12:2–5.

22. Hugh Ross, *Hidden Treasures in the Book of Job: How the Oldest Book in the Bible Answers Today's Scientific Questions* (Grand Rapids, MI: Baker Books, 2011), 78–80, 97–98.

23. Vern S. Poythress, "Rain Water Versus a Heavenly Sea in Genesis 1:6–8," *Westminster Theological Journal* 77 (2015): 181–191.

24. Jeffrey Burton Russell, *Inventing the Flat Earth: Columbus and Modern Historians* (New York: Praeger, 1991); Christine Garwood, *Flat Earth: The History of an Infamous Idea* (New York: Thomas Dunne Books, 2008).

25. Jeffrey Burton Russell, "The Myth of the Flat Earth: Summary," American Scientific Affiliation Conference, Westmont College, Santa Barbara, CA, August 4, 1997, veritas-ucsb.org/library/russell/FlatEarth.html.

Chapter 13: Ancient Near Eastern Science

1. Peter Enns, *Inspiration and Incarnation: Evangelicals and the Problem of the Old Testament*, 2nd ed. (Grand Rapids, MI: Baker Academic, 2015), 29.

2. Peter Enns, *The Evolution of Adam: What the Bible Does and Doesn't Say about Human Origins* (Grand Rapids, MI: Brazos Press, 2012), xiii.

3. John H. Walton and D. Brent Sandy, *The Lost World of Scripture: Ancient Literary Culture and Biblical Authority* (Downers Grove, IL: InterVarsity Press Academic, 2013), 49–51.

4. Walton and Sandy, *The Lost World of Scripture*, 48, 51, 53–54, 57; John H. Walton, *The Lost World of Genesis One: Ancient Cosmology and the Origins Debate* (Downers Grove, IL: InterVarsity Press Academic, 2009), 16.

5. Gerald S. Hawkins and John B. White, *Stonehenge Decoded*, 2nd ed. (New York: Hippocrene Books, 1988); Clive Ruggles, *Astronomy in Prehistoric Britain and Ireland* (New Haven, CT: Yale University Press, 1999); Mike Parker Pearson, *Stonehenge: A New Understanding: Solving the Mysteries of the Greatest Stone Age Monument* (New York: The Experiment, 2013); Peter F. Biehl, "9: Meanings and Functions of Enclosed Places in the European Neolithic: A Contextual

Approach to Cult, Ritual, and Religion," *Archeological Papers of the American Anthropological Association* 21, no. 1 (March 2011): 130–146, doi:10.1111/j.1551-8248.2012.01041.x; Daniel Brown, "An Introductory View on Archaeoastronomy," *Journal of Physics: Conference Series* 685, no. 1 (2016): id. 012001, doi:10.1088/1742-6596/685/1/012001; Alexander Thom and Archibald S. Thom, "Megalithic Astronomy," *Journal of Navigation* 30, no. 1 (January 1977): 1–14, doi:10.1017/S0373463300043575; Alexander Thom, Archibald S. Thom, and Aubrey Burl, *Stone Rows and Standing Stones: Britain, Ireland, and Brittany*, BAR International Series 560 (Oxford: British Archaeological Reports, 1990); J. Donald Fernie, "Marginalia: Alexander Thom and Archaeoastronomy" *American Scientist* 78, no. 5 (September–October 1990): 406–407, jstor.org/stable/29774177?seq=1.

6.   J. McKim Malville et al., "Astronomy of Nabta Playa," *African Skies* 11 (July 2007): 2–7, web. archive.org/web/20110608140813/http://www.saao.ac.za/~wgssa/archive/as11/as11_print. pdf; J. McKim Malville et al., "Megaliths and Neolithic Astronomy in Southern Egypt," *Nature* 392 (April 2, 1998): 488–491, doi:10.1038/33131; Thomas G. Brophy and Paul A. Rosen, "Satellite Imagery Measures of the Astronomically Aligned Megaliths at Nabta Playa," *Mediterranean Archaeology and Archaeometry* 5, no. 1 (June 2005): 15–24, web.archive.org/web/20080229170244/http://www.rhodes.aegean.gr/maa_journal/issues/past%20issues/volume%205%20no1%20june%202005/brophy.pdf.

7.   Frank Ventura, Giorgia Foderà Serio, and Michael Hoskin, "Possible Tally Stones at Mnajdra, Malta," *Journal of the History of Astronomy* 24, no. 3 (August 1, 1993): 171–183, doi:10.1177/002182869302400302; Tore Lomsdalen, "Possible Astronomical Intentionality in the Neolithic Mnajdra South Temple in Malta," in *SEAC 2011 Stars and Stones: Voyages in Archaeoastronomy and Cultural Astronomy: Proceedings of the SEAC 2011 Conference*, BAR International Series 2720 (Oxford: Archaeopress/British Archaeological Reports, May 2015), 182–186.

8.   John M. Steele, *Observations and Predictions of Eclipse Times by Early Astronomers* (Dordrecht, Netherlands: Kluwer Academic Publishers, 2000), doi:10.1007/978-94-015-9528-5; Kevin D. Pang, Kevin K. Yau, and Hung-hsiang Chou, "Astronomical Dating and Statistical Analysis of Ancient Eclipse Data," in S. M. R. Ansari, ed., *History of Oriental Astronomy: Astrophysics and Space Science Library*, vol. 275 (Dordrecht: Springer, 2015), 95–119, doi:10.1007/978-94-015-9862-0_9; J. K. Fotheringham, "A Solution of Ancient Eclipses of the Sun," *Monthly Notices of the Royal Astronomical Society* 81, no. 2 (December 1920): 104–126; Mayank Vahia, "Eclipses in Ancient Cultures" (2014), www2.nao.ac.jp/~mitsurusoma/WS2014/vahia.pdf.

9.   Marshall Clagett, *Greek Science in Antiquity* (New York: Collier Books, 1955), 116–118; Irene Fischer, "Another Look at Eratosthenes' and Posidonius' Determinations of the Earth's Circumference," *Quarterly Journal of the Royal Astronomical Society* 16 (June 1975): 152–167.

10.   Aristotle, "On the Heavens" 2.14, in *The Basic Works of Aristotle*, ed. Richard McKeon (1941; repr., New York: Random House, 1968), 436–437.

11.   Marta Mariotti Lippi et al., "Multistep Food Plant Processing at Grotta Paglicci (Southern Italy) around 32,600 Cal B. P.," *Proceedings of the National Academy of Sciences, USA* 112, no. 39 (September 8, 2015): 12075–12080, doi:10.1073/pnas.1505213112; Ainit Snir et al., "The Origin of Cultivation and Proto-Weeds, Long before Neolithic Farming," *PloS One* 10, no. 7 (July 22, 2015): id. e0131422, doi:10.1371/journal.pone.0131422; Amaia Arranz-Otaegui et al., "Archaeobotanical Evidence Reveals the Origins of Bread 14,400 Years Ago in Northeastern Jordan," *Proceedings of the National Academy of Sciences, USA* 115, no. 31 (July 16, 2018): 7925–7930, doi:10.1073/pnas.1801071115; Hugh Ross, "Confirmation That

Early Humans Were Making Bread," *Today's New Reason to Believe* (blog), Reasons to Believe, August 27, 2018, reasons.org/explore/blogs/todays-new-reason-to-believe/confirmation-that-early-humans-were-making-bread.

12. Alan H. Batten, "Aristarchus of Samos," *Journal of the Royal Astronomical Society of Canada* 75, no. 1 (January 1981): 29–35; Alan W. Hirshfeld, "The Triangles of Aristarchus," *The Mathematics Teacher* 97, no. 4 (April 2004): 228–231, doi:10.5951/MT.97.4.0448; Helge S. Kragh, *Conceptions of Cosmos: From Myths to the Accelerating Universe: A History of Cosmology* (New York: Oxford University Press, 2007), 26.

13. Batten, "Aristarchus of Samos"; Hirshfeld, "The Triangles of Aristarchus"; Kragh, *Conceptions of Cosmos.*

14. J. L. E. Dreyer, *History of the Planetary Systems from Thales to Kepler* (Cambridge, UK: Cambridge University Press, 1906), 135–148.

15. L. Jetsu et al., "Did the Ancient Egyptians Record the Period of the Eclipsing Binary Algol— The Raging One?," *Astrophysical Journal* 773, no. 1 (August 10, 2013): id. 1, doi:10.1088/0004-637X/773/1/1; Hugh Ross, "Ancient Egyptian Astronomy Yields New Discoveries," *Today's New Reason to Believe* (blog), Reasons to Believe, December 1, 2013, reasons.org/explore/publications/nrtb-e-zine/ancient-egyptian-astronomy-yields-new-discoveries.

16. North Greenland Ice Core Project members, "High-Resolution Record of Northern Hemisphere Climate Extending in to the Last Interglacial Period," *Nature* 431 (September 9, 2004): 147–151, doi:10.1038/nature02805.

17. Jochen Schmidt et al., "Carbon Isotope Constraints on the Deglacial CO_2 Rise from Ice Cores," *Science* 336, no. 6082 (May 11, 2012): 711–714, doi:10.1126/science.1217161; J. R. Petit et al., "Climate and Atmospheric History of the Past 420,000 Years from the Vostok Ice Core, Antarctica," *Nature* 399 (June 3, 1999): 433, doi:10.1038/20859.

18. Shaun A. Marcott et al., "A Reconstruction of Regional and Global Temperature for the Past 11,300 Years," *Science* 339 (March 8, 2013): 1198–1201, doi:10.1126/science.1228026; Carme Huguet et al., "Reconstruction of Sea Surface Temperature Variations in the Arabian Sea over the Last 23 kyr Using Organic Proxies (TEX_{86} and $U_{37}^{K'}$)," *Paleoceanography and Paleoclimatology* 21, no. 3 (September 2006): id. PA3003, doi:10.1029/2005PA001215; Stefan Schouten et al., "Distributional Variations in Marine Crenarchaeotal Membrane Lipids: A New Tool for Reconstructing Sea Water Temperatures?," *Earth and Planetary Science Letters* 204, no. 1–2 (November 2002): 265–274, doi:10.1016/S0012-821X(02)00979-2; Andy May, "A Holocene Temperature Reconstruction Part 4: The Global Reconstruction," *Watts Up With That?* (blog), June 9, 2017, wattsupwiththat.com/2017/06/09/a-holocene-temperature-reconstruction-part-4-the-global-reconstruction/; Andy May, "A Holocene Temperature Reconstruction Part 1: The Antarctic," *Watts Up With That?* (blog), June 1, 2017, wattsupwiththat.com/2017/06/01/a-holocene-temperature-reconstruction-part-1-the-antarctic/.

19. Matthew B. Osman et al., "Globally Resolved Surface Temperatures Since the Last Glacial Maximum," *Nature* 599 (November 11, 2021): 239–244, doi:10.1038/s41586-021-03984-4.

20. Daniel 1:4, 17.

Chapter 14: Biblical Cues to Earth's Age

1. Hugh Ross, *A Matter of Days*, 2nd ed. (Covina, CA: RTB Press, 2015); Hugh Ross, *Navigating Genesis* (Covina, CA: RTB Press, 2014); Stanley N. Gundry and J. B. Stump, *Four Views on Creation, Evolution, and Intelligent Design* (Grand Rapids, MI: Zondervan, 2017).

2. R. Laird Harris, Gleason L. Archer, and Bruce K. Waltke, *Theological Wordbook of the Old*

Testament, vol. 2 (Chicago: Moody, 1980), 730.

3.   Francis Brown, S. R. Driver, and Charles A. Briggs, *The Brown-Driver-Briggs Hebrew and English Lexicon* (1906; repr., Peabody, MA: Hendrickson, 1997), 822.

4.   Henry M. Morris, "Adam and the Animals," *Acts & Facts* 20, no. 2 (February 1, 1991), icr. org/article/339.

5.   C. John Collins, *Genesis 1–4: A Linguistic, Literary, and Theological Commentary* (Phillipsburg, NJ: P&R Publishing, 2006), 51; Rodney Whitefield, *Reading Genesis One: Comparing Biblical Hebrew with English Translation* (San Jose, CA: R. Whitefield Publisher, 2011), 10–11.

6.   Collins, *Genesis 1–4*.

7.   I have put this suggestion to the test with people who have had little or no exposure to modern science, the Bible, or to young-earth creationists. The majority concluded that Genesis was not teaching that creation was completed in only 144 hours.

8.   Irenaeus, "Against Heresies" 5.23.2, in *The Ante-Nicene Fathers*, ed. Alexander Roberts and James Donaldson, vol. 1, *Apostolic Fathers, Justin Martyr and Irenaeus* (1885; repr., Grand Rapids, MI: Eerdmans, 1981): 551–552.

9.   Augustine, "The Literal Meaning of Genesis" 5.2, in *Ancient Christian Writers: The Works of the Fathers in Translation*, ed. Johannes Quasten, Walter J. Burghardt, and Thomas C. Lawler, trans. and annotated by John Hammond Taylor, vol. 1 (New York: Newman Press, 1982), 148.

10. Augustine, "The Literal Meaning of Genesis" 4.27, 135.

11. Augustine, *Confessions* 13.51, in *The Fathers of the Church*, trans. Vernon J. Bourke, vol. 21 (New York: Fathers of the Church, 1953), 455.

12. John Millam, "Coming to Grips with the Early Church Fathers' Perspective on Genesis, Part 5 (of 5)," *Today's New Reason to Believe* (blog), Reasons to Believe, October 6, 2011, reasons.org/explore/publications/articles/coming-to-grips-with-the-early-church-fathers-perspective-on-genesis-part-5-of-5.

13. Travis R. Freeman, "Do the Genesis 5 and 11 Genealogies Contain Gaps?," in *Coming to Grips with Genesis: Biblical Authority and the Age of the Earth*, ed. Terry Mortenson and Thane H. Ury (Green Forest, AR: Master Books, 2008), 283–313; Jonathan Sarfati, *Refuting Compromise: A Biblical and Scientific Refutation of "Progressive Creationism" (Billions of Years), as Popularized by Astronomer Hugh Ross*, 2nd ed. (Atlanta: Creation Book Publishers, 2011), 283–293.

14. Freeman, "Genesis 5 and 11 Genealogies," 308.

15. Freeman, 308.

16. Harris, Archer, and Waltke, *Theological Workbook*, vol. 1, 5–6.

17. Harris, Archer, and Waltke, 5–6.

18. Harris, Archer, and Waltke, 5–6.

19. Daniel 5:9–11, 18–22.

20. Luke 3:35–36.

21. Exodus 12:40; 1 Kings 6:1.

22. Henry M. Morris, *The Genesis Record: A Scientific and Devotional Commentary on the Book of Beginnings* (Grand Rapids, MI: Baker Books, 1976): 127; Henry M. Morris, "The Logic of Biblical Creation," *Impact*, no. 205 (July 1990): iii–iv; Scott M. Huse, *The Collapse of Evolution*, 2nd ed. (Grand Rapids, MI: Baker, 1993), 78; Ian T. Taylor, *In the Minds of Men: Darwin and the New World Order* (Toronto: TFE Publishing, 1984), 294; Russell Humphreys, *Starlight and Time: Solving the Puzzle of Distant Starlight in a Young Universe* (Green Forest, AR: Master Books, 1994), 32–34; Lambert Dolphin, "The Uniqueness of Creation Week,"

accessed January 13, 2023, ldolphin.org/Unique.html; Ken Ham and Jonathan Sarfati, *Why Is There Death and Suffering?* Answers in Genesis, accessed January 13, 2023, academia. edu/5062699/Why_is_there_death_and_Suffering.

23. Michael T. Murphy et al., "Fundamental Physics with ESPRESSO: Precise Limit on Variations in the Fine-Structure Constant towards the Bright Quasar HE 051-4414," *Astronomy and Astrophysics* 658 (February 2022): id. A123, doi:10.1051/0004-6361/202142257; S. Muller et al., "A Study of Submillimeter Methanol Absorption toward PKS 1830-211: Excitation, Invariance of the Proton-Electron Mass Ratio, and Systematics," *Astronomy and Astrophysics* 652 (August 2021): id. A5, doi:10.1051/0004-6361/202140531; S. A. Levshakov et al., "An Upper Limit to the Variation in the Fundamental Constants at Redshift $z = 5.2$," *Astronomy and Astrophysics* 540 (April 2012), id. 9, doi:10.1051/0004-6361/201219042; S. A. Levshakov and M. G. Kozlov, "Fine-Structure Transitions as a Tool for Studying Variation of α at High Redshifts," *Monthly Notices of the Royal Astronomical Society: Letters* 469, no. 1 (July 2017): L16–L19, doi:10.1093/mnrasl/slx049; Michael T. Murphy, Adrian L. Malec, and J. Xavier Prochaska, "Precise Limits on Cosmological Variability of the Fine-Structure Constant with Zinc and Chromium Quasar Absorption Lines," *Monthly Notices of the Royal Astronomical Society* 461, no. 3 (September 21, 2016): 2461–2479, doi:10.1093/mnras/ stw1482; T. D. Le, "A Study of Space-Time Variation of the Gravitational Constant Using High-Resolution Quasar Spectra," *General Relativity and Gravitation* 53, no. 4 (April 2021): id. 37, doi:10.1007/s10714-021-02803-5; Jane H. MacGibbon, "Black Hole Constraints on Varying Fundamental Constants," *Physical Review Letters* 99, no. 6 (August 2007): id. 061301, doi:10.1103/PhysRevLett.99.061301.

24. Larry Vardiman, Andrew A. Snelling, and Eugene F. Chaffin, eds., *Radioisotopes and the Age of the Earth: A Young-Earth Creationist Research Initiative*, vol. 1 (El Cajon, CA: Institute for Creation Research; St. Joseph, MO: Creation Research Society, 2000), 42–44, 306–307, 312–313, 316–318, 334–337, 374, vol. 2 (El Cajon, CA: Institute for Creation Research; St. Joseph, MO: Creation Research Society, 2005), 736–738.

25. Vardiman, Snelling, and Chaffin, eds., *Radioisotopes and the Age of the Earth*, vol. 2, 738.

26. Vardiman, Snelling, and Chaffin, eds., *Radioisotopes and the Age of the Earth*, vol. 1, 337.

27. Vardiman, Snelling, and Chaffin, eds., *Radioisotopes and the Age of the Earth*, vol. 1, 307.

28. I have had two live radio debates with young-earth creationist scientists John Morris and Duane Gish. In these debates, the moderator John Stewart asked Morris and Gish whether they or any of their associates had ever met or heard of a scientist who became persuaded that the universe or Earth is only thousands of years old, based on scientific evidence and without any reference to an interpretation of the Bible. Both Gish and Morris unequivocally answered no. The statements by John Stewart and John Morris were made on the radio program *Bible on the Line*, aired on KKLA, North Hollywood, California, December 6, 1987. The statements by John Stewart and Duane Gish were made on the same radio program about a year later. Over a five-year period (1987–1993), John Stewart asked the same question he posed to John Morris and Duane Gish to several other young-earth creationist leaders in various radio interviews he conducted. He always received the same answer: no. John Stewart informed me of the results of his survey while I was on his radio show, *John Stewart Live*, KBRT, Costa Mesa, California, on April 14, 1993.

29. Ken Ham, Jonathan Sarfati, and Carl Wieland, *The Revised and Expanded Answers Book*, ed. Don Batten (Green Forest, AR: Master Books, 2000), 256–257; Douglas F. Kelly, *Creation and Change* (Geanies House, Fearn, Ross-shire, UK: Mentor, 1997), 97–98, 228–231; Henry

M. Morris, "Recent Creation Is a Vital Doctrine," *Impact*, no. 132 (June 1, 1984): 2.

Chapter 15: Science in Continual Flux?

1. John H. Walton, *The Lost World of Genesis One: Ancient Cosmology and the Origins Debate* (Downers Grove, IL: IVP Academic, 2009), 17.
2. Walton, *The Lost World of Genesis One*, 105.
3. Walton, 61.
4. Walton, 105.
5. Cornelis Van Dam, *In the Beginning: Listening to Genesis 1 and 2* (Grand Rapids, MI: Reformation Heritage Books, 2021), 46–47.
6. Thomas S. Kuhn, *The Essential Tension: Selected Studies in Scientific Tradition and Change* (Chicago: University of Chicago Press, 1977).
7. "I. Of the Holy Scripture," *The Westminster Confession of Faith*, paragraph 7, thewestminsterstandard.org/the-westminster-confession/.
8. 2 Peter 3:16.
9. Isaiah 55:9.
10. Walton, 17, 105; Johnny V. Miller and John M. Soden, *In the Beginning . . . We Misunderstood: Interpreting Genesis 1 in Its Original Context* (Grand Rapids, MI: Kregel Publications, 2012), 40; John H. Walton and D. Brent Sandy, *The Lost World of Scripture: Ancient Literary Culture and Biblical Authority* (Downers Grove, IL: InterVarsity Press Academic, 2013), 52.
11. Deuteronomy 4:2; Proverbs 30:5–6; Revelation 22:18–20.
12. I wrote about the COBE satellite discovery and its importance in scientifically establishing the validity of the big bang model in my book, *The Creator and the Cosmos*, 4th ed. (Covina, CA: RTB Press, 2018), 33–42.
13. Stephen Strauss, "An Innocent's Guide to the Big Bang Theory: Fingerprint in Space Left by the Universe as a Baby Still Has Doubters Hurling Stones," *Globe and Mail* (Toronto), April 25, 1992. Burbidge repeated his comment about "the First Church of Christ of the Big Bang" on the radio talk show *Live from LA* with host Phil Reid on KKLA in Los Angeles, CA. The program aired May 11, 1992 and included pre-recorded comments on the big bang ripples discovery from Drs. G. De Amici, Geoffrey Burbidge, Russell Humphreys, and Hugh Ross.
14. This evidence is described and documented in my book *The Creator and the Cosmos*, 4th ed., 33–198 and in the following articles: Hugh Ross, "How Hot a Bang Was the Big Bang," *Today's New Reason to Believe* (blog), Reasons to Believe, April 4, 2022, reasons.org/explore/blogs/todays-new-reason-to-believe/how-hot-a-bang-was-the-big-bang; Hugh Ross, "Dating the Cosmic Dawn and Testing Creation," *Today's New Reason to Believe* (blog), Reasons to Believe, September 13, 2021, reasons.org/explore/blogs/todays-new-reason-to-believe/dating-the-cosmic-dawn-cosmic-creation-test; Hugh Ross, "Resolving Hubble Constant and Creation Tension," *Today's New Reason to Believe* (blog), Reasons to Believe, August 2, 2021, reasons.org/explore/blogs/todays-new-reason-to-believe/resolving-the-hubble-constant-tension; Hugh Ross, "New Telescope Observations Provide Cosmic Creation Confirmations," *Today's New Reason to Believe* (blog), Reasons to Believe, February 22, 2021, reasons.org/explore/blogs/todays-new-reason-to-believe/new-telescope-observations-provide-cosmic-creation-confirmations; Hugh Ross, "Does a Cosmic Cold Spot Challenge Creation?," *Today's New Reason to Believe* (blog), Reasons to Believe, April 13, 2020, reasons.org/explore/blogs/todays-new-reason-to-believe/does-a-cosmic-cold-spot-challenge-creation; Hugh Ross, "The End of Cosmic Greatness and the Beginning of Life," *Today's New Reason to Believe* (blog), Reasons to Believe, March 9, 2020, reasons.org/explore/blogs/todays-new-reason-to-believe/the-end-of-cosmic-greatness-and-the-beginning-of-life; Hugh Ross, "Cosmic Inflation Confirmed

and Why We Need It," *Today's New Reason to Believe* (blog), Reasons to Believe, February 24, 2020, reasons.org/explore/blogs/todays-new-reason-to-believe/cosmic-inflation-confirmed-and-why-we-need-it; Hugh Ross, "Record-Breaking Star Gives More Evidence for Big Bang Creation Model," *Today's New Reason to Believe* (blog), Reasons to Believe, November 11, 2019, reasons.org/explore/blogs/todays-new-reason-to-believe/record-breaking-star-gives-more-evidence-for-big-bang-creation-model; Hugh Ross, "Gamma Ray Flares Constrain Beginning-of-Universe Speculations," *Today's New Reason to Believe* (blog), Reasons to Believe, August 12, 2019, reasons.org/explore/blogs/todays-new-reason-to-believe/gamma-ray-flares-constrain-beginning-of-universe-speculations; Hugh Ross, "Cosmic Creation Model Passes Key Helium Abundance Test," *Today's New Reason to Believe* (blog), Reasons to Believe, July 8, 2019, reasons.org/explore/blogs/todays-new-reason-to-believe/cosmic-creation-model-passes-key-helium-abundance-test; Hugh Ross, "Cosmic Creation Model Passes Another Test," *Today's New Reason to Believe* (blog), Reasons to Believe, January 21, 2019, reasons.org/explore/blogs/todays-new-reason-to-believe/cosmic-creation-model-passes-another-test.

Chapter 16: The Historicity of Genesis 1–11

1. See, for example, John N. Oswalt, *The Bible Among the Myths: Unique Revelation or Just Ancient Literature* (Grand Rapids, MI: Zondervan, 2009).
2. Peter Enns, *The Evolution of Adam: What the Bible Does and Doesn't Say About Human Origins* (Grand Rapids, MI: Brazos, 2012), 79.
3. Hugh Ross, *Navigating Genesis: A Scientist's Journey through Genesis 1–11* (Covina, CA: RTB Press, 2014), 25–84.
4. Hugh Ross, *A Matter of Days*, 2nd ed. (Covina, CA: RTB Press, 2015).
5. R. Laird Harris, Gleason L. Archer, and Bruce K. Waltke, *Theological Wordbook of the Old Testament*, vol. 1 (Chicago: Moody Press, 1980), 199.
6. Harris, Archer, and Waltke, *Theological Wordbook*, 252–253.
7. Harris, Archer, and Waltke, 688–689.
8. Harris, Archer, and Waltke, 734.
9. Isaac Newton, *The Correspondence of Isaac Newton*, ed. H. W. Turnbull, vol. 2, 1676–1687, (Cambridge, UK: Cambridge University Press, 1960), 234–235, 319, 330–334.
10. Thomas Chalmers, *On the Power, Wisdom and Goodness of God as Manifested in the Adaptation of External Nature to the Moral and Intellectual Constitution of Man*, vol. 1 (London: William Pickering, 1833; New York: Cambridge University Press, 2009).
11. Peter Bayne, *The Life and Letters of Hugh Miller*, vol. 2 (London: Strahan & Co., Publishers, 1871), 326–339, archive.org/details/lifelettersofhug02baynuoft/page/440/mode/2up; Hugh Miller, *The Footprints of the Creator* (Boston: Gould and Lincoln, 1850).
12. My meetings with Gleason Archer during the 1991 Kantzer Lectures in Systematic Theology led to us partnering with one another to write the contributions for the day-age view interpretation of Genesis 1 in the book David G. Hagopian, ed., *The Genesis Debate: Three Views on the Days of Creation* (Mission Viejo, CA: Crux Press, 2001).
13. William Lane Craig, *In Quest of the Historical Adam: A Biblical and Scientific Exploration* (Grand Rapids, MI: Eerdmans, 2021), 111.
14. Jean Astruc, *Conjectures sur les mémoirs originaux dont il parait que Moise s'est servi pour composer la Genèse, avec des remarques qui appuient ou éclaircissens ces conjectures* (Bruxelles, Fricx, 1753): 378, 439; Eamonn O'Doherty. "The Conjectures of Jean Astruc, 1753," *Catholic Biblical Quarterly*, 15 (1953): 300–304; Howard Osgood, "Jean Astruc," *Presbyterian and Reformed Review* 3 (1892): 97–101.

15. Robert Boyle, *The Excellence of Theology, Compared with Natural Philosophy*, I.1 The Nobility of Theology's Object: The Universe (1674), earlymoderntexts.com/assets/pdfs/boyle1674b. pdf, 11.

16. Ross, *Navigating Genesis*, 158.

Chapter 17: Recent Scientific Corroboration

1. Robert C. Newman, Perry G. Phillips, and Herman J. Eckelmann, *Genesis One and the Origin of the Earth*, 2nd ed. (Gloucester, MA: Interdisciplinary Biblical Research Institute, 2007); John C. Lennox, *Seven Days That Divide the World: The Beginning According to Genesis and Science* (Grand Rapids, MI: Zondervan, 2011); C. John Collins, *Genesis 1–4: A Linguistic, Literary, and Theological Commentary* (Phillipsburg, NJ: P & R Publishing, 2005); C. John Collins, *Reading Genesis Well: Navigating History, Science, and Truth in Genesis 1–11* (Grand Rapids, MI: Zondervan Academic, 2018).

2. Hugh Ross, *Navigating Genesis: A Scientist's Journey through Genesis 1–11* (Covina, CA: RTB Press, 2014); *Hugh Ross, A Matter of Days*, 2nd ed. (Covina, CA: RTB Press, 2015); Hugh Ross, *Improbable Planet* (Grand Rapids, MI: Baker Books, 2016); J. Ligon Duncan III, David W. Hall, Hugh Ross, Gleason Archer, Lee Irons, and Meredith G. Kline, *The Genesis Debate: Three Views on the Days of Creation*, ed. David G. Hagopian (Mission Viejo, CA: Crux Press, 2000).

3. Sarah M. Hörst et al., "Exploring the Atmosphere of Neoproterozoic Earth: The Effect of O_2 on Haze Formation and Composition," *Astrophysical Journal* 858, no. 2 (May 10, 2018): id.119, doi:10.3847/1538-4357/aabd7d.

4. A. J. Kaufman and S. Xiao, "High CO_2 Levels in the Proterozoic Atmosphere Estimated from Analyses of Individual Microfossils," *Nature* 425 (September 18, 2003): 279–282, doi:10.1038/nature01902; Linda C. Kah and Robert Riding, "Mesoproterozoic Carbon Dioxide Levels Inferred from Calcified Cyanobacteria," *Geology* 35, no. 9 (September 2007): 799–802, doi:10.1130/G23680A.1; James F. Kasting, "Theoretical Constraints on Oxygen and Carbon Dioxide Concentrations in the Precambrian Atmosphere," *Precambrian Research* 34, nos. 3–4 (January 1987): 205–229, doi:10.1016/0301-9268(87)90001-5; K. Zahnle, M. Claire, and D. Catling, "The Loss of Mass-Independent Fractionation in Sulfur Due to a Palaeoproterozoic Collapse of Atmospheric Methane," *Geobiology* 4, no. 4 (December 2006): 271–283, doi:10.1111/j.1472-4669.2006.00085.x; Alexander A. Pavlov et al., "Greenhouse Warming by CH_4 in the Atmosphere of Early Earth," *Journal of Geophysical Research: Planets* 105, no. E5 (May 25, 2000): 11,981–11,990, doi:10.1029/1999JE001134; Ross, *Improbable Planet*, 108–197.

5. Hörst et al., "Exploring the Atmosphere of Neoproterozoic Earth," 5.

6. Hörst et al., 1.

7. Sally P. Leys and Amanda S. Kahn, "Oxygen and the Energetic Requirements of the First Multicellular Animals," *Integrative and Comparative Biology* 58, no. 4 (October 2018): 666–676, doi:10.1093/icb/icy051.

8. Michael Bau and Andrea Koschinsky, "Oxidative Scavenging of Cerium on Hydrous Fe Oxide: Evidence from the Distribution of Rare Earth Elements and Yttrium between Fe Oxides and Mn Oxides in Hydrogenetic Ferromanganese Crusts," *Geochemical Journal* 43, no. 1 (2009): 37–47, doi:10.2343/geochemj.1.0005.

9. Bau and Koschinsky, "Oxidative Scavenging of Cerium," 37–47; James W. Moflett, "The Relationship between Cerium and Manganese Oxidation in the Marine Environment," *Limnology and Oceanography* 39, no. 6 (September 1994): 1309–1318, doi:10.4319/lo.1994.39.6.1309.

10. Eric J. Bellefroid et al., "Constraints on the Paleoproterozoic Atmospheric Oxygen Levels," *Proceedings of the National Academy of Sciences USA* 115, no. 32 (July 23, 2018): 8104–8109, doi:10.1073/pnas.1806216115; Xiao-Ming Liu et al., "A Persistently Low Level of Atmospheric Oxygen in Earth's Middle Age," *Nature Communications* 12 (January 13, 2021): id. 351, doi:10.1038/s41467-020-29484 7.

11. Noah J. Planavsky et al., "Low Mid-Proterozoic Atmospheric Oxygen Levels and the Delayed Rise of Animals," *Science* 346, no. 6209 (October 31, 2014): 635–638, doi:10.1126/science.1258410; Devon B. Cole et al., "A Shale-Hosted Cr Isotope Record of Low Atmospheric Oxygen during the Proterozoic," *Geology* 44, no. 7 (July 1, 2016): 555–558, doi:10.1130/G37787.1.

12. Donald E. Canfield et al., "Highly Fractionated Chromium Isotopes in Mesoproterozoic-Aged Shales and Atmospheric Oxygen," *Nature Communications* 9 (July 20, 2018): id. 2871, doi:10.1038/s41467-018-05263-9; G. J. Gilleaudeau et al., "Oxygenation of the Mid-Proterozoic Atmosphere: Clues from Chromium Isotopes in Carbonates," *Geochemistry Perspectives Letters* 2, no. 2 (May 24, 2016): 178–187, doi:10.7185/geochemlet.1618.

13. Changle Wang et al., "Strong Evidence for a Weakly Oxygenated Ocean-Atmosphere System during the Proterozoic," *Proceedings of the National Academy of Sciences USA* 119, no. 6 (January 2022): doi:10.1073/pnas.2116101119; Hugh Ross, "Oxygen and Carbon Dioxide History Affirms Divine Creation," *Today's New Reason to Believe* (blog), Reasons to Believe, April 18, 2022, reasons.org/explore/blogs/todays-new-reason-to-believe/oxygen-history-affirms-divine-creation.

14. Wang et al., "Strong Evidence," 6.

15. Hans O. Pörtner, Martina Langenbuch, and Anke Reipschläger, "Biological Impact of Elevated Ocean CO_2 Concentrations: Lessons from Animal Physiology and Earth History," *Journal of Oceanography* 60, no. 4 (August 2004): 705–718, doi:10.1007/s10872-004-5763-0.

16. Zaher S. Azzam et al., "The Physiological and Molecular Effects of Elevated CO_2 Levels," *Cell Cycle* 9, no. 8 (April 20, 2010): 1528–1532, doi:10.4161/cc.9.8.11196; Kris Permentier et al., "Carbon Dioxide Poisoning: A Literature Review of an Often-Forgotten Cause of Intoxication in the Emergency Department," *International Journal of Emergency Medicine* 10 (April 4, 2017): id. 14, p. 1, doi:10.1186/s12245-017-0142-y.

17. Stephan V. Sobolev and Michael Brown, "Surface Erosion Events Controlled the Evolution of Plate Tectonics on Earth," *Nature* 570 (June 5, 2019): 52–57, doi:10.1038/s41586-019-1258-4; Hugh Ross, "Why Do We Need Snowball Events?," *Today's New Reason to Believe* (blog), Reasons to Believe, August 5, 2019, reasons.org/explore/blogs/todays-new-reason-to-believe/why-do-we-need-snowball-events.

18. Douglas H. Erwin, James W. Valentine, and J. John Sepkoski Jr., "A Comparative Study of Diversification Events: The Early Paleozoic versus the Mesozoic," *Evolution* 41, no. 6 (November 1, 1987): 1183, doi:10.2307/2409086.

19. Ulf Linnemann et al., "New High-Resolution Age Data from the Ediacaran-Cambrian Boundary Indicate Rapid, Ecologically Driven Onset of the Cambrian Explosion," *Terra Nova* 31, no. 1 (February 2019): 49–58, doi:10.1111/ter.12368.

20. Kevin J. Peterson, Michael R. Dietrich, and Mark A. McPeek, "MicroRNAs and Metazoan Macroevolution: Insights into Canalization, Complexity, and the Cambrian Explosion," *BioEssays* 31, no. 7 (July 2009): 737, doi:10.1002/bies.200900033.

21. J. A. Jacobs, R. D. Russell, and J. Tuzo Wilson, *Physics and Geology* (New York: McGraw-Hill, 1959).

22. H. W. Nesbitt and G. M. Young, "Early Proterozoic Climates and Plate Motions In-

ferred from Major Element Chemistry of Lutites," *Nature* 299 (October 1982): 715–717, doi:10.1038/299715a0.

23.   J. W. Valley et al., "4.4 Billion Years of Crustal Maturation: Oxygen Isotope Ratios of Magmati Zircon," *Contributions to Mineralogy and Petrology* 150 (December 2005): 561–580, doi:10.1007/s00410-005-0025-8; I. N. Bindeman, A. Bekker, and D. O. Zakharov, "Oxygen Isotope Perspective on Crustal Evolution on Early Earth: A Record of Precambrian Shale with Emphasis on Paleoproterozoic Glaciation and Great Oxygenation Event," *Earth and Planetary Science Letters* 437 (March 1, 2016): 101–113, doi:10.1016/j.epsl.2015.12.029.

24.   I. N. Bindeman et al., "Rapid Emergence of Subaerial Landmasses and Onset of Modern Hydrologic Cycle 2.5 Billion Years Ago," *Nature* 557 (May 23, 2018): 545–548, doi:10.1038/s41586-018-0131-1.

25.   Ross, *Improbable Planet*, 144.

26.   Ross, 160–162.

27.   Erica L. McCormick et al., "Widespread Woody Plant Use of Water Stored in Bedrock," *Nature* 597, no. 7875 (September 9, 2021): 225–229, doi:10.1038/s41586-021-03761-3.

28.   Adrian L. Melott and Richard K. Bambach, "Do Periodicities in Extinction—with Possible Astronomical Connections—Survive a Revision of the Geological Timescale?," *Astrophysical Journal* 773, no. 1 (August 2013): id. 6, doi:10.1088/0004-637X/773/1/6.

29.   John J. Matese et al., "Why We Study the Geological Record for Evidence of the Solar Oscillation about the Galactic Midplane," *Earth, Moon, and Planets* 72 (February 1996): 7–12, doi:10.1007/BF00117495; John J. Matese et al., "Periodic Modulation of the Oort Cloud Flux by the Adiabatically Changing Galactic Tide," *Icarus* 116, no. 2 (August 1995): 255–268, doi:10.1006/icar.1995.1124; Michael R. Rampino, "Disc Dark Matter in the Galaxy and Potential Cycles of Extraterrestrial Impacts, Mass Extinctions, and Geological Events," *Monthly Notices of the Royal Astronomical Society* 448, no. 2 (April 1, 2015): 1816–1820, doi:10.1093/mnras/stu2708.

Chapter 18: The Original Human Pair and Original Sin

1.   Peter Enns, *The Evolution of Adam: What the Bible Does and Doesn't Say about Human Origins* (Grand Rapids, MI: Brazos Press, 2012), ix.

2.   Enns, *Evolution of Adam*, 82.

3.   Enns, 138.

4.   Enns, 82.

5.   Enns, 125.

6.   Enns, 81.

7.   Enns, 81.

8.   John H. Walton, *The Lost World of Adam and Eve: Genesis 2–3 and the Human Origins Debate* (Downers Grove, IL: InterVarsity Press Academic, 2015), 169.

9.   Walton, *Lost World of Adam and Eve*, 181.

10.   N. T. Wright, "Excursus on Paul's Use of Adam," in Walton, *The Lost World of Adam and Eve*, 177–178.

11.   Dennis R. Venema and Scot McKnight, *Adam and the Genome: Reading Scripture after Genetic Science* (Grand Rapids, MI: Brazos Press, 2017), 145.

12.   Venema and McKnight, *Adam and the Genome*, 145.

13.   Venema and McKnight, 187.

14.   Venema and McKnight, 189.

15.   Venema and McKnight, 189.

16. Venema and McKnight, 189.

17. Tremper Longman III, foreword to *Adam and the Genome*, by Venema and McKnight, vii.

18. William Lane Craig, *In Quest of the Historical Adam: A Biblical and Scientific Exploration* (Grand Rapids, MI: Eerdmans, 2021), 378.

19. Craig, *Historical Adam*, 380.

20. Ash Parton et al., "Alluvial Fan Records from Southeast Arabia Reveal Multiple Windows for Human Dispersal," *Geology* 43, no. 4 (April 2015): 295–298, doi:10.1130/G36401.1; Hugh Ross, "Did Arabia Provide a Migration Route for Early Humans?," *Today's New Reason to Believe* (blog), Reasons to Believe, May 28, 2015, reasons.org/explore/publications/articles/did-arabia-provide-a-migration-route-for-early-humans; Ignacio A. Lazagabaster et al., "Rare Crested Rat Subfossils Unveil Afro-Eurasian Ecological Corridors Synchronous with Early Human Dispersals," *Proceedings of the National Academy of Sciences USA* 118, no. 31 (August 3, 2021): e2105719118, doi:10.1073/pnas.2105719118.

21. Hugh Ross, "Errors in Human Origins Dates," *Today's New Reason to Believe* (blog), Reasons to Believe, June 29, 2020, reasons.org/explore/blogs/todays-new-reason-to-believe/errors-in-human-origins-dates.

22. Genesis 7:11–12, 17–19; 8:13–14.

23. Peter Enns, for example, wrote, "Paul shared with his contemporaries certain assumptions about the nature of physical reality, assumptions that we now know are no longer accurate," *The Evolution of Adam*, 94.

24. Dyson Hague, "The Doctrinal Value of First Chapters of Genesis," in *The Fundamentals: A Testimony to the Truth*, ed. R. A. Torrey et al., vol. 1 (Bible Institute of Los Angeles, 1917; Grand Rapids, MI: Baker, 1993), 283.

Chapter 19: Scientific Defense of an Original Human Pair

1. Fazale Rana with Hugh Ross, *Who Was Adam?*, 2nd ed. (Covina, CA: RTB Press, 2015).

2. Francis Brown, S. R. Driver, and Charles A. Briggs, *The Brown-Driver-Briggs Hebrew and English Lexicon* (1906; repr., Peabody, MA: Hendrickson, 1997), 1593.

3. R. Laird Harris, Gleason L. Archer, and Bruce K. Waltke, *Theological Wordbook of the Old Testament*, vol. 2 (Chicago: Moody Press, 1980), 587.

4. Johan J. Bolhuis and Clive D. L. Wynne, "Can Evolution Explain How Minds Work?," *Nature* 458 (April 16, 2009): 832–833, doi:10.1038/458832a; Thomas Nagel, "What Is It Like to Be a Bat?," *Philosophical Review* 83, no. 4 (October 1974): 435–450, doi:10.2307/2183914; C. B. G. Campbell and William Hodos, "The *Scale Naturae* Revisited: Evolutionary Scales and Anagenesis in Comparative Psychology," *Journal of Comparative Psychology* 105, no. 3 (September 1991): 211–221, doi:10.1037/0735-7036.105.3.211.

5. C. R. Raby and N. S. Clayton, "Prospective Cognition in Animals," *Behavioural Processes* 80, no. 3 (March 2009): 314–324, doi:10.1016/j.beproc.2008.12.005; Derek C. Penn, Keith J. Holyoak, and Daniel J. Povinelli, "Darwin's Mistake: Explaining the Discontinuity between Human and Nonhuman Minds," *Behavioral and Brain Sciences* 31, no. 2 (April 2008): 109–130, doi:10.1017/S0140525X08003543; Esther Herrmann et al., "Humans Have Evolved Specialized Skills of Social Cognition: The Cultural Intelligence Hypothesis," *Science* 317, no. 5843 (September 7, 2007): 1360–1366, doi:10.1126/science.1146282; Keith Jensen, Josep Call, and Michael Tomasello, "Chimpanzees Are Vengeful but Not Spiteful," *Proceedings of the National Academy of Sciences USA* 104, no. 32 (August 7, 2007): 13046–13050, doi:10.1073/pnas.0705555104; Alexandra Horowitz, "Disambiguating the 'Guilty Look': Salient Prompts to a Familiar Dog Behaviour," *Behavioural Processes* 81, no. 3 (July 2009):

447–452, doi:10.1016/j.beproc.2009.03.014; Mark Petter et al., "Can Dogs (*Canis familia-ris*) Detect Human Deception?," *Behavioural Processes* 82, no. 2 (October 2009): 109–118, doi:10.1016/j.beproc.2009.07.002.

6. Bolhuis and Wynne, "Can Evolution Explain?," 832.

7. Bolhuis and Wynne, 832.

8. Shoko Sugasawa et al., "Causes and Consequences of Tool Shape Variation in New Cale-donian Crows," *Current Biology* 27, no. 24 (December 18, 2017): 3885, doi:10.1016/j. cub.2017.11.028.

9. Sugasawa et al., "Causes and Consequences," 3885–3890.

10. M. Boeckle et al., "New Caledonian Crows Plan for Specific Future Tool Use," *Proceedings of the Royal Society B: Biological Sciences* 287, no. 1938 (November 11, 2020): id. 20201490, doi:10.1098/rspb.2020.1490; Romana Gruber et al., "New Caledonian Crows Use Mental Representations to Solve Metatool Problems," *Current Biology* 29, no. 4 (February 18, 2019): 686–692, doi:10.1016/j.cub.2019.01.008; A. M. P. von Bayern et al., "Compound Tool Con-struction by New Caledonian Crows," *Scientific Reports* 8, no. 1 (October 24, 2018): id. 15676, doi:10.1038/s41598-018-33458-z; Alice M. I. Auersperg, "Exploration Technique and Technical Innovations in Corvids and Parrots," in *Animal Creativity and Innovation*, ed. Allison B. Kaufman and James C. Kaufman (Amsterdam: Elsevier Academic Press, 2015), 45–72, doi:10.1016/C2013-0-18605-9; James J. H. St Clair and Christian Rutz, "New Cale-donian Crows Attend to Multiple Functional Properties of Complex Tools," *Philosophical Transactions of the Royal Society B: Biological Sciences* 368, no. 1630 (November 19, 2013): id. 20120415, doi:10.1098/rstb.2012.0415; Gavin R. Hunt and Russell D. Gray, "Direct Ob-servations of Pandanus-Tool Manufacture and Use by a New Caledonian Crow (*Corvus moneduloides*)," *Animal Cognition* 7 (April 2004): 114–120, doi:10.1007/s10071-003-0200-0; Simone Pika et al., "Ravens Parallel Great Apes in Physical and Social Cognitive Skills," *Scientific Reports* 10 (December 10, 2020): id. 20617, doi:10.1038/s41598-020-77060-8.

11. Seweryn Olkowicz et al., "Birds Have Primate-Like Numbers of Neurons in the Forebrain," *Proceedings of the National Academy of Sciences USA* 113, no. 26 (June 28, 2016): 7255–7260, doi:10.1073/pnas.1517131113; Felipe S. Medina et al., "Perineuronal Satellite Neu-roglia in the Telencephalon of New Caledonian Crows and Other Passeriformes: Evidence of Satellite Glial Cells in the Central Nervous System of Healthy Birds?," *PeerJ* 1 (July 25, 2013): id. 3110, doi:10.7717/peerj.110; Andreas Nieder, "Inside the Corvid Brain—Probing the Physiology of Cognition in Crows," *Current Opinion in Behavioral Sciences* 16 (August 2017): 8–14, doi:10.1016/j.cobeha.2017.02.005; Julia Mehlhorn et al., "Tool-Making New Caledonian Crows Have Large Associative Brain Areas," *Brain Behavior and Evolution* 75, no. 1 (March 2010): 63–70, doi:10.1159/000295151.

12. Andreas Nieder, "Consciousness without Cortex," *Current Opinion in Neurobiology* 71 (De-cember 2021): 69–76, doi:10.1016/j.conb.2021.09.010.

13. Johan J. Bolhuis, "Evolution Cannot Explain How Minds Work," *Behavioural Processes* 117 (August 2015): 82–91, doi:10.1016/j.beproc.2015.06.008; Natalie Uomini et al., "Extended Parenting and the Evolution of Cognition," *Philosophical Transactions of the Royal Society B* 375, no. 1803 (July 20, 2020): id. 20190495, doi:10.1098/rstb.2019.0495; Patrick R. Hof, Rebecca Chanis, and Lori Marino, "Cortical Complexity in Cetacean Brains," *The Anatomi-cal Record* 287A, no. 1 (November 2005): 1142–1152, doi:10.1002/ar.a.20258; Piero Amodio et al., "Grow Smart and Die Young: Why Did Cephalopods Evolve Intelligence?," *Trends in Ecology and Evolution* 34, no. 1 (January 2019): 45–56, doi:10.1016/j.tree.2018.10.010.

14. Simon Conway Morris, *Life's Solution: Inevitable Humans in a Lonely Universe* (New York:

Cambridge University Press, 2004); Simon Conway Morris, *From Extraterrestrials to Animal Minds: Six Myths of Evolution* (West Conshohocken, PA: Templeton Press, 2022); Simon Conway Morris, *The Deep Structure of Biology: Is Convergence Sufficiently Ubiquitous to Give a Directional Signal?* (West Conshohocken, PA: Templeton Foundation Press, 2008); Stephen Jay Gould, *Wonderful Life: The Burgess Shale and the Nature of History* (New York: W. W. Norton & Co., 1989).

15. Fazale Rana, *Creating Life in the Lab* (Grand Rapids, MI: Baker Books, 2011).
16. John D. Pettigrew, Shaun P. Collin, and Matthias Ott, "Convergence of Specialised Behaviour, Eye Movements and Visual Optics in the Sandlance (Teleostei) and the Chameleon (Reptilia)," *Current Biology* 9, no. 8 (April 22, 1999): 421–424, doi:10.1016/S0960-9822(99)80189-4; Michael F. Land, "Visual Optics: The Sandlance Eye Breaks All the Rules," *Current Biology* 9, no. 8 (April 22, 1999): R286–R288, doi:10.1016/S0960-9822(99)80180-8; Hugh Ross, "The Chameleon's Amazing Tongue Challenges Evolutionary Paradigm," *Today's New Reason to Believe* (blog), Reasons to Believe, July 11, 2016, reasons.org/explore/blogs/todays-new-reason-to-believe/the-chameleons-amazing-tongue-challenges-evolutionary-paradigm.
17. José M. Martín-Durán et al., "Convergent Evolution of Bilaterian Nerve Cords," *Nature* 553 (January 4, 2018): 45–50, doi:10.1038/nature25030; Caroline B. Albertin and Clifton W. Ragsdale, "More Than One Way to a Central Nervous System," *Nature* 553 (December 13, 2017): 34, doi:10.1038/d41586-017-08195-4.
18. Bolhuis, "Evolution Cannot Explain," 82.
19. Sadeq, "Do All African Greys Talk? (Find Out!!)," WooParrot, *African Greys, Behavior & Training*, accessed January 14, 2023, wooparrot.com/do-all-african-greys-talk-find-out/.
20. Penn, Holyoak, and Povinelli, "Darwin's Mistake," 109.
21. Hector M. Manrique et al., "Great Apes (*Pan troglodytes, Pan paniscus, Pongo abelii*) Exploit Better the Information of Failure Than Capuchin Monkeys (*Sapajus* spp.) When Selecting Tools to Solve the Same Foraging Problem," *Journal of Comparative Psychology* 135, no. 2 (May 2021): 273–279, doi:10.1037/com0000242; Crickette M. Sanz and David B. Morgan, "Chimpanzee Tool Technology in the Goualougo Triangle, Republic of Congo," *Journal of Human Evolution* 52, no. 4 (April 2007): 420–433, doi:10.1016/j.jhevol.2006.11.001; Elisa Bandini et al., "Naïve Orangutans (*Pongo abelii* and *Pongo pygmaeus*) Individually Acquire Nut-Cracking Using Hammer Tools," *American Journal of Primatology* 83, no. 9 (September 2021): id. e23304, doi:10.1002/ajp.23304; Juliane Bräuer and Josep Call, "Apes Produce Tools for Future Use," *American Journal of Primatology* 77, no. 3 (March 2015): 254–263, doi:10.1002/ajp.22341.
22. Human Origins Workshop 2020, hosted by Anjeanette Roberts, featuring Fazale Rana, Joshua Swamidass, William Lane Craig, Ken Keathley, Nathan Lents, Andrew Loke, Steve Schaffner, and Jeff Schloss, Covina, CA, January 18, 2020, reasons.org/single/humanoriginsworkshop2020.
23. Craig repeated this claim in his book, *In Quest of the Historical Adam* (Grand Rapids, MI: Eerdmans, 2022), 293–294.
24. B. L. Hardy et al., "Direct Evidence of Neanderthal Fibre Technology and Its Cognitive and Behavioral Implications," *Scientific Reports* 10 (April 9, 2020): id. 4889, doi:10.1038/s41598-020-61839-w.
25. Hardy et al., "Neanderthal Fibre Technology," 1.
26. Hardy et al., 1.
27. Becca Foley, "Prof. Hardy Gets Worldwide Attention for Neanderthal Research," *Kenyon Collegian*, April 23, 2020, kenyoncollegian.com/news/2020/04/prof-hardy-gets-worldwide-

attention-for-neanderthal-research.

28. Hardy et al., "Neanderthal Fibre Technology," 1.

29. Richard Roberts et al., "Optical and Radiocarbon Dating at Jinmium Rock Shelter in Northern Australia," *Nature* 393 (May 28, 1998): 358–362, doi:10.1038/30718; Hugh Ross, "Errors in Human Origins Dates," *Today's New Reason to Believe* (blog), Reasons to Believe, June 29, 2020, reasons.org/explore/blogs/todays-new-reason-to-believe/errors-in-human-origins-dates.

30. Ludovic Slimak et al., "Modern Human Incursion into Neanderthal Territories 54,000 Years Ago at Mandrin, France," *Science Advances* 8, no. 6 (February 9, 2022): id. eabj9496, doi:10.1126/sciadv.abj9496.

31. Jill D. Pruetz and David B. Morgan, "Savanna Chimpanzees, *Pan troglodytes verus*, Hunt with Tools," *Current Biology* 17, no. 5 (March 6, 2007): 412–417, doi:10.1016/j.cub.2006.12.042; Harry W. Green, "Evolutionary Scenarios and Primate Natural History," *American Naturalist* 190, no. S1 (August 2017): S69–S86, doi:10.1086/692830.

32. Jill D. Pruetz and Thomas C. LaDuke, "Brief Communication: Reaction to Fire by Savanna Chimpanzees (*Pan troglodytes verus*) at Fogoli, Senegal: Conceptualization of 'Fire Behavior' and the Case for a Chimpanzee Model," *American Journal of Physical Anthropology* 141, no. 4 (April 2010): 646–650, doi:10.1002/ajpa.21245.

33. A. C. Sorensen, E. Claud, and M. Soressi, "Neandertal Fire-Making Technology Inferred from Microwear Analysis," *Scientific Reports* 8 (July 19, 2018): id. 10065, doi:10.1038/s41598-018-28342-9.

34. Aylar Abdolahzadeh et al., "Investigating Variability in the Frequency of Fire Use in the Archeological Record of Late Pleistocene Europe," *Archaeological and Anthropological Sciences* 14, no. 4 (April 2022): id. 62, doi:10.1007/s12520-022-01526-1; Dennis M. Sandgathe et al., "Timing of the Appearance of Habitual Fire Use," *Proceedings of the National Academy of Sciences USA* 108, no. 29 (July 19, 2011): id. E298, doi:10.1073/pnas.1106759108; Dennis M. Sandgathe et al., "On the Role of Fire in Neandertal Adaptations in Western Europe: Evidence from Pech de l'Azé IV and Roc de Marsal, France," *PaleoAnthropology* (2011): 216–242, doi:10.4207/PA.2011.ART54.

35. Cara Ocobock, Sarah Lacy, and Alexandra Niclou, "Between a Rock and a Cold Place: Neanderthal Biocultural Cold Adaptations," *Evolutionary Anthropology* 30, no. 4 (July/August 2021): 262–279, doi:10.1002/evan.21894.

36. Michael Staubwasser et al., "Impact of Climate Change on the Transition of Neanderthals to Modern Humans in Europe," *Proceedings of the National Academy of Sciences USA* 115, no. 37 (September 11, 2018): 9116–9121, doi:10.1073/pnas.1808647115.

37. Mark Collard et al., "Faunal Evidence for a Difference in Clothing Use between Neanderthals and Early Modern Humans in Europe," *Journal of Anthropological Archaeology* 44, part B (December 2016): 235–246, doi:10.1016/j.jaa.2016.07.010.

38. Anna E. Goldfield, Ross Booton, and John M. Marston, "Modeling the Role of Fire and Cooking in the Competitive Exclusion of Neanderthals," *Journal of Human Evolution* 124 (November 2018): 91–104, doi:10.1016/j.jhevol.2018.07.006.

39. Marta Mariotti Lippi et al., "Multistep Food Plant Processing at Grotta Paglicci (Southern Italy) Around 32,600 Cal B. P.," *Proceedings of the National Academy of Sciences USA* 112, no. 39 (September 8, 2015): 12075–12080, doi:10.1073/pnas.1505213112; Hugh Ross, "Confirmation That Early Humans Were Making Bread," *Today's New Reason to Believe* (blog), Reasons to Believe, August 27, 2018, reasons.org/explore/blogs/todays-new-reason-to-believe/confirmation-that-early-humans-were-making-bread.

40. Adam van Casteren et al., "The Cost of Chewing: The Energetics and Evolutionary Significance of Mastication in Humans," *Science Advances* 8, no. 33 (August 17, 2022): id. eabn8351, doi:10.1126/sciadv.abn8451.
41. Chris Organ et al., "Phylogenetic Rate Shifts in Feeding Time during the Evolution of *Homo*," *Proceedings of the National Academy of Sciences USA* 108, no. 35 (August 22, 2011): 14555–14559, doi:10.1073/pnas.1107806108.
42. Callum F. Ross et al., "Ecological Consequences of Scaling of Chew Cycle Duration and Daily Feeding Time in Primates," *Journal of Human Evolution* 56, no. 6 (June 2009): 570–585, doi:10.1016/j.jhevol.2009.02.007.
43. Ross et al., "Ecological Consequences."
44. Van Casteren et al., "The Cost of Chewing," 3.
45. Paul Peter Anthony Mazza et al., "A New Palaeolithic Discovery: Tar-Hafted Stone Tools in a European Mid-Pleistocene Bone-Bearing Bed," *Journal of Archaeological Science* 33, no. 9 (September 2006): 1310–1318, doi:10.1016/j.jas.2006.01.006; Alfred F. Pawlik and Jürgen P. Thissen, "Hafted Armatures and Multi-Component Tool Design at the Micoquian Site of Inden-Altdorf, Germany," *Journal of Archaeological Science* 38, no. 7 (July 2011): 1699–1708, doi:10.1016/j.jas.2011.03.001.
46. Patrick Schmidt et al., "Birch Tar Production Does Not Prove Neanderthal Behavioral Complexity," *Proceedings of the National Academy of Sciences USA* 116, no. 36 (September 3, 2019): 17707–17711, doi:10.1073/pnas.1911137116.
47. Schmidt et al., "Birch Tar Production," 17707.
48. Itai Roffman et al., "Stone Tool Production and Utilization by Bonobo-Chimpanzees (*Pan paniscus*)," *Proceedings of the National Academy of Sciences USA* 109, no. 36 (September 4, 2012): 14500–14503, doi:10.1073/pnas.1212855109.
49. Alessandra Mascaro et al., "Application of Insects to Wounds of Self and Others by Chimpanzees in the Wild," *Current Biology* 32, no. 3 (February 2022): R112–R113, doi:10.1016/j.cub.2021.12.045; Mélodie Kreyer et al., "What Fecal Analyses Reveal about *Manniophyton fulvum* Consumption in LuiKotale Bonobos (*Pan paniscus*): A Medicinal Plant Revisited," *American Journal of Primatology* 84, no. 4–5 (August 21, 2021): id. e23318, doi:10.1002/ajp.23318; Michael A. Huffman, "Folklore, Animal Self-Medication, and Phytotherapy—Something Old, Something New, Something Borrowed, Some Things True," *Planta Medica* 88, no. 3–4 (March 2022): 187–199, doi:10.1055/a-1586-1665.
50. David R. Samson, Michael P. Muehlenbein, and Kevin D. Hunt, "Do Chimpanzees (*Pan troglodytes schweinfurthii*) Exhibit Sleep Related Behaviors that Minimize Exposure to Parasitic Arthropods? A Preliminary Report on the Possible Anti-Vector Function of Chimpanzee Sleeping Platforms," *Primates* 54, no. 1 (January 2013): 73–80, doi:10.1007/s10329-012-0329-z.
51. J. D. Pruetz, "Evidence of Cave Use by Savanna Chimpanzees (*Pan troglodytes versu*) at Fongoli, Senegal: Implications for Thermoregulatory Behavior," *Primates* 48, no. 4 (October 2007): 316–319, doi:10.1007/s10329-007-0038-1.
52. Dirk L. Hoffman et al., "Symbolic Use of Marine Shells and Mineral Pigments by Iberian Neanderthals 115,000 Years Ago," *Science Advances* 4, no. 2 (February 22, 2018): id. eaar5255, doi:10.1126/sciadv.aar5255; João Zilhão et al., "Symbolic Use of Marine Shells and Mineral Pigments by Iberian Neanderthals," *Proceedings of the National Academy of Sciences USA* 107, no. 3 (January 19, 2010): 1023–1028, doi:10.1073/pnas.0914088107.
53. Hoffman et al., "Marine Shells and Mineral Pigments," id. eaar5255.
54. Georges Sauvet et al., "Uranium-Thorium Dating Method and Paleolithic Rock Art," *Qua-*

ternary International 432, part B (March 8, 2017): 86–92, doi:10.1016/j.quaint.2015.03.053; Tebogo V. Makhubela and Jan D. Kramers, "Testing a New Combined (U,Th)–He and U/ Th Dating Approach on Plio-Pleistocene Calcite Speleothems," *Quaternary Geochronology* 67 (February 2022): id. 101234, doi:10.1016/j.quageo.2021.101234; Jan D. Kramers and Tebogo V. Makhubela, "(U,Th)-He Dating of Pleistocene Carbonates: Analytical Methods and Age Calculations," *MethodsX* 9 (2022): id. 101608, doi:10.1016/j.mex.2021.101608.

55.   Hugh Ross, "Errors in Human Origins Dates."

56.   R. E. Wood et al., "The Chronology of the Earliest Upper Palaeolithic in Northern Iberia: New Insights from L'Arbreda, Labeko Koba and La Viña," *Journal of Human Evolution* 69 (April 2014): 91–109, doi:10.1016/j.jhevol.2013.12.017; Joan Daura et al., "A New Chronological Framework and Site Formation History for Cova del Gegant (Barcelona): Implications for Neanderthal and Anatomically Modern Human Occupation of NE Iberian Peninsula," *Quaternary Science Reviews* 270 (October 15, 2021): id. 107141, doi:10.1016/j.quascirev.2021.107141.

57.   Ludovic Slimak et al., "Modern Human Incursion into Neanderthal Territories 54,000 Years Ago at Mandrin, France," *Science Advances* 8 (February 9, 2022): id. eabj9496, doi:10.1126/sciadv.abj9496.

58.   Anna Maria Kubicka et al., "A Systematic Review of Animal Predation Creating Pierced Shells: Implications for the Archaeological Record of the Old World," *PeerJ* 5 (2017): id. e2903, doi:10.7717/peerj.2903.

59.   Wil Roebroeks and Marie Soressi, "Neandertals Revised," *Proceedings of the National Academy of Sciences USA* 113, no. 23 (June 6, 2016): 6372–6379, doi:10.1073/pnas.1521269113.

60.   Marta Mariotti Lippi et al., "Multistep Food Plant Processing at Grotta Paglicci (Southern Italy) around 32,600 Cal B.P.," *Proceedings of the National Academy of Sciences USA* 112, no. 39 (September 2015): 12075–12080, doi:10.1073/pnas.1505213112.

61.   Takanori Kochiyama et al., "Reconstructing the Neanderthal Brain Using Computational Anatomy," *Scientific Reports* 8 (April 26, 2018): id. 6296, doi:10.1038/s41598-018-24331-0.

62.   Kochiyama et al., "Reconstructing the Neanderthal Brain," 1.

63.   Kochiyama et al., 1.

64.   Kochiyama et al., 5.

65.   Kochiyama et al., 5.

66.   Richard G. Coss, "Drawings of Representational Images by Upper Paleolithic Humans and Their Absence in Neanderthals Might Reflect Historical Differences in Hunting Wary Game," *Evolutionary Studies in Imaginative Culture* 1, no. 2 (Fall 2017): 15–38, doi:10.26613/esic.1.2.46.

67.   Kay Prüfer et al., "The Complete Genome Sequence of a Neanderthal from the Altai Mountains," *Nature* 505, no. 7481 (January 2, 2014): 43–49, doi:10.1038/nature12886; Fabrizio Mafessoni and Kay Prüfer, "Better Support for a Small Effective Population Size of Neandertals and a Long Shared History of Neandertals and Denisovans," *Proceedings of the National Academy of Sciences USA* 114, no. 48 (November 28, 2017): E10256–E10257, doi:10.1073/pnas.1716918114; Jean-Pierre Bocquet-Appel and Anna Degioanni, "Neanderthal Demographic Estimates," *Current Anthropology* 54, S8 (December 2013): S202–S213, doi:10.1086/673725.

68.   Krist Vaesen et al., "Inbreeding, Allee Effects and Stochasticity Might Be Sufficient to Account for Neanderthal Extinction," *PLoS One* 14, no. 11 (November 27, 2019): id. e0225117, doi:10.1371/journal.pone.0225117; Prüfer et al., "Complete Genome Sequence," 43–49.

69.   Mafessoni and Prüfer, "Better Support," E10256–E10257; Krist Vaesen, Gerrit L. Dussel-

dorp, and Mark J. Brandt, "An Emerging Consensus in Palaeoanthropology: Demography Was the Main Factor Responsible for the Disappearance of Neanderthals," *Scientific Reports* 11, no. 1 (March 1, 2021): id. 4925, doi:10.1038/s41598-021-84410-7; Frederico Sánchez-Quinto and Carles Lalueza-Fox, "Almost 20 Years of Neanderthal Palaeogenetics: Adaptation, Admixture, Diversity, Demography and Extinction," *Philosophical Transactions of the Royal Society B: Biological Sciences* 370, no. 1660 (January 19, 2015): id. 1660, doi:10.1098/rstb.2013.0374.

70. Mafessoni and Prüfer, "Better Support," E10256–E10257.

71. Adrian W. Briggs et al., "Targeted Retrieval and Analysis of Five Neandertal mtDNA Genomes," *Science* 325, no. 5938 (July 17, 2009): 318–321, doi:10.1126/science.1174462.

72. Matthias Meyer et al., "A Mitochondrial Genome Sequence of a Hominin from Sima de los Huesos," *Nature* 505 (January 16, 2014): 403–406, doi:10.1038/nature12788.

73. Rhys E. Green et al., "Implications of the Prevalence and Magnitude of Sustained Declines for Determining a Minimum Threshold for Favourable Population Size," *PLoS ONE* 15, no. 2 (February 12, 2020): id. e0228742, doi:10.1371/journal.pone.0228742; Georgina M. Mace et al., "Quantification of Extinction Risk: IUCN's System for Classifying Threatened Species," *Conservation Biology* 22, no. 6 (December 2008): 1424–1442, doi:10.1111/j.1523-1739.2008.01044.x; Ana D. Davidson et al., "Multiple Ecological Pathways to Extinction in Mammals," *Proceedings of the National Academy of Sciences USA* 106, no. 26 (June 2009): 10702–10705, doi:10.1073/pnas.0901956106; Marcel Cardillo et al., "Multiple Causes of High Extinction Risk in Large Mammal Species," *Science* 309, no. 5738 (August 19, 2005): 1239–1241, doi:10.1126/science.1116030; Owen L. Petchey and Andrea Belgrano, "Body-Size Distributions and Size-Spectra: Universal Indicators of Ecological Status?," *Biology Letters* 6, no. 4 (August 23, 2010): id. rsbl20100240, doi:10.1098/rsbl.2010.0240; Marcel Cardillo, "Biological Determinants of Extinction Risk: Why Are Smaller Species Less Vulnerable?," *Animal Conservation* 6, no. 1 (February 2003): 63–69, doi:10.1017/S1367943003003093.

74. Felisa A. Smith et al., "Body Size Downgrading of Mammals over the Late Quaternary," *Science* 360, no. 6386 (April 20, 2018): 310, doi:10.1126/science.aao5987.

75. Smith et al., "Body Size Downgrading," 310.

76. Smith et al., 310.

77. J. Tyler Faith et al., "Plio-Pleistocene Decline of African Megaherbivores: No Evidence for Ancient Hominin Impacts," *Science* 362, no. 6417 (November 23, 2018): 938–941, doi: 10.1126/science.aau2728.

78. Christopher Sandom et al., "Global Late Quaternary Megafauna Extinctions Linked to Humans, Not Climate Change," *Proceedings of the Royal Society B: Biological Sciences* 281, no. 1787 (July 22, 2014): id. 20133254, doi:10.1098/rspb.2013.3254.

79. Anthony D. Barnosky et al., "Assessing the Causes of Late Pleistocene Extinctions on the Continents," *Science* 306, no. 5693 (October 1, 2004): 70–75, doi:10.1126/science.1101476.

80. Barnosky et al., "Assessing the Causes," 70–75.

81. Barnosky et al., 70–75.

82. Francis S. Collins, *The Language of God: A Scientist Presents Evidence for Belief* (New York: Free Press, 2007).

83. Nuha Elhassan et al., "The Episode of Genetic Drift Defining the Migration of Humans Out of Africa Is Derived from a Large East African Population Size," *PLoS ONE* 9, no. 5 (May 20, 2014): id. e97674, doi:10.1371/journal.pone.0097674.

84. Renaud Kaeuffer et al., "Unexpected Heterozygosity in an Island Mouflon Population Founded by a Single Pair of Individuals," *Proceedings of the Royal Society B: Biological Sci-

ences 274, no. 1609 (February 22, 2007): 527–533, doi:10.1098/rspb.2006.3743.

85. S. Elizabeth Alter, Seth D. Newsome, and Stephen R. Palumni, "Pre-Whaling Genetic Diversity and Population Ecology in Eastern Gray Whales: Insights from Ancient DNA and Stable Isotopes," *PLoS ONE* 7, no. 5 (May 9, 2012): id. e35039, doi:10.1371/journal.pone.0035039.

86. Juan P. Torres-Florez et al., "High Genetic Diversity in a Small Population: The Case of Chilean Blue Whales," *Ecology and Evolution* 4, no. 8 (April 2014): 1398–1412, doi:10.1002/ece3.998.

87. Hiroki Goto et al., "A Massively Parallel Sequencing Approach Uncovers Ancient Origins and High Genetic Variability of Endangered Przewalski's Horses," *Genome Biology and Evolution* 3 (July 29, 2011): 1096–1106, doi:10.1093/gbe/evr067.

88. Catherine Lippé, Pierre Dumont, and Louis Bernatchez, "High Genetic Diversity and No Inbreeding in the Endangered Copper Redhorse, *Moxostoma hubbsi* (Catastomidae Pisces): The Positive Sides of a Long Generation Time," *Molecular Ecology* 15, no. 7 (June 2006): 1769–1780, doi:10.1111/j.1365-294X.2006.02902.x.

89. Steffen Roth and Robert Jehle, "High Genetic Diversity of Common Toad (*Bufo bufo*) Populations under Strong Natural Fragmentation on a Northern Archipelago," *Ecology and Evolution* 6, no. 6 (February 12, 2016): 1626–1636, doi:10.1002/ece3.1957.

90. Janna Kekkonen, Mikael Wikström, and Jon E. Brommer, "Heterozygosity in an Isolated Population of a Large Mammal Founded by Four Individuals Is Predicted by an Individual-Based Genetic Model," *PLoS ONE* 7, no. 9 (September 20, 2012): id. e43482, doi:10.1371/journal.pone.0043482; Suzanne L. Nelson, Scott A. Taylor, and Jon D. Reuter, "An Isolated White-Tailed Deer (*Odocoileus virginianus*) Population on St. John, US Virgin Islands Shows Low Inbreeding and Comparable Heterozygosity to Other Larger Populations," *Ecology and Evolution* 11, no. 6 (February 2021): 2775–2781, doi:10.1002/ece3.7230.

91. Frank Hailer et al., "Bottlenecked but Long-Lived: High Genetic Diversity Retained in White-Tailed Eagles upon Recovery from Population Decline," *Biology Letters* 2, no. 2 (June 22, 2006): 316–319, doi:10.1098/rsbl.2006.0453.

92. Teresa L. Santos et al., "Conservation Genetic Assessment of Savannah Elephants (*Loxodonta africana*) in the Greater Kruger Biosphere, South Africa," *Genes (Basel)* 10, no. 10 (October 2019): id. 779, doi:10.3390/genes10100779; Torres-Florez et al., "Chilean Blue Whales," 1398–1412; Lippé, Dumont, and Bernatchez, "Endangered Copper Redhorse," 1769–1780.

93. Joseph Milton, "Orangutans Join the Genome Gang," *Nature News* (January 26, 2011), doi:10.1038/news.2011.50.

94. Megan J. McAllister et al., "Energy Optimization during Walking Involves Implicit Processing," *Journal of Experimental Biology* 224, no. 17 (September 14, 2021): id. jeb242655, doi:10.1242/jeb.242655; Hugh Ross, "Humans Are Designed to Think while Walking," *Today's New Reason to Believe* (blog), Reasons to Believe, November 8, 2021, reasons.org/explore/blogs/todays-new-reason-to-believe/humans-are-designed-to-think-while-walking.

95. Michael I. Bird et al., "A Global Carbon and Nitrogen Isotope Perspective on Modern and Ancient Human Diet," *Proceedings of the National Academy of Sciences USA* 118, no. 19 (May 11, 2021): id. e2024642118, doi:10.1073/pnas.2024642118; Stefani A. Crabtree, Douglas W. Bird, and Rebecca Bliege Bird, "Subsistence Transitions and the Simplification of Ecological Networks in the Western Desert of Australia," *Human Ecology* 47 (April 2019): 165–177, doi:10.1007/s10745-019-0053-z; Jennifer A. Dunne et al., "The Roles and Impacts of Human Hunter-Gatherers in North Pacific Marine Food Webs," *Scientific Reports* 6 (February

17, 2016): id. 21179, doi:10.1038/srep21179; Stefani A. Crabtree, Jennifer A. Dunne, and Spencer A. Wood, "Ecological Networks and Archeology," *Antiquity* 95, no. 381 (April 30, 2021): 812–825, doi:10.15184/aqy.2021.38.

96. Ekaterina Stansfield et al., "The Evolution of Pelvic Canal Shape and Rotational Birth in Humans," *BMC Biology* 19 (October 11, 2021): id. 224, doi:10.1186/s12915-021-01150-w; Fazale Rana, "Life's Twists and Turns Are Designed to Start in the Birth Canal," *The Cell's Design* (blog), Reasons to Believe, February 16, 2022, reasons.org/explore/blogs/the-cells-design/lifes-twists-and-turns-are-designed-to-start-in-the-birth-canal.

97. R. McN. Alexander, "Bipedal Animals, and Their Differences from Humans," *Journal of Anatomy* 204, no. 5 (May 2004): 321–330, doi:10.1111/j.0021-8782.2004.00289.x; Herman Pontzer, David A. Raichlen, and Michael D. Sockol, "The Metabolic Cost of Walking in Humans, Chimpanzees, and Early Hominins," *Journal of Human Evolution* 56, no. 1 (January 2009): 43–54, doi:10.1016/j.jhevol.2008.09.001.

98. Kathryn A. Rose et al., "Outdoor Activity Reduces the Prevalence of Myopia in Children," *Ophthalmology* 115, no. 8 (August 1, 2008): 1279–1285, doi:10.1016/j.ophtha.2007.12.019; Xiaoyan Jiang et al., "Progress and Control of Myopia by Light Environments," *Eye and Contact Lens* 44, no. 5 (September 2018): 273–278, doi:10.1097/ICL.0000000000000548; Hidemasa Torii et al., "Violet Light Exposure Can Be a Preventive Strategy against Myopia Progression," *eBioMedicine* 15 (February 1, 2017): 210–219, doi:10.1016/j.ebiom.2016.12.007; Hugh Ross, "Eyes, Sun, and Earth Designed to Prevent Myopia," *Today's New Reason to Believe* (blog), Reasons to Believe, August 16, 2021, reasons.org/explore/blogs/todays-new-reason-to-believe/eyes-sun-and-earth-designed-to-prevent-myopia.

99. Pablo Aria, Pascal Belin, and Jean-Julien Aucouturier, "Auditory Smiles Trigger Unconscious Facial Imitation," *Current Biology* 28, no. 14 (July 23, 2018): PR782–PR783, doi:10.1016/j.cub.2018.05.084.

100. Thomas Kraft et al., "The Energetics of Uniquely Human Subsistence Strategies," *Science* 374, no. 6575 (December 24, 2021): id. 1576, doi:10.1126/science.abf0130.

101. Hans Rutger Bosker and David Peeters, "Beat Gestures Influence which Speech Sounds You Hear," *Proceedings of the Royal Society B* 288, no. 1943 (January 27, 2021): id. 20202419, doi:10.1098/rspb.2020.2419; Harry McGurk and John MacDonald, "Hearing Lips and Seeing Voices," *Nature* 264, no. 5588 (December 23, 1976): 746–748, doi:10.1038/264746a0; Elana M. Zion Golumbic et al., "Mechanisms Underlying Selective Neuronal Tracking of Attended Speech at a 'Cocktail Party," *Neuron* 77, no. 5 (March 6, 2013): 980–991, doi:10.1016/j.neuron.2012.12.037; Hans Rutger Bosker, Matthias J. Sjerps, and Eva Reinisch, "Spectral Contrast Effects Are Modulated by Selective Attention in 'Cocktail Party' Settings," *Attention, Perception, and Psychophysics* 82, no. 3 (June 2020): 1318–1332, doi:10.3758/s13414-019-01824-2.

Chapter 20: The Benefit of a Model Approach

1. Eugenia Torrance, "God of the Gaps or the God of 'Design and Dominion'? Re-Visiting Newton's Theology," *Zygon Journal of Religion & Science* (September 7, 2022), published ahead of print, doi:10.111/zygo.12825.

2. Dietrich Bonhoeffer, letter to Eberhard Bethge, May 29, 1944, in *Letters and Papers from Prison*, ed. Eberhard Bethge, trans. Reginald H. Fuller (New York: Touchstone, 1997), 310–312.

Chapter 21: A Modest Defense of Biblical Inerrancy

1.   Several examples are presented in the book by Anjeanette Roberts, Fazale Rana, Sue Dykes, and Mark Perez, *Thinking about Evolution: 25 Questions Christians Want Answered* (Covina, CA: RTB Press, 2020), 50–52, 55–57, 71–73, 157–174, 267–274.

Appendix: The Meaning of *Bara'* and *Asa*

1.   Ellen Van Wolde, "Why the Verb ברא Does Not Mean 'to Create' in Genesis 1.1–2.4a," *Journal for the Study of the Old Testament* 34, no. 1 (2009): 3–23, doi:10.1177/0309089209348155.
2.   R. Laird Harris, Gleason L. Archer, and Bruce K. Waltke, *Theological Wordbook of the Old Testament*, vol. 1 (Chicago: Moody Press, 1980), 127.
3.   John H. Walton, *The Lost World of Genesis One: Ancient Cosmology and the Origins Debate* (Downers Grove, IL: InterVarsity Press Academic, 2009), 113.
4.   Walton, *Lost World of Genesis One*, 153.
5.   Walton, 153.
6.   Walton, 44.
7.   Walton, 44.
8.   Walton, 43.
9.   Harris, Archer, and Waltke, *Theological Wordbook of the Old Testament*, 127.
10.   Harris, Archer, and Waltke, 701.
11.   John Walton, "The Goal and Purpose of Genesis 1: John Walton Responds," *Ancient Hebrew Poetry*, May 5, 2008, ancienthebrewpoetry.typepad.com/ancient_hebrew_poetry/2008/05/the-goal-and-pu.html.

Index

Hoyle, Fred, 88
Hugh of St. Victor, 52
human exceptionalism, 182–185, 196, 198–199
Human Genome Project, 68–69, 173, 208
human origins, 46–47. *See also* Adam and Eve
Hume, David, 70

ice age, 130–131, 159, 165, 175–176
image of God. *See* God, image of
inbreeding, 192
Ingersoll, Robert Green, 29–30
initial conditions, 73–74
Institute for Creation Research, 78
intelligent design, 185
International Council on Biblical Inerrancy (ICBI), 24–25, 33, 40–41, 46, 56, 59, 61, 87, 132
interplanetary space travel, 96
Irenaeus, 50, 137
Islam. *See* concordism and Islam

Jacobs, Jack, 166
Jaki, Stanley, 70
Jehovah's Witnesses. *See* concordism and Christian cults
Jerome, 51
Jet Propulsion Laboratory, 91
jewelry, 189–190
Job, 45, 61, 70, 75, 84–86, 89, 109, 119–120
junk DNA, 209

Kaiser, Walter, 33, 38
Kant, Immanuel, 70
Kantzer, Kenneth, 33
Keel, Othmar, 115
Kepler, Johannes, 55, 125
Kissling, Paul, 118
Knox Theological Seminary, 39
Koko, 184–185
Kolob, 100–101
Kuhn, Thomas, 144
Kuyper, Abraham, 54–55

Lambert, Wilfred, 115
Lamoureux, Denis, 46, 68
    The Bible & Ancient Science, 46
Langton, Stephen, 136
last universal common ancestor (LUCA), 110–111, 184
laws of motion, 145
laws of physics, 72, 88, 139–140, 145–146

About the Author

Hugh Ross is senior scholar and founder of Reasons to Believe (RTB), an organization dedicated to demonstrating the compatibility of science and the Christian faith.

With a degree in physics from the University of British Columbia and a PhD in astronomy from the University of Toronto, Hugh—initially a skeptic, always curious, and eventually a Christian—continued his research on quasars and galaxies as a postdoctoral fellow at the California Institute of Technology. After five years there, he transitioned to full-time ministry. In addition to founding and leading RTB, he remains on the pastoral staff at Christ Church Sierra Madre. His writings include journal and magazine articles, blogs, and numerous books—*The Creator and the Cosmos*, *Why the Universe Is the Way It Is*, and *Designed to the Core*, among others. He has spoken on hundreds of university campuses as well as at conferences and churches around the world.

Hugh lives in Southern California with his wife, Kathy.

About Reasons to Believe

Reasons to Believe (RTB) exists to open people to the gospel by revealing God in science. Based in Covina, California, RTB was established in 1986 and since then has taken scientific evidence for the God of the Bible to more than a dozen countries. Our ongoing work is providing content for all who desire to explore the connection between science and the Christian faith.

RTB is unique in its range of resources. The curious can explore articles, podcasts, and videos. Those who want to learn more can delve into books, events, and online courses. Donors enable us to continue this important work.

For more information, visit reasons.org.

For inquiries, contact us via:
818 S. Oak Park Rd.
Covina, CA 91724
(855) REASONS | (855) 732-7667
ministrycare@reasons.org

Scientific, philosophical, and theological perspectives on transhumanism

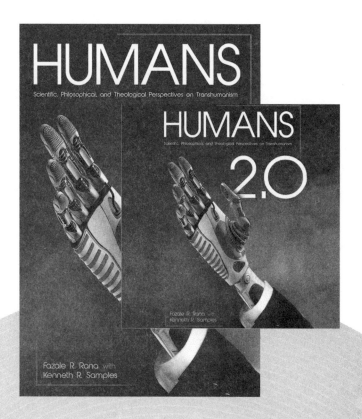

Should we discourage advances in biotechnology and bioengineering that can be used for human enhancement? Or should we take control of our own "evolution" and usher in a posthuman age? Is there another option?

Examine the challenging topic of transhumanism in *Humans 2.0*—also available in audiobook format. Get your copy now at **reasons.org/h2**.

Discover the reason . . .

In our video podcast *Stars, Cells, and God*, RTB scholars discuss new discoveries taking place at the frontiers of science that have theological and philosophical implications, as well as new discoveries that point to the reality of God's existence.

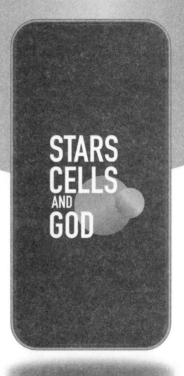

Watch now at **youtube.com/reasonstobelieve1**
or scan the QR code above.